The Exclusively Animal Free
VEGAN SHOPPER

First published June 1991
Second edition published June 1993
Third edition published April 1995
Fourth edition published November 1997
Fifth edition published June 2000

ISBN 0 907337 23 6

Design by Taylor McKenzie,
58 Charlotte Road, London

Printed on 50% totally chlorine free
and 50% recycled fibre by
KSC Printers Ltd
High Brooms Industrial Estate
Tunbridge Wells, Kent TN2 3DR

Published by The Vegan Society,
Donald Watson House,
7 Battle Road, St Leonard's-on-Sea,
East Sussex TN37 7AA,
United Kingdom
(Tel 01424 427393)

CONTENTS

multiple outlet quick reference guide ii
key iii
guidelines iv

introduction 1
why animal-free? 8
  animal rights/welfare 8
  health 14
  ecology 17
  resource use 18
  spiritual 19

food 23
drink 91
toiletries & cosmetics 119
health care 169
baby, infant & child care 185
footwear & clothing 191
home & office 203
animal care 215
garden & leisure 221

animal-free criteria 226
additives 228
Vegan Society trade mark 230
glossary of animal substances 231
animal-free shops 235
suggested reading 236
contact networks 242
useful addresses 248
multiple outlet contacts 254
mail order addresses 255
index 264

MULTIPLE OUTLET QUICK REFERENCE GUIDE

Aldi 24, 26, 34, 43, 46, 55, 57, 64, 72, 74, 76, 80, 92, 95, 97, 102, 104

Alldays No own brand products.

ASDA Able to supply details of animal-free food and drink. 24, 26, 34, 39, 41, 43, 46, 47, 48, 50, 51, 53, 55, 57, 65, 66, 69, 70, 72, 74, 76, 77, 78, 80, 92, 94, 95, 96, 97, 103, 104

Body Shop No vegan list available.

Boots 178

Budgens Vegan list available soon.

Co-op 24, 27, 35, 39, 43, 46, 47, 49, 51, 52, 54, 56, 58, 65, 67, 69, 72, 74, 76, 80, 96, 98, 105, 121, 125, 127, 137, 141, 143, 146, 150, 160, 163, 164, 187, 188, 204, 206, 207, 208, 209, 210

Culpeper 72, 99, 129, 141, 163

Holland & Barrett No questionnaire returned.

Iceland No questionnaire returned.

Kwik Save Now Somerfield.

Lo Cost Stores Now Co-op.

Londis Holdings Now Nisa Today.

Marks & Spencer Able to supply details of animal-free food and soft drinks. 25, 28, 35, 40, 42, 44, 48, 49, 51, 52, 55, 60, 65, 67, 71, 73, 74, 76, 78, 81, 82, 99

Netto Foodstores Ltd No vegan list available.

Nisa Today Vegan list available soon.

Safeway Able to supply details of animal-free food and drink. 25, 29, 37, 40, 42, 45, 47, 48, 50, 51, 53, 54, 55, 56, 61, 66, 67, 69, 71, 73, 75, 77, 78, 80, 81, 95, 96, 100, 103, 107

Sainsbury's Able to supply details of animal-free baby food, health care products and toiletries. 73, 123, 124, 126, 128, 133, 137, 139, 142, 145, 147, 156, 165, 177, 180, 186, 187, 188

Somerfield Able to supply details of animal-free food and drink. 25, 31, 37, 40, 45, 47, 48, 50, 53, 54, 56, 62, 66, 68, 70, 71, 73, 75, 77, 81, 94, 100

Spar No vegan list available.

Superdrug List "not exhaustive". 123, 127, 128, 132, 133, 135, 136, 137, 139, 140, 141, 142, 145, 147, 156, 158, 164, 188, 192

Tesco Able to supply details of animal-free food and hot/soft drinks. 25, 32, 37, 39, 40, 45, 47, 48, 50, 51, 53, 56, 57, 62, 66, 68, 70, 72, 73, 75, 77, 81, 82, 96, 101

Thorntons 43, 45

Waitrose Able to supply details of animal-free food, drink, health care products and toiletries. 26, 32, 37, 40, 43, 46, 47, 48, 50, 51, 53, 54, 56, 57, 63, 66, 68, 70, 72, 73, 75, 77, 78, 82, 94, 95, 96, 102, 104, 114, 127, 128, 146, 165, 180

Wine Rack 114

The entire range of the company's products is animal-free
*(see **ANIMAL-FREE CRITERIA**, page 226)* √

Some or all of the company's products are available by mail order
*(see **MAIL ORDER ADDRESSES**, page 255)* Ø

The company is an authorised user of the Vegan Society Trade
Mark (but not all its animal-free products may be registered)
*(see **VEGAN SOCIETY TRADE MARK**, page 230)* ™

The company has at least one vegan proprietor §

The company has a policy of ensuring that
(as far as possible and practical) the production
of its products has not involved the use
of genetically modified material
*(see **GENETICALLY-MODIFIED ORGANISMS**, page 16)* π

The company has a policy of not
conducting nor commissioning animal testing Ω

The company has signed up to the
Humane Cosmetics Standard
*(see **ANIMAL TESTING CRITERIA**, page 3)* Δ

The company has a policy of using only ingredients which have not
been tested on animals by, or at the initiative of, the company or its
suppliers since a specified date (Note: In the product listings, the year
follows this symbol — eg a 1976 cut-off date appears as **fcd76**) *(see
ANIMAL TESTING CRITERIA, page 3)* **fcd**

*products in **bold** are free from involvement with genetically modified
material at every stage of production*

w = with (product listings only)

GUIDELINES

- Although, as far as is practical, the publisher has taken care to ensure the accuracy and reliability of information supplied to it, the reader should bear in mind that manufacturers may make alterations to the constituents, derivation and testing of their products *at any time*. The diligent vegan shopper always checks a product's ingredients listing (where one is provided!) before making a purchase. (Note: *A current errata slip for this publication may be obtained by sending an SAE marked 'AFVS Update'* to: The Vegan Society, Donald Watson Hse, 7 Battle Rd, St Leonard's-on-Sea, E Sussex TN37 7AA.)

- The absence of an (apparently) animal-free product does not necessarily mean it does not meet the Society's **ANIMAL-FREE CRITERIA** *(page 226)*. Product categories which are obviously or typically animal-free (tinned fruit, tea, coffee, nuts, dried pulses, beans etc) have been excluded. Additionally, despite repeated approaches, some manufacturers/distributors (including a number whose products have appeared in previous editions) failed, or simply refused to supply the information requested.

- In order to make effective use of this *guide*, it is suggested that the new reader familiarises her/himself with the location of the **KEY** *(page iii)* and **CONTENTS** *(page i)* — and, at least initially, regularly consults the **INDEX** *(page 264)*.

- The inclusion of a product should not be construed as constituting Vegan Society approval for the product, its intended use, or its manufacturer/distributor *(see **OTHER ETHICAL CONSIDERATIONS**, page 4)*.

- The listing of products under 'health care' is not intended to take the place of advice provided by health care professionals.

Welcome to the fifth edition of the *Vegan Shopper* — the guide to products which are free of animal substances and involve no animal testing. Here at the Vegan Society (an educational charity) we have been encouraging the development of animal-free — ie *vegan* — products since 1944. In the last few decades the Society has seen a dramatic expansion in the availability of such products, paralleling the rapid growth of the animal rights, vegetarian/vegan and green movements — and heightened interest in health, diet, nutrition and food safety.

The *Vegan Shopper* caters not only for vegans but also vegetarians seeking to move further along their ethical path; the dairy intolerant; those recognising the environmental and resource consequences of livestock farming; and individuals wishing to take the first step towards reducing their dependence on the products of animal exploitation.

In 1993, the Realeat/Gallup survey into Meat-Eating and Vegetarianism put the number of vegans in the UK at around 100,000. By 1995 this figure had risen to an impressive 170,000. And the 1997 survey estimates that UK vegans total 224,000 — nearly $1/4$ million!

Amongst the rest of the population, the British appetite for animal foods is waning. The National Food Survey Annual Report, published in November 1996, shows that during the last ten years the consumption of liquid whole milk, cheese, butter, eggs, beef and veal, mutton and lamb, and pork all declined — some considerably. For example: liquid whole milk consumption has reduced from 1676ml to 776ml per person per week; butter from 64g to 39g per week; and pork from 103g to 73g. Then in 1998, another Realeat/Gallup survey found over 7 million UK consumers (13%) never, or hardly ever, eat dairy products — and a third are atttempting to reduce their consumption of dairy foods.

Concerns over Bovine Spongiform Encephalopathy (BSE), the now proven link with 'new variant' Creutzfeldt Jakob Disease (*nv*CJD), salmonella, and *E coli*, will doubtless accelerate the move towards safer, plant-based foodstuffs — as will the increasing prominence of vegans in entertainment and sport.

Celebrity or sporting vegans include: Bryan Adams (singer), Drew Barrymore (actress), Sally Eastall (Olympic marathon runner), Moby (DJ, musician), Sinead O'Connor (singer), Pat Reeves (British Powerlifting Champion), Dave Scott (triathlete, Ironman winner 5 times), Judith Shakeshaft (Welsh Cyclo-Cross Champion), Alicia Silverstone (actress), Lucy Stephens (triathlete), Wendy Turner (TV presenter, writer) and Benjamin Zephaniah (poet, actor).

Animal-free shoppers are in good company!

MISSING, PRESUMED VEGAN

It is important to emphasise that if an apparently animal-free product does not appear in this guide, this does not, in itself, mean the product has to be avoided. There are many reasons why a handful of animal-free products did not make it for inclusion, the main ones being:

- companies repeatedly failing to respond to questionnaires, telephone calls and faxes
- lack of confidence on the part of the compilers that the manufacturer/supplier actually understood the **ANIMAL-FREE CRITERIA** (see page 226)
- companies supplying incomplete or inadequate product information
- companies refusing to have their products listed because they did not wish to be associated with a 'minority interest' publication
- the information requested being 'commercially sensitive'

PLAYING DETECTIVE

Though experienced in investigating the animal-free credentials of a product, there are limits to the Vegan Society's capabilities. Food processing technology is a vast, complex and rapidly changing subject. At the end of the day, unless it obtains evidence to the contrary — or the details provided are clearly suspect — the Vegan Society has to accept the information provided to it (normally in the form of a written declaration) in good faith.

However, playing detective isn't the sole province of the Society. An increasing number of companies understand a vegan's requirements and enquiries from members of the public are often at least as effective as those from an organisation. Use the **ANIMAL-FREE CRITERIA** (see page 226) as the basis for your approach and check **ADDITIVES** (see page 228) to identify E numbers that could be animal-derived. You will quickly be able to determine whether the person responding to your enquiry is sufficiently knowledgeable to provide you with plausible product information. Confirming the animal-free status of a product can be thrilling but be prepared also for frustration and disappointment! That said, discovering that an apparently animal-free product is not suitable certainly isn't wasted effort. Manufacturers take note of consumer interest and will, sooner or later, act. Recent examples of companies deciding to alter their products in response to 'animal-free shopper demand' include: Cadbury's changing the ingredients of the Fry Chocolate Cream range; Kellogg's removing D_3 from Frosties and Coco Pops; Ecover producing a new 'whey-free' washing-up liquid; and Sainsbury's introducing a vegan Easter egg.

In addition to drawing the attention of manufacturers to the unmet needs of animal-free shoppers, it is equally important to tell them that you buy their animal-free products precisely because they are animal-free! It is all-to-easy to complain and accuse companies of 'discriminating against vegans' or 'condoning animal suffering', but letters and phone calls of an encouraging nature are more likely to elicit a receptive response and, ultimately, produce the desired outcome.

ANIMAL TESTING CRITERIA

It remains the case that animal protection groups and manufacturers promote a number of variations on the 'not tested on animals' theme. Depending on one's perspective or strategy, all have their strengths and weaknesses.

The criterion used to complete the *Vegan Shopper (see **ANIMAL-FREE CRITERIA**, page 226)* recognises that most substances have been, and some may continue to be, animal tested and simply requires that a product's manufacturer, or 'related' company, has not initiated testing on either the finished product or, where applicable, the ingredients.

For those readers who prefer companies using either a fixed cut-off date *(see below)* or the new international Not Tested on Animals Cosmetics Standard *(see below)*, an appropriate symbol *(see KEY, page iii)* appears in the product listings after the company name.

HUMANE COSMETICS STANDARD

In response to pressure from animal protection groups and consumers across Europe, the European Parliament proposed a ban on the marketing of animal tested cosmetics (Directive 93/35). However, early in 1997, to widespread dismay, the European Union (EU) postponed its 1 January 1998 target date until into the new century. An international coalition of animal protection groups from across the EU and North America drew up an international Humane Cosmetics Standard and launched a major campaign calling on all manufacturers and retailers to adopt it and thereby voluntarily meet the EU's original 1 January 1998 deadline.

Co-ordinated (in the UK) by the British Union for the Abolition of Vivisection (BUAV), the Standard requires companies not to *conduct, commission, nor be a party to any animal testing either now or in the future*, nor to *purchase ingredients, formulations or products from suppliers which have conducted, commissioned, or been party to animal testing on them after the date on which the company's policy takes effect*.

Note: Although there are no laws or regulations requiring finished cosmetic products to be tested on animals in the UK or EU, there are British, EU and even international regulations requiring *new ingredients* to be safety (effectively animal) tested.

FIXED CUT-OFF DATE

A company which has adopted a fixed cut-off date has a policy of using only ingredients which have not been tested on animals by, or at the initiative of, either it or its suppliers since a specified date. In addition, the company will not initiate animal tests on its finished products.

The Cosmetics Industry Coalition for Animal Welfare (CICAW) encourages cosmetic companies to adopt an animal testing fixed cut-off date — preferably 1976 (the year the EU required all *new* ingredients to be safety (animal) tested).

OTHER ETHICAL CONSIDERATIONS

To qualify for inclusion in the *Vegan Shopper* a product need only be free of animal ingredients and animal testing. However, whilst choosing to avoid products which have a *direct* animal involvement is a coherent and far-reaching ethical stance in itself, many animal-free shoppers also take into consideration a wide range of ethical issues concerning humans, animals and the environment — such as:

• **vegan ownership** Some shoppers prefer to support those companies which are wholly or partly owned by vegans *(see KEY, page iii).*
• **product range** Many companies manufacture or distribute both animal and non-animal products. Given the choice, many animal-free shoppers prefer to buy from those companies whose entire

range is animal-free *(see **KEY**, page iii)*.

- **company activities** A number of companies manufacturing or distributing animal-free (and animal) products are involved directly in animal abuse — such as the meat and dairy industries.
- **company connections** Some seemingly innocuous companies have parent, sister or subsidiary companies which are involved directly in animal abuse.
- **company affiliations** Possible animal abuse affiliations include: The British Industrial Biological Research Association (BIBRA), Research Defence Society (RDS), British Field Sports Society (BFSS), Game Conservancy.
- **company sponsorships & donations** Common areas include animal-connected medical research and sporting events.
- **organised boycotts** Even large multi-national companies have ceased an objectionable activity when threatened with, or subjected to, a boycott campaign. Though not always successful, it is argued that boycotts are, nevertheless, a useful means by which to heighten public awareness.
- **use of by-products** The production of animal-free goods may involve the generation of by-products which are then employed for purposes the animal-free shopper would not normally support. Examples include: *white flour* — bran — animal feed; *wheat etc* — straw — animal bedding; *linseed, rapeseed, soya* — cake/meal — animal feed; *sugar beet* — pulp — animal feed.
- **genetically-modified organisms** *(see **GENETICALLY-MODIFIED ORGANISMS**, page 16 and **KEY**, page iii)*.
- **microbiological testing** In order to ensure the safety of their products, and to forestall damaging law suits which might arise following the discovery of a defect, many manufacturers test batches of their products for the presence of bacterial contaminants. The nutrient media 'fed' to the bacteria (in order to identify them) are commonly derived from the slaughterhouse or the dairy industry. Virtually all foodstuffs, and most toiletries and cosmetics, are subject to testing involving the use of animal derivatives. Unfortunately, animal-free shoppers cannot avoid microbiologically-tested foodstuffs, which not only include processed foods but also unprocessed fruits and vegetables — and even drinking water!

Recognising that human and animal rights are inextricably linked and that all life is dependent upon the well-being of the planet, the animal-free shopper might also wish to avoid companies involved in or with: cash crops, environmentally damaging practices, irresponsible marketing, land rights, low wages and poor conditions, and oppressive regimes.

FURTHER INFORMATION

The Ethical Consumer Research Association Unit 21, 41 Old Birley St, Manchester M15 5RF **t** 0161 226 2929

Publishes *The Ethical Consumer*, a magazine providing information on companies behind brand names across a range of ethical issues — including 'Animal Testing', 'Factory Farming' and 'Other Animal Rights'.

ACKNOWLEDGEMENTS

This edition of the *Vegan Shopper* would not have been possible without the substantial and invaluable contributions given, on a voluntary basis, by Amanda Rofe, Eileen Hardy and Wendy Waller.

LOOKING AHEAD . . .

Research for the *Vegan Shopper* never ceases and the Vegan Society needs you to be part of this process! If you stumble across a new animal-free product, or discover that a manufacturer has introduced an animal ingredient into a product that was hitherto animal-free, please share your finding by contacting us at: The Vegan Society, Donald Watson Hse, 7 Battle Rd, St Leonard's-on-Sea, E Sussex TN37 7AA **t** 01424 427393 **f** 01424 717064 **e** info@vegansociety.com

To keep up-to-date with new animal-free products why not subscribe to *The Vegan* magazine? Contact the address above for details.

7

WHY ANIMAL FREE?

There are five main reasons why people avoid animal products — animal rights/welfare, health, environment, resource use, and spiritual growth. In the last ten years the arguments for veganism have been radically strengthened as it became increasingly clear to vegetarians that all the benefits of their diet come from its vegan component.

Since the last edition of the *Vegan Shopper*, there have been lots of developments in the areas of mad cow disease, TB in cattle, global warming, abolition of vivisection, food poisoning and of course genetically modified organisms (GMOs). With the information below you'll be primed for those frequent discussions about why you're avoiding animal products — whether with bewildered relatives, mystified mates, or the local press, radio and TV.

ANIMAL RIGHTS/WELFARE

Meat

Animals slaughtered in the UK in 1998 included 2 330 000 cows, 16 691 000 sheep, 30.66 million turkeys, 30.38 million spent egg laying hens (boiling fowl), 745.55 million meat-only chickens (broilers) and 6.47 million spent broiler breeders. To these can be added around 13 million ducks, 1 million geese, plus rabbits, goats, pheasants, pigeons, frogs (for their legs), snails, ostriches, emus, crocodiles, kangaroos and other animals making a total of over 860 million.

The value of livestock sold at markets in England and Wales fell by 28% in 1998. Cattle numbers fell by 3%, sheep by nearly 6%, pigs by 2% and calves by 10%.

This Government strongly prefers meat to be exported as carcasses rather than as live animals but two judgements of the European Court of Justice have confirmed that the UK does not have the legal powers, on the grounds of public morality or otherwise, to introduce a ban on live exports.

Poultry

The majority of the broilers reared each year in the UK are factory farmed. They are kept in huge windowless sheds which are so overcrowded that one can barely see the floor so thickly is it 'carpeted' with chickens. The major welfare problem is that the birds have been selectively bred to reach their slaughter weight in 42 days, which is half the time they took 35 years ago. The muscle grows quickly, while the supporting structure of legs, joints, heart and lungs fails to keep pace. As a result, each year millions of chickens suffer from painful, sometimes crippling leg disorders and millions more die of heart disease.

Sea Life

In 1997 UK fishing vessels landed 891.3 thousand tonnes of fresh and frozen fish, including 142 000 tonnes of shellfish worth £621.9 million. In 1998 the UK used 260 000 tonnes of fishmeal, 45 000 tonnes of which was home produced. Fishmeal is used to feed poultry, fish, pigs and ruminants.

Fish farming — known as aquaculture — is one of the fastest growing sectors in world food production. Intensive fish farms produce high volumes of biological waste, primarily from uneaten food and waste material. Other problems include disease outbreaks, chemical pollution, and escapes of genetically modified fish, which can dilute the gene pool of wild fish and displace them altogether.

Dairy

The EU milk production in 1999 is estimated at 119.9 million tons — a reduction since 1998. Cow numbers are expected to continue their long term downward trend. In 1998 the UK consumed 6 948 and the EU 32 641 000 metric tons of fluid milk. In the same year the UK produced 14 637 and the EU as a whole 120 426 000 metric tons of cow's milk. The EU herd contained 21 270 000 dairy cows.

The value of UK milk production was £431 million (14%) lower in 1998 than in 1997. The dairy breeding herd decreased by 2% with 2 439 000 dairy cows. Average yield per cow was 5 793 litres per annum, compared to 5 302 in 1994. There is a steady decrease in fertility in the UK dairy herd. Poor fertility is one of the strongest signals that a cow is stressed past her 'critical point of coping'. Newer procedures on dairy farms include forcing cows to undergo extended lactations of 18 months instead of 12 months. Over half the national herd suffers some form of lameness each year. Leptospirosis infection was been identified in over 80% of selected milk samples.

Calves

In the dairy industry, approximately a quarter of cows are replaced annually with dairy heifers. With the current target of each cow producing one calf per year, this results in 3 out of 4 calves born being used for meat. Milk and meat are the same business.

BSE (see also CJD under Health)

The first cow with bovine spongiform encepalopathy was identified in 1984. In 1988 BSE became a notifiable disease and the government instigated a mass cattle slaughter policy. Milk from infected cows was also destroyed. In 1990, after full compensation was offered, a surge of BSE cases indicated farmers had been under-reporting.

In 1996 UK beef was banned from being exported. In addition, meat and bonemeal fertiliser were banned from agricultural land. Maternal transmission of BSE to offspring was discovered. As at July 1999, the total number of cases was 175 065. Over 63% were located in dairy farms and over 81% of the total number of cases were from dairy cattle.

Eggs

In 1998 hens produced 10 812 million eggs. 83% of the UK's eggs still come from battery hens. Usually 5 hens are crammed into a cage so small that the birds cannot even stretch their wings. They are prevented from engaging in nearly all of their natural behaviour such as pecking and scratching at the ground, perching, dustbathing and nest-building. The lack of exercise and excessive egg production leads to battery hens having such brittle bones that 33% have broken ones by the time they come to be slaughtered. Wire meshed floors cause foot deformities. Close confinement results in aggression, feather loss and cannibalism. 2 million die annually in their cages. The survivors are slaughtered at 76 weeks of age for use in soup, pastes and pet food.

The EU's Scientific Veterinary Committee has condemned the battery cage saying that "it has inherent severe disadvantages for the welfare of hens". The keeping of laying hens in battery cages will be banned in the EU from 2012.

The 'humane' veneer of the so-called 'free range' systems is eggshell thin. The stocking density of such systems can be 1000 to 20 000 birds per house. Insufficient 'pop' holes (exits) deter birds from venturing outdoors. Monetary considerations require the culling of poor layers at around 2 years of age. Around 14% of free range hens have broken bones prior to arrival at the slaughterhouse. For each laying hen, an unwanted male chick was gassed or crushed at 1-3 days to be used for animal feed or fertiliser.

Unscrupulous packers have been conning consumers for years by passing battery eggs off as free-range and charging up to 50% more. MAFF reveal that in October 1997, 341,000 cases were sold as free-range despite the fact that only 285,000 cases were produced in the UK. Imported eggs may make up some of the shortfall. Free range eggs account for 13% of eggs sold in the UK.

Honey

Bees are manipulated in similar ways to other farmed animals to provide a range of products: honey, beeswax, propolis, bee pollen, bee brood, royal jelly (bee milk) and venom.

Hives are forced to remain in a single location by manipulation of the queen (wing clipping). The queen is also routinely artificially inseminated by sperm from decapitated bees (they would normally mate in flight). The queen is routinely killed after 2 years due to the decline in her egg-laying abilities. A new queen, often purchased by mail order from specialist breeding companies, replaces her.

Honey, used by the bees for the lean winter months, is removed for human use and replaced with nutrient deficient glucose or corn syrup. Synthetic pesticides and antibiotics are also used.

A bee will fly about 800km in its working life to produce just half a teaspoon of honey.

Fur

The trade in wild furs is responsible for the decline of many species and the extinction of some. As the larger cats became commercially extinct or protected, the fur trade turned to the smaller ones. Thousands of lynx and bobcat are still being trapped each year in North America. Animals are trapped using steel leg-hold traps (banned in Europe) which do not kill the animal outright, and cause immeasurable suffering.

World-wide, over 30 million minks and foxes are imprisoned in row upon row of wire cages to produce fur (1997 figures). In the UK there are currently (1999) 13 fur farms rearing mink. Animals kept in fur factory farms show stereotypical behaviour, self mutilation and cannibalism. They are killed by gassing (vehicle exhaust), neck breaking, lethal injection or anal electrocution. In the UK there are no qualifications or training required for this procedure.

Leather

Vegans don't eat the inside and, increasingly, they also don't wear the outside. Leather is simply fur with the hairs scraped off one side and the meat scraped and chemically removed from the other side during the tanning process. The sale of leather makes a sizeable contribution to the viability of the meat industry. Synthetic alternatives such as lorica — from which vegetarian shoes and jackets are made — are superior to leather, with micropores which allow perspiration out but don't allow water droplets in, and thus do not become waterlogged or need drying out. There was an 11% decrease in the turnover of UK leather products in 1997. Global trade in bovine hides and skins decreased in 1998. The clothing section of this new edition of the *Vegan Shopper* contains a number of new vegan footwear suppliers.

Wool and Lanolin

The sheep breeding flock, geared primarily to the production of meat, increased for the second consecutive year (by 3%) in 1998 and this, along with lower lamb mortality rates, led to a 5% increase in lambs under one year old. Total sheep and lamb numbers in 1998 were 44 471 000 (excluding clip wool). However the value of production of sheep and lambs was 5% or £57 million lower in 1998 than in 1997. The UK produced 67 000 tonnes of wool in 1998.

The majority of animals are shorn for the first time at 14-15 months and thereafter annually. Early season shearing — in wet, windy and cold conditions — can result in severe chilling, a high incidence of mastitis or even death.

Australia is the world's largest wool-producing country with 123.2 million sheep. 20-40% of Australian lambs die either at birth or before the age of 8 weeks, from exposure after shearing, starvation, heat exhaustion, or following castration, tail docking, muesling (removing strips of flesh, without anaesthetic, from around anal and vaginal areas to deter egg-laying flies) and other stock operations. Lambs are susceptible to shock, blood poisoning, tetanus, dislocated joints and arthritis.

Raw wool contains 10-25% grease or lanolin, which is recovered during the scouring process. Lanolin consists of a highly complex mixture of esters, alcohols, and fatty acids and is used in adhesive tape, printing inks, motor oils, and auto lubrication. It can also be refined for use in cosmetics and pharmaceuticals.

Silk

In 1997 the UK imported 63 metric tons of raw silk worth £924,000.00.

The most common species of silkworm (moth larvae) used in commercial silk production, *Bombyx mori*, has been 'cultivated' over many centuries and no longer exists in the wild. The female annually lays 300-400 eggs on mulberry trees, secreting a sticky substance to fasten them to the surface.

The silkworm secretes a fine thread to make a cocoon around itself consisting of around 300 000 figure of eight movements. The pupa stage should be followed by the production of an alkali substance which would eat through the threads, allowing the subsequent emergence of a moth. However, the industry requires the threads to remain intact and so, upon the cocoon's completion, the pupa is 'stifled' (killed) by immersion in boiling water, steaming, oven drying or exposure to the hot sun.

The usable silk from each cocoon is minute — it takes around 500 silkworms (80kg of cocoons) and 200kg of mulberry leaves to produce just 1kg of silk. The stifled pupae are typically composted to feed the mulberry trees.

Gelatine

The UK produced around 10 000 tonnes of gelatine in 1998 by boiling up cow bones (31%), cow hides (27%) and pig skin (42%). Gelatine is one of the principal animal ingredients lurking mainly in foods of all kinds (71%), pharmaceuticals (16%), photographic film (9%) and other applications (4%).

Shellac

Lac are scale insects (*Lacifer lacca*) living on lac trees, where the female secretes a protective resin over herself. It is this resin, along with encrusted live insects, which is scraped from the trees and manufactured into shellac. 100 000 lac insects are killed for 333g of shellac. India is the world's main producer of shellac at around 20 000 tonnes per year.

Shellac is used as a glaze for fruit such as those surprisingly shiny supermarket apples, nuts, coffee beans; in paint, varnish, tablets, cosmetics, confectionery, floor polish; and in hats as a stiffener. Whilst synthetic resin could replace shellac entirely, public demand for 'natural' products may be encouraging greater production.

Cochineal

Cochineal, a purple dye used in clothing and foodstuffs, consists of dried bodies of the female insects of *Dactylopius coccus* indigenous to central and south America. The female insects are picked by hand after mating and dried in shade for 20-30 days. About 100,000 to 150,000 insects yield 1 kg of raw cochineal. Total world production of cochineal, though fluctuating, is estimated at 150 to 180 tonnes per year, with Peru accounting for 90%. The rest comes from the Canary Islands.

Vivisection

In 1997 2 635 969 experiments were carried out on 2 573 088 animals in the UK, including 7 240 dogs, 1 446 cats, 9 413 horses and donkeys, 750 great apes, 27 baboons, 1 999 marmoset and tamarin monkeys, 1 868 macaque monkeys, 35 129 sheep, 7 717 pigs, 6 804 cattle, 724 goats, 223 deer, 44 996 rabbits, 84 173 guinea-pigs, 636 694 rats, 8 791 hamsters, 6 916 gerbils, 1 517 888 mice, 3 462 other rodents, 1 833 ferrets, 1 923 other carnivores, 14 squirrel, owl and spider monkeys, 102 656 domestic fowl, 5 620 turkeys, 2 516 quail, 10 047 other birds, 15 166 amphibians, 94 reptiles and 119 583 fish.

Some animals are used more than once in an experiment. Every year in the UK a further 400 000 animals are bred and killed so their body parts can be used for test tube research. These animals do not show up on the government's 'living animals' statistics listed above.

The numbers of experiments has decreased by 3% since 1996. Roughly 64% of experiments are carried out without anaesthetic, and 13% involved genetically manipulated animals (a 17% since 1996). The largest single field of research is pharmaceuticals, accounting for 501 000 experiments. Around 1 300 experiments a year are carried out for testing cosmetics, compared to 1 935 experiments in 1995.

Alternatives to animal testing include using humans, human tissue from cadavers or removed during surgery, imaging techniques, epidemiological (population) studies, plants and microbes, computer programmes, artificial animal models and substances that have been tried and tested over many years.

HEALTH

All the health benefits of the vegetarian diet come from its vegan component. Meat has around 40% of calories from fat, whilst cheese has around 70%. An egg is the richest source of cholesterol, about 290mg per egg — which is 71% of a person's recommended daily cholesterol intake.

In the USA the four food groups (meat, dairy, grains, fruit and veg) have been abolished as a result of lobbying by doctors in the Physicians' Committee for Responsible Medicine (PCRM) and replaced by a food pyramid which, though not entirely vegan, is moving towards PCRM's new four food groups of grains, legumes (beans, peas and lentils), vegetables, and fruit.

Recent research results

Several international studies have demonstrated that a plant-based diet is linked to a much lower risk of death from heart disease when compared to the general population. There appears to be a clear advantage in moving toward a vegan diet (*J Am C Nutr* 1998;17:407-8).

An uncooked vegan diet ('living food diet') provides significantly more dietary antioxidants than does the cooked, omnivorous diet, and the long-term adherents to this diet have a better anti-oxidant status than do omnivores (*Am J Clin Nutr* 1995;62:1221-7).

Compared to lacto-ovo-vegetarians, vegans exhibit significantly higher intakes of nutrients which are associated with reduced risk of cardiovascular disease, including fibre, vitamin C, potassium, magnesium, vitamin B6 and folate, as well as lower intakes of sodium. They also ingest less total and saturated fat, and have lower levels of lipids, including total cholesterol, LDL cholesterol, triglycerides, and serum total cholesterol: HDL cholesterol. Both systolic and diastolic blood pressure were inversely correlated with plasma vitamin C (*J Am C Nutr* 1998;17:425-34).

There are clear differences in the adipose tissue composition of vegans, which contain more unsaturated and fewer saturated fatty acids compared with omnivores and vegetarians. The vegan subjects had a significantly lower intake of saturated fatty acids and higher intake of polyunsaturated fatty acids than either the omnivore or the vegetarian groups (*Lipids* 1996;31).

Prevention of Cancer

A major new report by the World Cancer Research Fund in association with the American Institute for Cancer Research was published in 1997 and provides the most comprehensive world-wide review of diet and research, presenting new dietary guidelines for prevention, public policy recommendations and a thorough review of the science.

10 million new cases of cancer occurred around the world in 1996. By 2001 that number is expected to rise to 14.7 million. The report suggests that high intakes of animal protein might increase the risk of a number of colorectal, breast and endometrial cancers. An increase in animal fat consumption may increase the risk of lung, colon, rectum, breast, endometrium and prostate cancers. Diets high in milk and dairy products may increase the risk of prostate and kidney cancer.

Protein of plant origin from cereals and pulses was heralded as being as good as protein of animal origin and the typical Western-style diet was condemned: " ... within the last 50 years, the trend has been to invest in the very resource-intensive rearing of animals. The consumption of fatty meats and of meat, milk and other dairy products has also been promoted with the incorrect message that such foods are especially healthy."

"Increasing consumption of meat and fatty foods will lead to a massive increase in incidence of a large number of diseases that are expensive to treat. It reflects the impact of widespread perceptions of a cultural link between affluence and Western lifestyles. Traditional diets, when adequate and varied, are likely to be generally more healthy."

(*Food, Nutrition and the Prevention of Cancer: a global perspective.* World Cancer Research Fund, 105 Park St, London W1Y 3FB t 020 7343 4200. American Institute for Cancer Research, 1759 R St NW, Washington, DC 20009 t 001 709 329 7744 f 001 202 328 7226)

Dairy Allergy & Intolerance

In the UK, 31% (17 million people) of all consumers are attempting to reduce their consumption of dairy products. 13% (over 7 million people) never or hardly ever eat dairy foods. 22% claim to 'regularly' purchase non-dairy products like soya milk.

Food Poisoning

Studies have demonstrated that 53% of bovine carcasses and 83% of pig carcasses were contaminated with *E coli*. 18% of raw chicken from Britain and 64% of imported poultry contained salmonella. In a 1996 study, more than half of UK-bred chickens purchased from retail outlets contained campylobacter. Eggs and egg-containing foods were involved in 27% of salmonellosis in England and Wales in 1992. In 1998 53 273 cases of food poisoning have been formally notified (provisional data) in England and Wales, with 23 420 cases of salmonella. Diarrhetic, paralytic and amnesic shellfish poisoning has been found in several areas of the UK.

CJD

There is now convincing evidence that the agent which causes BSE is the same as that which causes new variant Creutzfeld Jacob Disease (nvCJD) in humans. By June 1999 the total number of definite and probable cases was 43, including a high number of dairy farmers.

BSE cannot be destroyed by cooking and all beef-containing foods are potential carriers, especially burgers, sausages and pies, but also products containing gelatine and animal fat such as sweets, cakes, jellies, pies, biscuits and gelatine vitamin capsules.

Prions, the 'rogue' proteins believed to be responsible for BSE and CJD, have not been found in milk or milk products. However, the prion agent is contained within white blood cells and the presence of such cells in milk is legally permitted. White blood cells are found in the pus discharged into milk by cows suffering mastitis — around $1/3$ of the national herd at any one time.

Should vegans be concerned about BSE? As far as we know, there are no cases of cow pus, blood or prions being observed in rice, oat or soya milk!

Antibiotics

British farmers are some of the heaviest users of antibiotics in Europe, accounting for more than 20% of the 1225t of antibiotics used annually on farm animals. Antibiotic resistant bugs — long feared, but now found for the first time in a Glasgow hospital — have resulted from the use of antibiotic growth promoters in farm animals, not the overuse of antibiotics in hospitals. For example Vancomycin is chemically identical to Avoparcin which from 1976 until 1997 was the most widely used antibiotic growth promoter in the UK being fed to most chickens, turkeys, pigs and about 30 per cent of all cattle. DNA sequencing showed that Vancomycin resistance in bugs infecting humans has come entirely from the use of Avoparcin and not the use of Vancomycin. Approximately 1 tonne of Avoparcin was used for every 1kg of Vancomycin.

GMOs

Of concern to the consumer wishing to avoid genetically modified organisms (GMOs), because of possible long term effects on their health or the implications of releasing them into the environment, is the presence in the UK food supply of GM soya, containing genes derived from a bacterium, a virus and a petunia. Soya is found in around 50% of all processed foods.

So far there has been very little research done to assess the health and safety implications of GMOs. The insertion of foreign genes can have many harmful unexpected effects, eg the insertion of a brazil nut gene into soya resulted in a reaction in people allergic to nuts. There is a risk of increasing antibiotic resistance in bacteria. Critics warn of unexpected and irreversible effects on agriculture and biodiversity. They condemn the immorality of the 'patenting of life' — transgenic animals, plants and seeds. From a vegan perspective, even if no animal gene was used during the modification process, it is likely that animal-derived enzymes were employed.

GM material can cross species barriers to other crops and weeds, and once released it is impossible to 'clean up' any unforeseen consequences. Plants designed to kill pests can kill beneficial insects as well and stimulate the development of resistance in pests. Those engineered for herbicide resistance will encourage increased use of chemicals. Most American farmers who have turned to GM crops seem to be getting yields no better than farmers who grow traditional varieties. They also appear to be using similar quantities of pesticides.

The Soil Association believes that genetic modification has no place in the production of safe and healthy food. Organic farming systems aim to produce food with care for human health, the environment and animal welfare.

In keeping with its vegan ethic, the Vegan Society is totally against the use of animal genes or animal substances in the development and production of GMOs. The Vegan Society believes that all foods that contain, may contain, or have involved GMOs should be clearly labelled, and has signed up to the Five Year Freeze campaign for a moratorium on genetic engineering and patenting in food and farming.

ECOLOGY

Land

25% of the world's land surface is given over to grazing more than 1.25 billion cattle. They weigh more and eat more than the human population and produce a lot more waste. A more efficient and sustainable use would be to grow trees for timber, fuel and food — such as nuts and fruits. Currently one third of the world's land suffers desertification through clearing forests for grazing, overgrazing, overcultivating croplands to feed farm animals (as well as people), and using poor irrigation techniques. A vegan requires just one eighth of the land needed to feed a meat eater.

Global Warming

Beef is a greenhouse-intensive food because cattle belch and fart methane, which is produced during fermentation in their guts. A typical animal emits 48 kilograms of methane a year, with more bubbling out of its manure. Beef farming makes other indirect contributions to the greenhouse effect. For instance, fossil fuels are burnt to generate the energy to produce the fertiliser that feeds the fodder crops on which many animals feed. Rearing beef is also land-intensive.

Water

Every year farmers spread about 200 million tonnes of animal manures and other organic farm wastes onto the land as fertiliser. Slurry and silage effluent can pollute a nearby river or stream, taking oxygen out of the water and in the worst cases killing all the fish. Slurry, which contains manure and urine, can be up to 100 times more polluting than raw untreated domestic sewage. Silage effluent, the liquid produced when preserving crops for fodder, is up to 200 times more polluting.

A day's food for a meat eater requires over 15 000 litres of water, compared with 5 000 for a vegetarian and a mere 1 500 for a vegan.

Tanneries

In its natural state as hide or skin, leather would be totally unsuitable for its current uses and rot rapidly. To make it pliable and longer lasting, hide is treated with a wide range of environmentally damaging chemicals such as lime, sodium sulphate solution, emulsifiers, non-solvent degreasing agents, salt, formic acid, sulphuric acid, chromium sulphate salts, lead, zinc, formaldehyde, fats, alcohol, sodium bicarbonate, dyes, resin binders, waxes, coal tar derivatives and cyanide based finishes. Tannery effluent contains large amounts of other pollutants such as proteins and hair. Overall the production of leather is far more polluting than the modern synthetic versions such as lorica.

Environment Emergency Hotline

The Environment Agency's emergency hotline number 0800 807060 operates 24 hours a day, 365 days a year for people to report pollution, fish in distress, illegal disposal of waste, poaching and danger to the natural environment.

RESOURCE USE

Nearly 1 billion people are undernourished or starving, despite the world producing enough food to feed twice its population of 6 billion. One third of the grain we grow is fed to farm animals.

World-wide, the production of beef and mutton depends heavily on natural range-lands, which are being pushed to the limits of their carrying capacity and beyond.

For most of the world's population, grain is the primary source of nutrition and may become more so in the years ahead. But less than one half of the world's land area is suitable for agriculture. Nearly all of the world's productive land, flat and with water, is already exploited. Currently ruminant livestock like cattle and sheep graze about half of the cultivable land area. In addition, about one quarter of world cropland is devoted to producing grains and other feed for livestock. About 38% of the world's grain production is now fed to livestock. In the USA this amounts to about 135 million tons of grain, sufficient to feed a population of 400 million on a vegan diet. If humans, especially in developed countries, moved toward more vegetable protein diets rather than their present diets, which are high in animal protein foods, a substantial amount of grain would become available for direct human consumption.

SPIRITUAL

Central to the beliefs of many of those following an animal-free lifestyle is the conviction of harmlessness or reverence for life, embodied in the spirit of *ahimsa*, the Sanskrit word for non-killing and non-injury popularised by Mahatma Ghandi.

Some animal-free shoppers are allied to a particular church such as the pacifist Society of Friends (Quakers) or Seventh Day Adventists; or to a particular faith, such as Buddhism, Jainism or Christianity; or empathise with paganism (eg wicca, druidry) or humanism.

Many consider that their animal-free lifestyle, its practical application and sense of inner peace, provide for most of their spiritual needs. There is a tendency towards vegetarianism and then veganism within the modern spiritual/personal growth movements.

The liberation of animals from human tyranny, health benefits, ecological, resource use and spiritual considerations, are five very good reasons for adopting an animal-free vegan lifestyle. With the *Vegan Shopper* in your pocket, it's very easy to be vegan and it's FUN!

THE VEGAN SOCIETY
TRADE MARK

The only truly international symbol of veganism, providing peace of mind for the vegan consumer and an established and growing audience for the producer. From beers to baby food, candles to cosmetics, the logo works for manufacturers, retailers and service providers, whether household names or small businesses. Phone us now to discover the vast range of approved products and companies, and how you can benefit as a purchaser or provider of vegan products or services.

food

biscuits	24
breads, rolls, pizza bases etc	26
breakfast foods	34
'burgers', 'sausages', 'meat' slices etc	37
cakes & cake mixes	39
'cheese' & 'cheese' spreads	40
chocolate	41
confectionery & sweet snacks	43
cooking aids — savoury	46
cooking aids — sweet	47
crackers, crispbreads etc	48
cream replacers	50
desserts	50
dips & dressings	51
egg replacers	53
gravies & stocks	53
hampers	54
'ice creams', sorbets etc	55
margarines, fats etc	56
pastry	57
pickles, sauces, vinegars etc	57
pies & pasties	64
savouries — canned/bottled	64
savouries — chilled/fresh	66
savouries — dried	69
savouries — frozen	70
seasonal foods	72
snacks — savoury	74
soups	76
soya and other 'milks'	77
spices	78
spreads — savoury	80
spreads — sweet	82
tofu, tempeh, miso etc	83
'yoghurts'	84
notes	*85*

BISCUITS

ALDIπ

Belmont Rich Tea; *Westside:* Bourbon Creams, Chocolate Chip Cookies, Ginger Snaps

ASDA

Bourbon Creams, Fruit Shortcake, Ginger Nuts, Ginger Thins, Instore Bakery Empire, Morning Coffee, Rich Tea; *Farm Stores:* Choc Chip Cookies, Fruit Shorties

BLACKFRIARS BAKERYπΩfcd

Flapjacks: Apple & Sultana, Apricot, Cherry & Coconut, Date & Walnut, Fruit, Original, Raspberry

BURTON'S BISCUITS

Fruit Snapjacks, Rich Tea, Snapjacks, Trim Rich Tea

CO-OPπΩ∆fcd85

Bourbon Creams, Coconut Crumble Creams, Coconut Rings, Country Crunch, Everyday Digestive, Everyday Rich Tea, Fruit Country Crunch, Fruit Shortcake, Ginger Nuts, Ginger Thins, Morning Coffee, Rich Tea, Round Lemon Puffs, Royal Duchess

CRAWFORD'S

Bourbon Creams, Morning Coffee, Oat & Wholemeal, Pink Wafer

DOVES FARM FOODSøπ

Cookies: Chocolate Chip, Lemon, Muesli, Roman, Seven Seed; *Digestives:* Organic, Fruity Oat, Organic Plain Chocolate; *Flapjacks:* Apple & Sultana, Chocolate Chip & Coconut, Chocolate Fruit & Nut

FOX'S BISCUITSπ

Classic Plain, Ginger Snaps, Original Thick Tea; *Crinkle Crunch:* Coconut, Ginger

GOBBLINπΩfcd86

Flapjacks: Apricot & Cinnamon, Coconut, Fruit & Nut

GOODNESS FOODSøπΩfcd

Coffee & Walnut Topped Chunky Jacks; *Chunky Jacks (untopped):* Apricot, Date & Walnut, Mulled Fruit, Traffic Jam

GRANNY ANN'S

Premier Protein Gluten Free Biscuits: Fruit & Nut, Plain

GREEN & BLACK'Sø§π

Organic Cookies: Fruit, Russian

HEMP FOOD INDUSTRIES ASSOC.ø§πΩ

Hemp Flapjack

JACOBSπ

Bourbons, Lemon Puffs, Fig Rolls

KALLO

Organic Chocolate Thin Slice Rice Cakes; *Organic Biscuits:* Muesli, Raisin, Sesame

LYME REGISøπ

Traditional Flapjacks: Apricot, Fruit & Nut

MA BAKER

Giant Bars: all; *Organic Bars:* Apple, Apricot, Orange; *Wild About... Nut

Bars: all

McVITIES

Abbey Crunch, Fruit Shortcake, Go Ahead Ginger Crisp, Hob Nobs, Lincoln, McVitie's Cake Hob Nob Flapjacks, Noddy Rich Tea Finger

MARKS & SPENCER

9 Fruit Cookies, Bourbon Creams, Break In [12 pack], Butter Puffs, Digestives, Fruit Snap Jacks, Ginger Snaps, High Fibre Digestives, Oat Crunchies, Rich Tea, Rich Tea Fingers; *Reduced Fat:* Digestives, Rich Tea

MARYBAKE

Traditional Flapjack: Apricot & Hazelnut, Banana & Apricot, Cherry & Almond, Ginger, Original, Pineapple & Coconut, Sultana, Toffee

MOLENAARTJEø

Bio-Carob, Bio-Malt Digestive

MRS MOON'S√øπΩfcd

Organic Cinnamon Raisin Cookie Mix

PAMELA'Sπ

Ginger Cookies

PENNYWISE

Bourbon Creams, Shortcake; *Finger:* Nice, Rich Tea

PREWETT'S

Carob Finger: Fig Orange, Oatflake; *Wholemeal:* Brazil Nut, Oatbran

RJ FOODS™

Flapjack: Apple & Apricot, Cherry & Coconut, Cherry & Sultana, Date & Walnut, Fig, Fruit Bar, Mincemeat Bar, Muesli, Plain, Raspberry, Rum & Raisin, Organic Chocolate

RAKUSEN'S™

Digestive, Chocolate Digestive, Fruit Flapjack, Fruit Shortcake, Ginger Crunch, Nice, Shortcake, Viennese Star

SAFEWAY

Bourbon Creams, Chocolate Mint Crisp Cookies, Digestive Fingers, Fig Rolls, Fruit Shortcake, Ginger Cookies, Gingernuts, Morning Coffee, Orange Finger Creams, Pecan Cookies, Rich Tea Fingers, Shortcake; *Savers:* Rich Tea, Shortcake

SOMERFIELD

Coconut Crumble Cream, Coconut Rings, Fat Reduced Digestive, Fruit Shortcake, Ginger Crunch, Ginger Thins, Morning Coffee, Nice, Oat Crunch, Rich Tea Finger

SUMMERBRIDGE BAKERY§πΩ

Double Choc Flapjack *w* Hempseed; *Muesli Bar:* Apricot & Banana *w* Hempseed, Fig & Orange *w* Hempseed, *w* Hempseed

SUNWHEEL NATURAL FOODS

Flapjack: Cherry & Coconut, Fruit & Nut, Maple Flavour Syrup & Sultana

TESCO

Fruit Shortcake, Ginger Nuts, Oat Digestive & Choc Chip, Oat Digestive *w* Peanuts; *25% Less Fat:* Oatbakes, Rich Tea; *Value:* Bourbon Creams, Digestive,

Rich Tea

TRUFREE™

Bourbons, Chocolate Chip Cookies, Custard Creams, Gingernut Cookies, Shortcake

VILLAGE BAKERYøπΩ

Sultana & Cashew Nut Flapjack

VITALINEAπ

Fig Rolls

WAITROSE

Coconut Creams, Flapjack, Fruit Shortcake, Plain Chocolate Ginger Crunch, Plain Chocolate Orange, Rich Tea, Rich Tea Finger, Sweetmeal Digestive, Womble; *Flapjack:* Apple & Sultana, Chocolate Chip; *Reduced Fat:* Digestives, Rich Tea

WHOLEBAKEπ

Hemp Seed Flapjack; *Crisp Bar:* Cherry & Almond, Cranberry, Original, Pecan; *Fruit Filled Slice:* Apple & Cinnamon, Apricot & Apple, Date, Fig, Plum; *Luxury Flapjack:* Apricot, Date & Walnut, Fruit & Nut, Original, Cranberry, Cherry & Coconut; *Organic Flapjack:* Coconut, Hazelnut, Original, Sunflower

BREADS, ROLLS, PIZZA BASES ETC

ALDIπ

White Finger Rolls; *Spinaca Sliced Bread:* Medium Brown, Medium White, Thick White; *Village Green:* Crumpets (**not** Village Green Scottish Crumpets), Gold Farmhouse Loaf, White Bread Premium, Wholemeal Bread Medium, Wholemeal Thick Sliced Bread

ALLINSON

HiBran Sliced Bread: Medium, Sliced, Thick; *Wholemeal Sliced:* Family Soft Wax Wrapped, Medium, Sliced, Thick; *Wholemeal:* Muffins, Rolls

ASDA

4 Instore Bakery Petit Pain, 6 Potato Cakes, Family Malt Loaf, Jaws 2 Teacakes, Tex Mex Wheatflour Tortilla, Traditional Pizza Base Mix; *Baps:* 4 Granary, 4 White Sliced, 4 White Sandwich, 4 Wholemeal, 4 Wholemeal Sandwich, 6 Big White, 6 Big Wholemeal, 6 Large White, 6 White Sandwich, 6 Wholemeal Big, 8 Granary, 8 White Sandwich, 8 Wholemeal, 8 Wholemeal Sandwich, 12 White Sandwich, 12 Wholemeal Sandwich, 16 Granary, 16 White Sandwich, 16 Wholemeal Sandwich; *Bread:* Bakers Gold Medium Sliced , Hot & Spicy, Multigrain Brown; *Bread Sticks:* Garlic, Pizza, Plain, Sesame; *Crumpets:* 6 Farm Stores, 6 Plain Scotch, 6 Scotch Fruit, 8 Pack, 12 Pack; *Danish White Bread:* Medium, Medium Sliced, Sliced, Thick; *Farm Stores Bread:* Medium Sliced Brown, Medium Sliced White, Thick Sliced White; *HC Softgrain White Sliced Loaf:* Medium, Thick; *Long Life Medium Sliced Bread:* White, Wholemeal; *Muffins:* 6 White, 12 Oven Bottom; *Petits Pains:* 4 Instore Bakery, 12; *Rolls:* 8 Finger White, 12 Finger White Farm Stores, 12 White Fresh for a Week, 16 Finger White; *Speciality Breads:* 2 Mushroom & Garlic

Focaccia, 6 Chapatis, 8 Tortillas, Onion Pitta; *Square Cut Sliced Loaf:* Medium Brown, Medium Softgrain, Medium White, Medium Wholemeal, Thick Softgrain, Thick White, Thick Wholemeal; *White Sliced Big Loaf:* Medium, Thick

BAKOVEN π

Pretzel; *Bread:* Blackforest, Danish Three-Seed Malted, Fruit & Nut Muesliz, Mischbrot, Muesli Roll, Pumpkin & Sunflower, Wholemeal; *Farmhouse Bread:* Bloomer, Ring; *Goldgrain Bread:* Goldgrain, Walnut, w Sesame; *Rye Bread:* 100% Loaf, Bloomer, Caraway, Danish Light, Light w Caraway, Malted, Onion, Stick, Stick w Onion, Square; *Pretzel:* Crescent, Roll, Selection, Stick

BESTFOODS

Napolina Pizzeria Bases: 2 Standard, 4 x 4 Mini Bases, Deep Pan, Stone Baked

BIONA

Wholemeal Raisin & Cinnamon Bread

BRAKE BROS

Frozen Bread Specialities Pitta Bread; *Frozen:* Pre-Cut Teacakes, Provencette Ciabatta; *Frozen Breads & Rolls:* all; *Frozen Create Your Own Pizza Crusts:* Deep Pan (9", 14"), Traditional (7", 9", 12"); *Frozen Tortillas:* 6" Corn, Flour (6", 10")

BREWHURST

Pleniday Bread Mix

CO-OP π Ω ∆ fcd85

Crumpets, Finger Crumpets, Fruit Brack, Medium Sliced Brown Bread, Pitta, Piz-

za Base Mix, Potato Breads, Potato Cakes; *Baps:* Goodlife Wholemeal, Granary, Large White, Soft White, White, Wholemeal; *Buns:* Burger, Large White Burger, Unsliced Burger, White Burger; *Danish Sliced Loaf:* Medium, Thick; *Everyday Sliced:* White Medium, White Thick, Wholemeal Medium; *Granary & Malted Bread:* Medium Sliced Brown Granary, Multigrain Medium; *Part Baked:* Granary Petit Pain, White Batons, White Petit Pain; *Pitta Bread:* Garlic, Wholemeal; *Premium Sliced Loaf:* Medium, Thick White; *Rolls:* Brown Snack, Crusty, Finger, Long White Finger, Morning, Scotch, Soft White Finger, White Snack; *Softgrain Loaf:* Medium, Thick; *White Loaf:* Extra Thick Sliced, Medium, Medium Sliced, Square Sliced Medium, Thick Sliced, Thin Sliced; *Wholemeal Loaf:* Extra Thick Sliced, Medium, Medium Sliced, Medium Soft Sliced, Thick Sliced

COOPLANDS (DONCASTER) π

Bread: all

COUNTRY CHOICE

Rolls: Harvester, White, Wholemeal

DAYOFRESH

White Sliced Bread: Medium, Thick; *Rolls:* Brown, White

EVERFRESH NATURAL FOODS √ ø

Organic Breads: Fruit-T Loaf, Malted Raisin Loaf, Mixed Grain Gluten Free, Spicy Onion Gluten Free, Wheat Sourdough; *Organic Sprouted Bread:* Date, Fruit & Almond, Onion, Raisin, Stem Ginger, Sunseed, Wheat, Wheat Banana,

Wheat Carrot & Raisin, Wheat Chocolate Chip; *Organic Rye Bread:* Sourdough, *w* Caraway Seed, *w* Mixed Seed, *w* Onions, *w* Poppy Seed, *w* Sunflower Seed; *Sunnyvale Organic Loaf:* 100% Rye, Fruit, Gluten-Free Mixed Grain, Malt, Natural Sourdough Wholewheat, Rye *w* Poppy Seed; *Sunnyvale Organic Sprouted Grain Bread:* Banana, Carrot Raisin, Chocolate Chip, Date, Fruit & Almond, Original, Raisin, Stem Ginger, Sunseed

GOSWELL BAKERIESπ

Light Rye Bread: all; *Wholemeal Bread:* Cranks Organic, Prewetts

GREEN & BLACK'Sø§π

Organic Pizza Bases

HEINZ

Weight Watchers Danish Bread: Brown, Malted, Oat, White; *Weight Watchers Soft Rolls:* Brown, Malted Grain, White

HEMP FOOD INDUSTRIES ASSOC.ø§πΩ

Hemp & Wheat Sprouted Bread

HETHERTON'S ORIGINAL

White Sliced: Medium, Thick

INTERNATIONAL HARVEST

White Pitta

KINGSMILL

6 White Rolls; *Bread:* Country Gold Malted Wheat, Gold White Farmhouse, Square Cut White Sliced, White Sliced

MARKALø

Organic Pizza Bases

MARKS & SPENCER

4 Plain Bagels, 6 Potato Farls, 8 Wraps, Fruit Buns, Half Baguette, Harvest Brown, Hi Bran, High Fibre White, Hovis, Italian Country, Multiseed, Plain Loaf, Poppy Seed Swirl, Potato & Rosemary, Roast Onion, Soft Grain Medium, Tuscan Rosemary, Walnut, Wholemeal Medium Sliced; *95% Fat Free:* Tea Loaf, Teacakes; *Baguette (Eire):* Half, Large, Regular; *Bakers Choice:* Golden Wholemeal, Multigrain, White; *Bakers Choice Rolls:* 4, 4 Granary, 4 Soft, 6, White; *Batch:* Brown, Seeded, Soft White, Soft Wholemeal; *Bloomer:* Country Grain, English, Sliced, Vienna; *Ciabatta:* 1, 2, 2 Olive, Organic; *Cob:* Crusty, Loaf; *Count On Us:* Farmhouse, Granary; *Farmhouse:* Golden, Oatmeal, Organic Wholemeal, Sliced, Sliced Brown, Sliced White, Sliced Wholemeal, Soft Grain, Soft White, White, Wholemeal; *Granary:* Loaf, Sliced; *Long Life Sliced:* White, Wholemeal; *Muffins:* 4, 4 Raisin & Bran, 9 Plain, Wholemeal; *Pittas:* 8, 12 Mini; *Rolls:* 12 Split, 4 Breakfast Morning, 4 Ciabatta, 4 Crusty White, 4 Organic Wholemeal, 6 Soft Wholemeal, 6 Split, 8 White Homebake, Finger, French Crusty (Eire), Soft Crusty White; *Sandwich:* White, Wholemeal Medium, Wholemeal Thick; *Soft Crusty:* White, Wholemeal

MESTEMACHER

Bread: Pumpernickel, Rye; *Organic Bread:* Sunflower Seed, Wholemeal Rye

MIGHTY WHITE

Softgrain Sliced Bread: Medium, Thick

NEW YORK BAGEL CO

Bagels: Blueberry, Cinnamon & Raisin, Onion, Plain, Poppy, Sesame Seed, Strawberry

ODENWALD

Par Baked: **Baguette, Pistolet, Pistolet Wholewheat**

SAFEWAY

Delicatessen: Deep Pan Pizza Base, Thin & Crispy Pizza Base, Wheat Flour Tortillas; *Instore Bakery:* Crosscut Batard, Granary Stick, Grand Rustique, Guernsey Planche, Mexican Style Chilli, Parisienne, Petit Parisienne, Pumpkin Seed, Spiced Fruit Feast; *Instore Bakery Bagel:* Onion, Plain, Sesame; *Instore Bakery Baguette:* French, Petite, Sandwich; *Instore Bakery Baps:* White, Wholemeal; *Instore Bakery Bloomer:* Brown, Brown Poppy Seeded, Brown Sesame Seeded, White, White Poppy Seeded, White Sesame Seeded; *Instore Bakery Cob:* Small Granary, Small Pot Wholemeal, Wheatgerm, White Twin; *Instore Bakery Farmhouse:* Granary, White, Large White, Large Wholemeal; *Instore Bakery French:* Baton, Boule, Roll, Stick; *Instore Bakery Hovis:* Large White, Large Wholemeal Country Grain, Small Brown; *Instore Bakery Loaf:* Coarse Brown Country, Wholemeal; *Instore Bakery Organic:* Brown, White; *Instore Bakery Pain:* Rustique, Siegle; *Instore Bakery Rolls:* Crusty Round, Soft Brown Cottage, Soft White, Soft White Cottage, White Bouchon; *Instore Bakery Sandwich:* Large White, White; *Instore Bakery Soft White Roll Knotted Seeded :* Poppy, Sesame; *Instore Bakery White*

Loaf: Extra, Large Family, Small Tinned, Split Tin; *Pre-packed:* Bacon Flavour Potato Scones, Breakfast Pack, Crumpets, Finger Crumpets, Football Baps, French Stick, Fruit Teacakes, Herb Rustique, Keeps Fresh Crumpets, Mediterranean Style Vegetable Folded Flatbread, Muffins, Potato Scones, Rosemary Ciabattini, Teacakes, Traditional Potato Farls, Traditional Style Potato Scones, Veda Malt Loaf, White Baps, Wholemeal Baps; *Pre-packed Bread:* Brown, Danish White, Farmhouse Premium Wholemeal, Fibrewhite, Gold Premium White, Granary Malted Brown, Granary Thick Sliced, Keeps Fresh Family White, Keeps Fresh Family Wholemeal, Medium Sliced Brown, Multigrain, Premium Pan, Savers White, Savers Wholemeal, Scottish Plain, Softgrain, Standard White, Traditional Style Plain White, White Batch, White Medium Sliced, White Pan, Wholemeal; *Pre-packed Buns:* Burger, Chocolate & Orange Mini, Currant, Seeded, Topped Wholemeal, White Sliced Burger; *Pre-packed Delicatessen:* 2 Deep Pan Pizza Bases, 2 Thin & Crispy Pizza Bases; *Pre-packed Focaccia:* Garlic & Mushroom, Mediterranean, Rosemary, Tomato; *Pre-packed Hovis:* Premium Brown, Premium White, Premium Wholemeal, Wheatgerm; *Pre-packed Italian Style:* Ciabatta, Ciabatta Flute, Ciabatta Rolls, Ciabattini, Mediterranean Bread, Olive Ciabatta, Sun-dried Tomato Ciabatta; *Pre-packed Muffins:* Cinnamon & Raisin, Fruit & Spice; *Pre-packed Pitta Bread:* Mini White, Mini Wholemeal, White, Wholemeal; *Pre-packed Rolls:* Farmhouse White, Farmhouse Wholemeal,

Finger, Premium White, Premium White Split, Savers Brown, Savers White, Scottish White Morning, Scottish Wholemeal Morning, Soft Brown, Soft White, Split White, Traditional Style Brown Morning, Traditional Style Malted Brown, Traditional Style White, Traditional Style White Morning, White Finger, Wholemeal, Wholemeal Snack

SOMERFIELD

Bakery: Basics Teacakes, English Toasting Crumpets, Family Malt Loaf, Finger Crumpets, Fruited Teacakes, Muffins, Pikelets, Potato Cakes, Round Crumpets, Spiced Fruit Muffins, White Pitta Bread, Wholemeal Muffins, Wholemeal Pitta Bread; *Bakery Baps:* Granary Malted Brown Salad, Stoneground Wholemeal, White Farmhouse, White Salad, Wholemeal Sandwich; *Bakery Bread:* Basics Wholemeal, Medium Sliced Long Life White, Medium Sliced Brown, Medium Sliced Danish White, Medium Sliced Premium White, Medium Sliced Premium White Toaster, Medium Sliced Soft Wholemeal, Medium Sliced Softgrain, Medium Sliced Wax Wrapped White, Medium Sliced White, Medium Sliced Wholemeal, Thick Sliced Danish White, Thick Sliced Long Life White, Thick Sliced Premium White, Thick Sliced Softgrain, Thick Sliced Wax Wrapped White, Thick Sliced White, Thick Sliced Wholemeal, Traditional Roll, White Crusty Cobs, White French Stick, White Half Baguettes; *Bakery Buns:* Basics Currant, Chelsea, Currant, Mini Fruit, Spiced Fruit, White Burger; *Bakery Rolls:* Basics White, Large Petit Pain Harvester, Large Petit Pain White, Large Soft Brown Split,

Premium White, Soft Brown, Soft White, Soft White Split, White Bridge, White Finger, Wholemeal Scotch; *In Store Bakery Bread:* Coburg White, Cottage White, Danish White, Farmhouse White, French Baguette, French Seeded Baton, Harvester, Poppy Seeded Bloomer, Soft Bake, Soft Bloomer, Soft Farmhouse, Soft Sandwich, Soft Split, Soft White Tin, Split Tin White, White Bloomer, White Sandwich, Wholemeal; *In Store Bakery Roll:* French, Pain Complete, Pain Rustique, Ploughmans, Ploughmans Harvester, Poppy Seeded Knot

SOREEN

Lincolnshire Plum Loaf

SOY FOODSø™π

Seed Coated Baguettes, Teacakes; *Bread:* Cornutopia & Sweetcorn, Herb, Light Rye, Malthouse, Sechskorn 6 Grain, Spelt Wheat, White Unbleached, Wholewheat & Mixed Seed, Wholewheat; *Fancy Bread:* Foccacia *w* Olive Oil, Olive Bread *w* Olives, Basil Bread *w* Pesto, White Tabatiere Triangles; *Rolls:* Plain, Sesame Seeds, Small Mixed Topping; *Sourdough or Yeast-Free Bread:* Pain de Campagne, Spelt Wheat, Wholewheat, Wholewheat 4 Seed, Wholewheat & Brown Rice, Wholewheat & Sprouted Kamut; *Yeast-Free (Sourdough) & Wheat-Free Bread:* Barley (Tsampa), Rye, Rye *w* Corn

SUMMERBRIDGE BAKERY§πΩ

Bread: all

SUNBLEST

Currant Buns, Fruited Teacakes, Pikelets, Standard White Muffins, Sun-malt Loaf; *Bread:* Brown Sliced, Danish Toaster, White Unsliced; *Crumpets:* English Toasting, Finger; *Rolls:* Farmhouse Baps, Seeded Burger Buns, Soft Brown, Soft White; *White Sliced Bread:* Danish, Medium, Scottish Plain, Thick, Thin

TESCO

4 Orange & Sultana Ginger Buns, 4 Potato Farls, 4 White Muffins, 6 Bakers Premium Crumpets, 6 Potato Cakes, 6 Tomato Wraps, 6 White Muffins, 8 Crumpets, 8 Pikelets, 8 Potato Farls, 10 Mini White Pitta Breads, 12 Crumpets, Coffee Shop Loose White Morning Rolls, Continental Style Light Rye Brown Bread, Softgrain Medium Thick White Bread; *Bakers Premium White Bread:* Medium, Plain, Stay Fresh Medium, Stay Fresh Thick, Thick, Toaster Extra Thick, Wax Doorstep; *Baps:* 4 Granary, 4 Large Granary, 4 Large Wholemeal, 6 Brown, 6 Godzilla, 6 Large White, 6 Soft White, 6 Wholemeal, 12 Sliced White, 12 Wholemeal; *Brown Bread:* Bakers Premium Gold Malted, Oatmeal White Thick, Standard Medium Sliced; *Buns:* 6 Large White Burger, 6 Wholemeal Burger, 12 Sliced Sesame Seeded Burger; *Homebake Bread & Rolls:* 2 Garlic Baguettes, 2 Half Baguettes, 4 Crusty Garlic Continental Rolls, 6 Mini Petit Pains, Crusty White Loaf; *Instore Bakery Farmhouse Bread:* Crusty White, Crusty White Sliced; *Mega Value Packs:* 4 Large White Baps, 12 Finger Rolls & 12 Baps, 24 White Rolls, 32 White Finger Rolls; *Rolls:* 4 American White Deli, 4 American Wholemeal Deli, 4 Bakers Premium Granary Brown, 4 Bakers Premium Wholemeal, 4 Large White Hot Dog, 6 Brown Finger, 6 Brown Morning, 6 Scottish White Morning, 6 White Finger, 6 White Morning, 12 Wholemeal Snack; *Speciality White Bread:* Ciabatta, Garlic & Parsley Focaccia, Garlic & Herb Mini Focaccia, Olive Ciabatta, Red Onion & Basil Mini, Three Seed; *Standard White Bread:* Medium, Plain, Stayfresh Medium, Stayfresh Thick, Thick, Thin, Toaster Extra Thick; *Truly Fruity:* Currant Buns, Sliced Fruit Loaf; *Value Packs:* 12 Teacakes, 12 White Rolls, Medium Wholemeal Bread; *White Danish Bread:* Medium, Thick; *Wholemeal Bread:* Bakers Premium Gold, Multigrain, Organic, Soft Medium, Soft Thick, Stayfresh Medium, Stayfresh Thick

VILLAGE BAKERYøπΩ

4 Large Sandwich Rolls; *Baps:* 6 White, 6 Wholemeal; *Bread:* Baltic Rye, Borodinsky, Campagne, Gluten-Free, Hadrian, MaltGrain, Pane Toscano, Raisin Borodinsky, Rossisky, Sunflower, White Cob, White Tin, Wholemeal, Wild Mushroom & Garlic

WAITROSE

12 Garlic Dough Balls, Casareccio, Foccacia, Grande Mange Blanc, Grande Mange Paysan, Grande Rustique, Pain de Campagne, Pain Fermier, Paysan Rustique, Petit Parisienne, Plain Bagel, Seeded Gallego; *Bake Off:* Granary Baton, Large Flute, Organic Baguette, Pain au Levain, Pain Rustique; *Bap:* Granary 5", Multi Seeded White, White

Floured; *Batch:* Organic Fruit, Wholemeal Seeded; *Bloomer:* Large, White, White Poppy Seeded, White Seeded, Wrapped; *Bread:* Greek Olive, Malted Wheat Sandwich; *Brown:* Ascot, Organic, *w* Malted Wheat Grains; *Buns:* 4 Fruit, 4 Wholemeal Spiced; *Ciabatta:* Plain, Tomato; *Danish Bread:* Light Rye, Malted, Toaster, White; *Foccacia:* Mixed Pack, Trio, *w* Rosemary; *French Style:* Baguette, Stick; *Frozen Part Bake:* Knots, Petit Pain; *Farmhouse:* Plain, Tin, White, White Sesame, Wholemeal, Wholemeal Tin; *Granary:* Long Tin, Malted Brown Cob, Malted Brown Tin, Malted Stick, Sandwich Thick, Tin, *w* Sesame Seeds; *Muffins:* 4 White, 4 Wholemeal; *Pane:* Anello, Bruno; *Part Bake:* 3 Small Baguettes, 6 Petit Pain, Long White Tin; *Pitta Bread:* 6 White Traditional, 6 Wholemeal, 8 White Picnic, 8 Wholemeal Picnic; *Premium Bread:* Heyford Wholemeal, Organic White Thick Sliced, Organic Wholemeal Medium Sliced, Organic Wholemeal Thick Sliced; *Ready-to-Bake:* 3 Baguettes, 9 Petit Pain, Assorted; *Rolls:* 9 Brown, 8 Finger, 9 Soft White Snack, 12 Bridge Rolls, 12 White Bridge, Braces Heyford, Ciabatta, Granary, Granary Malted Brown, Organic Brown, White Cottage, White Crusty, White Soft, White *w* Organic Flour; *Rye Bread:* 100%, Light, Seedless Light, Stick, Stick *w* Onion; *Sandwich:* Tin, White, White Tin, Wholemeal; *Tin:* Heyford, Long Split, Long White, Organic Malted, Small White, Wholemeal Long, Wholemeal Organic, Wrapped; *White:* Extra Thick Sliced, Healthy Eating, Medium Sliced, Organic, Soft Grain Thick Sliced, Thick

Sliced, Thin Sliced, Traditional; *Wholemeal:* Devon Flat, Medium Sliced, Mixed Grain Seed, Organic, Seeded, Sliced, Stoneground Organic, Thick Toast, Traditional, *w* Oats

WARBURTON'S SOREEN π

Loaf: Cornish Saffron, Lincolnshire Plum

WILLIAM JACKSON

Brown Sliced, Crumpets, Fruit Tea Cakes, Multigrain Sliced, Super Toaster; *Buns:* Value White, Wholemeal; *Danish White:* Sliced, Toaster; *Golden Slice:* Medium, Thick; *Granary:* Sliced, Thick; *Hovis:* Family, Handy; *White:* Finger Rolls, Medium, Sliced, Stays Fresh Medium, Thick, Thin, Toaster; *Wholemeal:* Medium, Sliced, Thick; *Yorkshire:* Bread Cakes, Dusties

WRIGHT'S π

Bread Mix: **Malty, Mixed Grain, Premium White, Sunflower, Wholemeal**

BREAKFAST FOODS

ALARA WHOLEFOODS √ § π

Organic Rich Muesli

ALDI π

Harvest Morn: Fruit n Fibre, Wheat Bisks; *New Day:* Bubble Rice, Wheaties

ASDA

Healthy Choice Wheat Bisks, Malted Wheaties, Vanilla & Almond Cereal; *Bran:* Flakes, Hi Fibre, Sultana; *Muesli:* Fruit & Fibre, Luxury, Wholewheat

BIOFORCE

Muesli

BREWHURST

Pleniday Muesli

CO-OPπΩΔfcd85

Bran Flakes, Cornflakes, Crisp Rice, Frosted Flakes, Malt Crunchies, Porridge Oats & Bran, Wholewheat Biscuits; *Muesli:* Everyday, Luxury Fruit, Luxury Fruit & Nut

COUNTRY ORGANICS√πΩfcd

Puffed Spelt

DOVES FARM FOODSøπ

Corn Flakes, Easy, Multi Flake, Tasty

FAMILIA SWISS FOODS

Traditional Swiss Muesli

GOOD FOOD DISTRIBUTORSøπΩfcd74

Muesli: all

GOODNESS FOODSøπΩfcd

Muesli: Alpine, Apricot Crunchy, Base, Deluxe, Fibre Rich, Gluten Free, Organic, Rich Fruit, Tropical

GRANNY ANN'S

High Fibre Cooked Soya Bran

GRANOVITAπ

Classic Flakes, Maxiwheat

GREEN & BLACK'Sø§π

Crunch: **Almond, Orange;** *Organic:* **All Your Fibre, Classic Cornflakes, Cornflakes, Swiss Style Muesli, Total Bran**

GREEN CITY WHOLEFOODSøπ

Muesli: Base, Crispy, Crunchy, Deluxe, Five Star, Gluten-Free, High Fibre, Organic Base, Organic Deluxe, Organic Special (No Coconut), Organic Special, Super, Super (No Coconut), Traditional

HEMP FOOD INDUSTRIES ASSOC.ø§πΩ

Hemp Muesli

HEMP UNIONø™§πΩfcd93

Organic Hemp Muesli

JORDANS

Crunchy: **Maple & Pecan, Organic;** *Muesli:* **Natural, Organic**

KALLO

Natural Organic Puffed Rice Cereal

KELLOGG'S

All Bran Buds, Coco Pops, Common Sense Oat Bran Flakes & Fruit, Corn Flakes, Frosties, Just Right, Fruit 'n' Fibre, Raisin Wheats, Rice Krispies

KRAFT JACOBS SUCHARD

Grape Nuts

MAPLETONS

Fru Grains

MARKALø

Organic Muesli: **Energy w Fruit & Nuts, Standard**

MARKS & SPENCER

Bran Sticks, Cornflakes, Crispy Rice, Frosted Flakes; *Muesli:* Luxury, Organic, Tropical Fruit, Unsweetened

NATURAL COLLECTIONø

Muesli: Base, Deluxe

NESTLÉ

Force, Shredded Wheat, Shredded Wheat Bitesize

PILLSBURYπ

Thomas Toasters: Apple, Chocolate

PREWETT'S

Oatbran & Oatgerm, Wholewheat Flakes

QUAKER OATS LTD

Oat Bran Crispies, Oat Krunchies, Oat So Simple Original, Puffed Wheat

RYECROFT FOODSπ

Marshalls: Bran Breakfast Cereals, Fruit & Fibre, Malt Crunchies

SAFEWAY

Choc Teddies, Cornflakes, Farmyard Crunch, Fibre Bran, Instant Hot Oat Cereal, Mixed Berry Wheat Bites, Rice Crunchies, Scottish Porridge Oats, Sultana Bran, Tropical Wheat Bites, Unsweetened Wholewheat Muesli, Wheat Bisks, Wheat Bites; *Flakes:* Bran, Frosted, Tropical Fruit; *Luxury Muesli:* Fruit, Fruit & Nut, Tropical

SHEPHERDBOYøπ

Organic Muesli *w* Hempseed

SOMERFIELD

Breakfast Bran, Bran Fibre Muesli, Malted Wheats, Porridge Oats, Porridge Oats *w* Bran, Puffed Wheat; *Basics:* Corn Flakes, Porridge Oats

SUNBLESTøπ

Cornflakes, Frosted Flakes

SUNWHEEL NATURAL FOODS

Special Deluxe Muesli

TESCO

Cornflakes, Frosted Flakes, Instant Hot Oat Cereal, Malt Wheats, Tropical Feast, Wheat Biscuits; *Muesli:* Crispy, Luxury Fruit, Wholewheat; *Value:* Bran Flakes, Cornflakes, Frosted Flakes

TRAIDCRAFTπΩ

Muesli: Fruit, Nut

WAITROSE

High Fibre Bran, Wheat Cereal Biscuit; *Muesli:* Fruit & Fibre, Fruit & Nut; *Oats:* Porridge, Scottish Porridge

WEETABIXπ

Advantage, Country Home Bran Flakes, Crunchy Bran, Frutibix, Original Ready Brek, Weetabix

WHOLE EARTH

Orange Crunch; *Muesli:* All Your Fibre Organic Breakfast Cereal, Organic; *Organic Cornflakes:* Classic, Whole Grain

XVø§πΩ

Muesli: Base, Deluxe

'BURGERS', 'SAUSAGES', 'MEAT' SLICES ETC

AMBROSIAN VEGETARIAN FOODS√ø™§π

Savoury Herb Burgettes; *Burgers:* Chilli

Bean, Hemp Seed, Savoury, Sesame & Nut, Smokey BBQ; *Mix:* Burger, Sosage; *Sosage Rolls:* Savoury Herbs, Tomato & Garlic; *Sosages:* Hot As Mustard, Plain, Savoury Herb, Smoked Mushroom & Tomato, Tandoori, Tomato & Garlic

BRAKE BROS

Frozen: Nut Cutlettes, Spicy Bean Burger, Spicy Vegetable Burger, Vegebanger

BRUNO FISHER

Burger Mix: Chestnut, Maize, Oatflake, Spelt

CAULDRON FOODS LTD√π

Burgers: Chilli, Savoury, Spicy Bean, Vegetable

CLEAR SPOT

Organic Tofu-Sesame Rissoles

CLIVE LOWEøπ

Organic Soysage Rolls

DIRECT FOODS

Protoveg: 95% Fat Free Sosmix, Burgamix, Burgamix w Onion & Herb, Organic Burgamix, Organic Sosmix, Sosmix, Sosmix Country Herb

DRAGONFLY FOODSøπ

Organic Beany: Baked, Curry, Fruity, Nut, Mushroom, Natural, Smoky, Spicy, Tomato

GOODLIFEπ

Bangers: Herb, Spicy, Spicy Bean; *Burg-* ers: Mexican, Nut, Organic Vegetable

GRANOSE

Vegetable Sausage [frozen]

GRANOVITAπ

Vegetarian Mix: Burger, Organic Burger, Organic Sausage, Sausage, Sausage & Burger

HEINZ FROZEN & CHILLED FOODSπ

Linda McCartney [frozen]: Sausage Rolls, Sausages

HEMP UNIONø™§πΩfcd93

Burgamix

JUST WHOLEFOODS

Organic Vegetarian: Banger Mix, Burger Mix

LONGA LIFE

Meat-Free Vegetarian Slices: Not Chicken, Not Ham

LUNN LINKS√øπΩ

Kitchen Garden Organic TVP: Flavoured, Plain

MORNINGSTAR FARMS

Hard Rock Cafe Veggie Burger

REALEAT

Fishless Fish Cakes, VegeMenu, VegeMince; *VegeBanger:* Herb, Meaty Style, Spicy; *VegeBurger:* Chilli Style, Herb & Vegetable, No Salt

REDWOOD√ø§π

Cheatin Roast Beef Turkey, Cheatin Vegetarian Style Rashers; *Cheatin*

Chicken Bites: 5 Spice, BBQ, Savoury, Tikka; *Cheatin Slices:* Chicken, Garlic Sausage, Ham, Pepperoni, Roast Beef, Turkey; *Organic:* Frankfurter, Lincolnshire Sausage; *Vegi-Deli Gourmet Sausages:* Oregano & Basil, Sage & Marjoram; *Vegi-Deli Slices:* Boston Baked Bean, Provençal, Spicy Chilli, Spicy Thai

SOY FOODSø™π

Burgers: Bengal, Herb, Mexican, Nut

TAIFUN

Organic: Hot Dogs, Peanut Butter Burgers

TESCO

Nut Cutlets, Quarter Pound Mexican Bean Burgers

VEGETARIAN'S CHOICE√™§πΩ

Vegetable Protein: Burgers, Sausage Mix, Sausages

VEGGIES√ø™§π

Frozen: Burgers, Chilli Burgers, Savoury Sosages, Sosages, Tomato Sosages; *Mix:* Burger, Hemp Seed, Sosage

WICKEN FENøπΩfcd

Cajun & Red Pepper Kebab; *Vegetarian Sausages:* Country Herb, Courgette Spinach & Nutmeg, Mediterranean Vegetable, Mushroom & Tarragon, Thai Spinach, Tomato & Garlic

YAKSO

Temmo Tempeh Burgers

CAKES & CAKE MIXES

ASDA

Farm Stores Apple Pies, Kitchen Fun For Kids Jam Tarts, Ready to Decorate Gingerbread Ducks; *Instore Bakery:* 5 Jam Donuts, Rhubarb Pie

BLACKFRIARS BAKERYπΩfcd

Eccles Cake

BRAKE BROS

Frozen: Apple Turnovers, Individual Seven Fruits Summer Pudding, Mini Baked Apple Pies, Spotted Dick

BREWHURST

Pleniday Cake Mix

CO-OPπΩΔfcd85

Jam Doughnuts, Rock Cake Mix

EVERFRESH NATURAL FOODS√øπ

Sunnyvale Organic Cakes: Banana, Carrot w Raisins, Carrot w Raisins & Almonds, Cherry Genoa, Choc N Cherry, Choc N Orange, Chocolate Chip, Coconut, Date & Pecan, Fig & Orange, Fruit, Lemon, Mandarin, Orange, Rich Fruit, Stem Ginger

GOBBLINπΩfcd86

Banbury Cake, Barmbrack, Bread Pudding, Eccles Cakes; *Slices:* Almond Fruit (ask for 'no honey'), Apple (ask for 'no honey'), Apricot, Black Cherry, Date, Fig

LYONS CAKES

Traffic Jams

MARKS & SPENCER

6 Jam Doughnuts

MR KIPLING

Apple & Blackcurrant Pies, Fruit Pies Selection — Apricot Pies, Jam Tarts Selection, Slices Selection — Treacle Lattice Tart, Treacle Lattice Tart; *Fruit Pie Bars:* Apple & Blackcurrant, Bramley Apple

MRS MOON'S√øπΩfcd

Organic Apple Sultana Streusel Muffin Mix

ORGRANø

Pancake Mix: **Apple Cinnamon, Buckwheat**

SAFEWAY

Assorted Jam Tarts, Savers Apple Pies, Summer Fruit Pie Selection, Instore Bakery Apple Turnover; *Instore Bakery Gingerbread:* Man, Snowman & Scarf Kit, World Cup Striker England Kit, World Cup Striker Scotland Kit; *Instore Bakery Individual Pie:* Apple, Rhubarb

SOMERFIELD

Apricot & Peach Lattice

SOY FOODSø™π

Apple & Fruit Strudel, Fruit Pie *w* Kuzu; *Cake:* Banana & Date Slice, Fruit & Ginger

STILETTOπ

Mrs Crimble's Dutch Fruit Loaf

TESCO

2 Individual Summer Fruit Pudding, 6 Value Apple Pies, Jam Doughnuts

TRA'FO

Waffles: **Hazelnut, Malt**

VILLAGE BAKERYøπΩ

Celebration Fruit Cake; *Slice:* **Apricot, Date**

WAITROSE

Kirsch Hawaii; *Pies:* Apple & Blackberry, Family Apple, Family Apple & Blackberry, Small Fruit

XVø§πΩ

Celebration Cake

'CHEESE' & 'CHEESE' SPREADS

BIDDY MERKINS√™πΩ

Vegerella (hard): Italian, Mexican

BUTE ISLAND√§π

Scheese (hard): **Blue, Cheddar, Cheddar w Chives, Cheshire, Edam, Emmental, Gouda, Hickory Cheddar, Mozzarella**

GALAXY FOODSπ
Soya Slices (hard): **Cheddar Style, Mozzarella Style**

KALLO

Fromsoya: w Dill, *w* Garlic & Herb, *w* Horseradish, *w* Onion

REDWOOD√ø§π

Cheezly (hard): **BBQ Style, Garlic &**

Parsley Style, Pizza Style, Red Cheddar, White Cheddar, White Cheddar *w* Bacon Style Pieces; *Cheezly (soft):* Garlic & Herb, Original Cream, Sour Cream & Chive

ST GILES FOODS

Parmazano

TOFUTTI√§π

Better Than Cream Cheese: French Onion, Garlic & Herbs, Herbs & Chives, Plain; *Better Than Sour Cream:* all; *Tofutti Light:* all

VEGIE KAASπΩ

Hard: Cheddar Style, Mozzerella Style

CHOCOLATE

ALLERGYCARE√øπ

Whizzers: Chocolate Beans, Chocolate Footballs, Mint Balls, Speckled Eggs

ANIMAL AID√ø§πΩ∆fcd76

Handmade Vegan Chocolate: Assortment, Rose & Violet Cremes

ASDA

Plain Chocolate: Drops, Flavour Cake Covering

CADBURY

Fry's Chocolate Cream: Chocolate, Orange, Peppermint; *Fry's Spirit:* Berry Margarita, Pina Colada, Velvet Dream

CHAPEL CHOCOLATESøπ

Hazelnut Rocher, Plain Chocolate Truf-

fles; *Cluster:* **Almond & Raisin, Hazelnut & Apricot**

D&D CHOCOLATESø

Dark Chocolate: Bar, Flowers, Hazelnut Praline, Large Chuckling Bunny, Net of 8 Mini Bunnies

DR HADWEN TRUST√ø§

Champagne Liqueurs, Chocolate Covered Stem Ginger, Mint Cremes, Orange Cremes, Strawberry Fourre, Vegan Chocolate Assortment

EQUAL EXCHANGEπ

Plain Chocolate Brazil Nuts

GRANNY ANN'S

Chunky Eggs

GREEN & BLACK'Sø§π

Organic Chocolate: **Dark, Hazelnut & Currant, Maya Gold**

HOUSE OF DORCHESTERøø§π

Plain Chocolate: Luxury Bars, Mint Discs, Mint Slims, Vegan Range Of Weigh Out; *Plain Chocolate Cremes:* Coffee, Orange, Peppermint, Rose & Violet, Violet

KINGSWAY

Smooth Plain Chocolate

LEAF

Elizabeth Shaw Plain Chocolate: After Dinner Mints, Mint Crisp, Orange Crisp

LINDT & SPRUNGLI

Excellence: 70% Cocoa Mini-eggs, 85% Cocoa Bar, Plain Chocolate, Plain Chocolate 70% Cocoa Bar, Plain Chocolate 70% Cocoa Thins; *Swiss:* Dark Tafel Surfin Bar, Dark Thins

LYME REGISøπ

Chocolate Coated Marzipan: Organic, Plain

MARKS & SPENCER

Extra Fine Swiss Dark Chocolate

MOLLE SKOVLY

After All Mini Mint, Cafe Choco, Mint Heart; *Dark Choco:* Almond, Hazelnut, Peanut, Raisin

NESTLÉ

After Eight Mints

NORFOLK TRUFFLE COMPANYø™§π

Organic Dairy Free Organic Chocolate: **Cognac Flambéd Banana Truffle, Expresso Truffle, Ginger Wine Truffle, Hazelnut Apricot Cluster, Hazelnut Crunch Rocher, Maple Almond Truffle, Roast Almond & Raisin Cluster, Truffle, Xmas Wine Truffle**

NORWOOD HOUSE CHOCOLATEø

Dark Chocolate: Bars, Coated Almonds, Coated Hazelnuts, Cooking Chocolate, Cups, Discs, Hearts, Pearls, Spheres, Squares, *w* Pistachios & Almond Marzipan; *Dark Chocolate Dipped Fruits:* Grapefruit, Lemon, Orange

PAYNES

Just Brazils In Plain Chocolate, Just Ginger In Plain Chocolate

PLAMIL√™§π

Chocolate Bars: **Hazelnut, Martello, Mint, Plain; *Organic Chocolate Bars:* Expressions, Mint, Orange, Plain**

PREMIER ORGANIC FOOD

Bonbon Jeannette: **Dark Chocolate Covered Hazelnuts & Raisins, Dark Chunky Nut Brittle, Vegan Chocolate Assortment Box; *Bonbon Jeannette Bars:* Dark Chocolate, Dark Hazelnut, Dark Marzipan, Dark Orange**

RAPUNZEL

Plain, Plain & Almond

RITTER SPORT

Plain Chocolate, Plain Chocolate *w* Marzipan Filling, Plain Chocolate *w* Peppermint Filling

ROCOCO CHOCOLATESøπΩ

Dusted Scorched Almonds; *Artisan Bars:* Caramelised Almond, Cardamon, Chilli Pepper, Crystallised Ginger, Earl Grey Tea, Juniper, Lavender, Nutmeg, Orange & Geranium, Orange Confite, Petitgrain, Pink Peppercorn, Rosemary, Tarragon, Thyme, Wild Mint Leaves; *Plain Chocolate Bars:* 60%, 85%; *Valrhona Grand Cru Plain Chocolate:* Caraibe, Guanaja, Manjari; *Valrhona Grand Cru Chocolate Bars:* 99% Plain, Caraibe, Guanaja, Manjari, Organic Plain, Sugar & Dairy Free Plain

SAFEWAY

Thin Chocolate Mint Creams

THORNTONS

Dark Bar: Chocolate, Ginger

TRAIDCRAFTπΩ

Continental Organic Plain Chocolate

TREBOR BASSETTΩ

Barker & Dobson Chocolate Mint Crisp; *Jameson Chocolate Creams:* **Orange, Strawberry**

TROPICAL SOURCEø

Dairy-Free Chocolate: all; *Organic Dairy-Free Chocolate:* all

VEGAN SOCIETY√ø§Ω

Fine Mint Chocolates, Organic Gourmet Chocolate Truffles

VIVA!√ø§π

Finest Vegan Plain Chocolate Bar, Handmade Vegan Chocolates

WAITROSE

After Dinner Mints, Chocolate Limes, Chocolate Peppermint Creams, Liquer Chocolates, Mint Crisps, Plain Chocolate Brazil Nuts; *Chocolate Bars w Filling:* Mint, Strawberry

YORK FOODS√™π

Chocolat Menier

CONFECTIONERY & SWEET SNACKS

ALDIπ

Mint Imperials

ALLERGYCARE√øπ

Original Silhouette Carob Bar; *Whizzers:* Mint Humbugs, Toffees

ASDA

Crystal Clear Mints, Flying Saucers, Fruity Soft Centres, Pick n Mix Crystal Clearmints, Sherbet Fruit Cocktails

AUSTRALIAN NOUGAT COMPANYø™π

Macadamia Bliss Nougat: **Nuts & Fruit, Nuts & Pistachios**

BOND'Sπ

Aniseed Twist, Apple & Custard, Army & Navy, Barley Sugar, Cola Cubes, Cough Candy, Fizz Bombs, Garden Fruits, Menthol & Eucalyptus, Old English Cloves, Rainbow Crystals, Rhubarb & Custard, Strawberries & Cream, West Indian Limes, Winter Mixture; *Drops:* Acid, Fruit, Pear; *Pips:* Cola, Sherbet; *Pops:* Corn Fizz, Mixed Fruit, Rhubarb & Custard, Strawberry Fizz, Traffic Light, Tutti Frutti; *Sherbets:* Lemon, Strawberry

CAROLE MONTEITH√ø™π

Twistees

CO-OPπΩΔfcd85

Clear Mints

D&D CHOCOLATESø

Carob: Bar, Bunny, Gluten Free No Added Sugar Drops, Orange Bar, Teddy

DOBSON'Sπ

Army & Navy, Bulls Eyes, Gogs, Rhubarb & Custard, Rosy Apple, Sherbet Lemons, Strawberry & Cream; *Balls:* Kola, Pineapple; *Drops:* Fruit, Pear, Tom Thumb; *Pips:* Kola, Spearmint

DR HADWEN TRUST√ø§

Bonbons In Embossed Decorated Cat Tin, Caramel Toffees, Chocolate Dipped 'Bee Free' Honeycomb, Chocolate Dipped Peanut Brittle, Jellies In World Globe Money Box Tin, Rose & Lemon Turkish Delight, Sugared Almonds, Vanilla Fudge

EQUAL EXCHANGEπ

Barrita Sesame Bar

EVERGREEN

Organic Apple Crumbles

FLEUR

Mixed Fruit Lollipops; *Fruit Drops:* **Alpine Herb, Blackcurrant, Mix, Tropical Mix**

GRANNY ANN'S

Granymel Toffees: Caramel, Liquorice, Mint, Treacle

GRANOVITAπ

Wild Fruit Bar; *Castus Fruit Bars:* **Date & Apricot, Raisin;** *Organic Gourmet Bars:* **Almanda, Noisette**

HEMP UNIONø™§πΩfcd93

Hemp Muesli Bar: Banana, Double Chocolate, Double Seed, Fig & Orange

HEMP FOOD INDUSTRIES ASSOC.ø§πΩ

Pow! Hemp Bar

KETTLE VALLEYøπ

Grabber 100 % Fruit Energy Bar: Apricot, Mountain Berry, Raspberry, Strawberry; *Real Fruit Snack:* **Apple, Apricot, Blueberry, Cherry, Raspberry, Strawberry, Tutti Frutti, Wildberry**

LYME REGISøπ

Fruit Bar: **Banana, Date & Fig, Ginger & Pear;** *La Fruit:* **Apricot, Raspberry;** *Ricci Carob Coated Fruit Bar:* **Coconut, Lime, Orange;** *Zaps Fruit Bar:* **Apricot, Orange**

MARKS & SPENCER

3 Lollipops, Apple Slices, Fizzy Fish, Ultra Fruity; *Chewing Gum:* Blackcurrant, Coolmint, Grapefruit, Peppermint; *Crumbles:* Lemon, Mint, Spearmint; *Lolly:* Bus, Large; *Strawberry & Almond Cereal:* Bar, Carton

MARS

Skittles, Starburst, Tunes

MITOKUø

Sweet Crunch Brown Rice; *Sweets:* **Butterscotch, Ginger, Lemon, Peppermint, Sour Plum, Vanilla**

MOLLE SKOVLY

Nougat

NESTLÉ

Fox Glacier Fruit, Jelly Tots, Mints, Polo Fruits; *Polo Mints:* Extra Strong, Original, Spearmint, Sugar Free

NEW EARTH

9 Bar, Organic Hemp Seed 9 Bar

ORGRAN∅

Carob & Fruit Log, Fruit Bars; *Clusters:* Carob & Coconut, Carob & Peanut

PANDAπ

Energy Bar

PAYNES

Army & Navy Boiled Sweets

PLAMIL√™§π

Carob Bar: Hazelnut, No Added Sugar, Orange, Plain; *Carob Drops:* No Added Sugar, Sweetened

POWER HEALTH∅π**Ω**

White Aniseed Balls; *Herb Candy Sticks:* Aniseed, Barley Sugar, Blackcurrant, Cinnamon, Lemon, Liquorice Juice, Orange, Pineapple, Strawberry; *Sugar Free:* Fruits, Mints

RADFORDS∅π

Dairy Free Fudge: Cherry, Chocolate, Coconut Ice, Gift Boxes, Ginger, Rum & Raisin, Vanilla, Walnut

RIDPATH PEKπ

Sesame Crunch

SAFEWAY

Connoisseur Stuffed Dried Fruit Selection, Crystallised Ginger, Extra Strong Mint Humbugs, Flying Saucers, Fruit Flavoured Slices, Fruit Lollies, Sparkling Mints

SANO MIO

Frutty Sweets: Peppermint, Strawberry; *Minthy Sweets:* Peppermint, Strawberry

SHEPHERDBOY∅π

Fruit & Nut Bar: Apple, Banana (*w* VS Trademark only), Carob, Coconut, Ginger, Organic *w* Sunflower Seeds, Multi-Fruit, Tangy, *w* Sunflower Seeds; *Just So Carob Bar:* Crispy, Orange, Peppermint, *w* Ginger

SOMERFIELD

Clear Mints

SPEAKEASY∅

Chewing Gum: all; *Organic Mints:* all

SUNITA

Sultanas & Grape Juice Halva

SWEET STARSπ

Cola Cubes, Cough Candy, Garden Fruits, Lemon Sherbets; *Drops:* Cola, Pear

TESCO

Acid Drops, Coffee Shop Caramel Popcorn, Sparkling Mints

THORNTONS

Barley Sugar, Cola Snail Jelly, Diabetic Mint Creams, Hugs & Kisses, Mint Crumbles, Orange Jelly Fish, Princes & Frogs, Raspberry Spider; *Hard Boiled Fruit:* Citrus, Mixed

TREBOR BASSETTΩ

Craven Chocolate Limes; *Bards/Butterkist:* Salty Microwave Popcorn, Sugared Popcorn; *Barker & Dobson:* Best English Mints; *Barratt:* Anglo Bubbly Bubble Gum, Astro Belts, Fruit Flavoured Lollies (all), Sherbet Dippers (all); *Bassett's Fundays:* **American Hard Gums, Barley Sugar, Cough Candy Twist, Fruit Bonbons, Mint Creams, Murray Mints, Pear Drops, Real Chocolate Limes, Sherbet Lemons;** *Beechnut Sugar Free Chewing Gum:* **Peppermint, Spearmint;** *Hacks:* **Blackcurrant, Original;** *Maynard:* **American Hard Gums;** *Pascall:* **Barley Sugar, Cherry Drops, Chocolate Limes, Cough Candy, Fruit Bonbons, Pear Drops, Pineapple Chunks, Sherbet Lemons, Sherbet Strawberries, Sweet Peanuts;** *Trebor:* **Assorted Fruit Jellies, Clarnico Mint Creams, Coolmints Sugar Free Mints**

TROPICAL SOURCEø

Organic Hard Candies: **all**

VEGAN SOCIETY√ø§Ω

Vegan Macadamia Bliss Nougat

VILLAGE BAKERYøπΩ

Organic Trophy Bars: **4 Fruit, 4 Fruit Dispenser, 4 Nut, 4 Seed**

VIVA!√ø§π

Dairy-Free Fudge

WAITROSE

Clear Mints, Grenoble, Mint Imperials

WILLIAM SANTUSøπfcd

Uncle Joe's Mint Balls

WRIGLEY'S

Airwaves; *Extra:* Peppermint, Spearmint, Winter Fresh; *Orbit:* Doublemint, Ice White, Lemon Fresh, Spearmint; *Wrigley's:* Doublemint, Juicy Fruit, PK Peppermint, Spearmint

XVø§πΩ

Fruit Bars

COOKING AIDS — SAVOURY

ALDIπ

Sweet Harvest: Instant Mashed Potato

ALLERGYCARE√øπ

Herb & Onion Stuffing Mix

ASDA

Farm Stores: Instant Mashed Potato; *Sauce Mix:* Bread, Parsley; *Stuffing Mix:* Parsley & Thyme, Sage & Onion

BLUE DRAGON

Rice Flour Pancakes for Spring Rolls

CLEARSPRING√ø§π

Kuzu

CO-OPπΩΔfcd85

Bread Sauce Mix, Golden Breadcrumbs, Instant Mashed Potato; *Stuffing Mix:* Parsley & Thyme, Sage & Onion, Speciality Chestnut, Speciality Country Herb, Speciality Garlic & Herb

DREI STERREN

Gomasio

GR LANE

Herb Salt

HALDANE

Organic Nut Roast Mix

JUST WHOLEFOODS

Organic Wholemeal Breadcrumbs, VegeRen Vegetarian Rennet; *Stuffing Mix:* Chestnut, Country Style, Sage & Onion

MARIGOLD HEALTH FOODSπ

Engevita Yeast Flakes

MITOKUø

Gomasio, Mochi, Shiso, Tekka, Wasabi

SAFEWAY

Broth Mix, Bruscetta Topping, Instant Mashed Potato, Sage & Onion Stuffing Mix; *Purée:* Double Concentrated Tomato, Garlic

SANCHIø

Furikake Seasoning, Wasabi Powder; *Seaweeds:* all

SEAGREENS√ø™π

Culinary Seaweed Ingredient, Seaweed Table Condiment

SOMERFIELD

Luxury Stuffing Mix: Apricot Sultana & Amaretto, Vine Fruit Port & Cranberry; *Stuffing:* Apple & Herb, Chestnut, Garlic & Herb, Parsley Thyme & Lemon, Sage & Onion

TESCO

Italian Sun-dried Tomato Paste, Smokey BBQ Breadcrumbs; *Stuffing Mix:* Country Herb, Garlic & Herb, Sage & Onion, Speciality Sun-dried Tomato

WAITROSE

Crispy Seaweed, Garlic Purée, Lightly Salted Croutons, Mashed Potato, Toasted Croutons; *Stuffing Mix:* Chestnut & Tarragon, Date Orange & Ginger, Garlic & Herb, Herb & Peppercorn, Parsley & Thyme, Sage & Onion

COOKING AIDS — SWEET

ASDA

Cut Mixed Peel, Glacé Cherries; *Marzipan:* Golden, White

BIONOVA

Apple Purée

CARABAY√øπΩfcd

Irish Carrageen Moss

CLEARSPRING√ø§π

Natura Nuovo Fruit Purée: **Apple, Apricot, Bilberry, Prune;** *Organic Amazake:* Brown Rice, Millet

CO-OPπΩΔfcd85

Custard Powder, Glacé Cherries, Mixed Peel, Ready to Roll White Icing; *Food Colourings:* Blue, Green, Red, Yellow; *Food Flavourings:* Almond, Brandy, Lemon, Peppermint, Rum, Vanilla; *Marzipan:* White, White Almond

GR LANEøπΩΔfcd87

Gelozone Vegetarian Gelling Powder

GREEN & BLACK'Sø§π

Cocoa Powder

JUST WHOLEFOODS√πΩ

All Natural Custard Powder

LYME REGISøπ

Marzipan: Non Organic, Organic

MARKALø

Fruit Purée: Apple, Blackcurrant, Strawberry

MARKS & SPENCER

Berries In Port, Cherries In Kirsch, Maple Syrup, Peach Halves In Brandy, Pears In Sweet Wine; *Sauce:* Lemon, Raspberry

MERIDIAN

Syrup: Date, Organic Maple

RAYNER BURGESSπ

Angelica, Cocktail Cherries; *Topping Syrup:* Butterscotch, Chocolate, Raspberry, Strawberry

RENSHAW SCOTTπ

Regalice; *Marzipan:* Brandy, Classic, Golden Colour, Natural, Roll; *Regalice:* & Marzipan Dual Pack, Celebration, Roll

SAFEWAY

Crumble Mix; *Sweeteners:* all

SHARWOOD'S

Creamed Coconut Sachets

SOMERFIELD

Custard Powder, Cut Mixed Peel, Glacé Cherries, Mixed Fruit; *Marzipan:* Golden, White

SUPERCOOK

Colour: Black, Blue, Green, Pink, Yellow; *Flavour:* Almond, Banana, Brandy, Coffee, Lemon, Peppermint, Rum, Strawberry, Vanilla

TESCO

Glacé Cherries, Luxury Crumble Mix, Tablet Sweeteners; *Glacé Cherries:* Chopped, Natural Coloured

WAITROSE

Apricot & Papaya *w* Rum, Apricot Halves in Amaretto, Cane Molasses, Cereal Topper, Cherries *w* Kirsch, Cocoa, Clementines *w* Orange Liqueur, Cocktail Cherries, Cut Mixed Peel, Forest Fruits in Cherry Brandy, Glacé Cherries, Green Figs *w* Cognac, Kumquats *w* Orange Brandy, Mixed Fruit *w* Cognac, Mixed Peel, Peaches *w* Cinnamon Syrup, Satsumas in Orange Liqueur, Tropical Fruit Cocktail Salad, Whole Peaches *w* Cognac; *Fruit Filling:* Apple & Blackberry, Apple & Raspberry , Apricot, Black Cherry, Blackcurrant, Red Cherry; *Marzipan:* Golden, White

WHOLE EARTHø§π

Organic Cocoa Powder; *Syrup:* Barley Malt, Brown Rice, Maize Malt

YAKSO

Amazake: Millet, Rice

CRACKERS, CRISPBREADS ETC

ALLINSONø

Wholemeal Crackerbread

ASDA

Butter Puffs, Melba Toast, Poppy &

Sesame Thin Biscuits; *Bread Sticks:* Garlic, Pizza, Plain, Sesame; *Crackers:* 50% Less Fat, Cream, Selection; *Ready to Eat Poppadums:* Plain, Spicy

BURTON'S BISCUITS

Lightly Salted Potato Puffs

CARR'S

Table Water Biscuits: Large, Small, *w* Sesame

CLEARSPRING√ø§π

Japanese Rice Crackers: Brown Sesame Wafers, Brown *w* Tamari; *Rice Cakes:* Brown Rice Sesame, Double Sesame, Sesame Garlic, Teriyaki

CO-OPπΩΔfcd85

High Bake Water Biscuits; *Crackers:* 50% Reduced Fat Cream, Cream, Savoury Wheat, The Traditional; *Crispbread:* Savoury Wheat, Wheat

COURTNEYSø

English Water Crackers: **Classic Flavour, Cracked, Savoury Herb, Sundried Tomato**

DOVES FARMøπ

Rye Crackers

EREWHONø

Japanese Brown Rice Crackers *w* Sea Salt

FOX'S BISCUITSπ

Biscuits & Herbs, Biscuits & Pepper

GOOD FOOD DISTRIBUTORSøπΩfcd74

Sticks: Garlic, Sesame

JACOBSπ

Cornish Wafer; *Crackers:* Bran, Cream, Water High Bake

KALLO

Savoury Yeast Extract Organic Rice Cakes; *Natural Rice Cakes:* No Added Salt, Slightly Salted; *Original Thick Slice Organic Rice Cakes:* No Added Salt, Sesame No Added Salt, Sesame Slightly Salted, Slightly Salted; *Snack Size Organic Rice Cakes:* No Salt, Pepper - Slightly Salted, Slightly Salted; *Thin Slice Organic Rice Cakes:* No Added Salt, Sesame Slightly Salted, Slightly Salted

MCVITIES

Butter Puffs, Krackawheat Multigrain

MARKS & SPENCER

Ciabatta Crispbreads, Poppadums, Scottish Oat Cakes

MITOKUø

Japanese Rice Crackers: Brown Rice *w* Sesame, Harvest Moon

NAIRN'Sπ

Oatcakes: **Organic, Rough, Traditional**

ORGRANø

Corn Cakes; *Crispbreads:* **Corn, Organic Rice, Rice & Cracked Pepper, Rice & Garden Herbs, Rice & Millet, Salsa Corn**

PATAK'Sπ

Pappadums: Garlic, Hot Spiced, Plain

RAKUSEN'S™

Crackers: 99% Fat Free, Hilo, Matzo,

Nice & Spicy Matzo, Savoury Bit Matzo; *Matzos:* Tea, Traditional, Wheaten

RYVITAøπ

Allinson Wholemeal Crackerbread; *Crackerbread:* High Fibre, Original Wheat; *Ryvita Crispbread:* Dark Rye, Multibran, Original, Sesame

SAFEWAY

High Baked Water Biscuits, Melba Toast, Rough Scottish Oatcakes; *Breadsticks:* Assortment, Garlic, Mini Assortment, Pesto Flavour, Pizza Flavour, Plain; *Crackers:* Cream, Half Fat Cream, Selection; *Crispbread:* Brown Rye, Sesame; *Thins:* Onion & Sesame, Poppy & Sesame

SANCHIø

5-Flavour Arare Rice Puffs, Brown Rice Crackers, Nori Maki Rice Crackers

SIMMERSπ

Abernethy, Butter Biscuits, Macvita, Mini Oatcakes, Scottish Savoury Selection

SOMERFIELD

Basics Cream Cracker, Brown Rye Crispbread, Cream Crackers; *Biscuits:* Healthy Selection Wheat, High Bake Water; *Breadsticks:* Classic, Garlic, Sesame; *Thins Savoury Biscuits:* Poppy & Sesame, Sesame & Onion

TESCO

Cornish Wafers, Rough Oatcakes, High Baked Water Biscuits, Onion & Sesame Seed Brown Crackers, Wholegrain

Crackers; *Breadsticks:* Garlic, Mini, Original, Torinesi, Wholewheat; *Ready-to-Eat Puppadums:* Plain, Plain Mini, Spicy

VILLAGE BAKERYøπΩ

Oatcakes, Savoury Seed Biscuits

VITALINEAπ

Cream Cracker

WAITROSE

Rough Griddle Oatcakes; *Breadsticks:* Garlic, Plain, Sesame; *Crackers:* Cream, High Bake

WHOLEFOOD WHOLESALE CO-OP√™πρ

Organic Oatcakes: Low Salt, No Salt

CREAM REPLACERS

GRANOSE

Soya Creem

PROVAMELπ

Soya Dream

RICH'S

Coffee Rich Non-Dairy Creamer, Ready-to-Use Whip Topping

DESSERTS

ASDA

Frozen Strudel: Apple, Fruits of the Forest; *Instore Bakery:* Apple & Blackberry Crumble, Rhubarb Crumble; *Vegetarian Jelly Crystals (Sugar Free):* Lemon, Orange, Strawberry

BIONA

Creme Desserts: Blueberry, Strawberry, Vanilla

CO-OPπΩΔfcd85

Chilled Summer Pudding; *Frozen Strudel:* Apple, Summer Fruit

DRAGONFLY FOODSøπ

Organic Beany Sweet: Chocolate, Fruity

GEORGE SKOULIKASπΩfcd

Sunita Grape Juice & Sultana Halva

IMAGINEø

Pudding: Banana, Butterscotch, Chocolate, Lemon

JUST WHOLEFOODS√πΩ

Jelly Crystals: Lemon, Raspberry, Strawberry, Tropical

LIMAø

Soya Dessert: Chocolate, Vanilla, Yannoh

MARKALø

Soya Desserts: Nut, Vanilla

MARKS & SPENCER

Reduced Fat Layered Dessert; *Compote:* Blackberry & Apple, Summer Fruit

MAXIM MARKETING√ø™§πΩΔfcd95

Weikfield Jelly Crystals: Cherry, Mango, Orange, Pineapple, Raspberry, Strawberry

ORGANIC VALLEY LTD√ø™π

Dairy Free Rice Pudding

PLAMIL√™§π

Rice Pudding w Sultanas: Sugar Free, Sweetened

PROVAMELπ

Dessert Pots: Chocolate, Hazelnut, Vanilla; *Organic Dessert:* Chocolate, Vanilla

ROWNTREE'S

Ready To Eat Jelly: all

SAFEWAY

2 Summer Puddings, Summer Fruit Medley, Summerfruit Compote, Winter Pudding

TESCO

Strudel: Apple, Apple & Strawberry, Woodland Fruit

WAITROSE

Pudding: Summer, Winter

DIPS & DRESSINGS

ANNIE'S NATURALSπ

Organic Dressing: Goddess, Green Garlic, Tuscany Italian; *Organic Vinaigrette:* Horseradish w Echinacea, Shiitake & Sesame

ASDA

Salad Cream Low Fat, Tex Mex Fresh Salsa Dip; *Salsa Chunky Dip:* Fruity, Hot, Mild; *Dressing:* French Vinaigrette, Sundried Tomato

food

BIDDY MERKINS√™πΩ

Egg Free: Alavon Mayonnaise, Coleslaw, Garlic Flavoured Coleslaw

BIONOVA

Salad Dressing: w Dijon Mustard, *w* Herbs, *w* Wholegrain Mustard

BRAKE BROS

Frozen: Guacamole, Salsa

CO-OPπΩΔfcd85

Salsa Dip, Virtually Fat Free Vinaigrette

GRANOVITAπ

Egg & Dairy Free Alternative to Mayonnaise: Garlic, Lemon, Original; *Mayola Egg & Dairy Free Mayonnaise:* Garlic, Lemon, Organic, Plain

HEINZ

Hot Salsa

JETHROSø

Vinaigrettes: Classic, Ginger & Sesame, Mojo Chilli, Orange & Oregano, Raspberry & Walnut

KITE WHOLEFOODS

Egg Free Mayonnaise: Garlic, Plain

KRAFT JACOBS SUCHARD

Italian Vinaigrette w Garlic: Fat Free, Regular

MARKS & SPENCER

Fresh Chunky Salsa, Green Olive Tapenade; *Dressing:* 95% Fat Free French, Classic French, Classic Italian, French, Italian Style, Roasted Red Pepper

MERIDIANøπ

Salsa: Hot, Mild

NESTLÉ

Waistline Dressing: Reduced Fat, Reduced Fat Cocktail

ORGANIC VALLEY LTD√ø™π

Salad Cream

PLAMIL√™§π

Egg Free Mayonnaise: Chilli, Garlic, Organic, Plain, Tarragon

RAYNER BURGESSπ

Steven Saunders Salsa: Jalapeno & Mango, Peppered Pineapple

ST GILES FOODS

La Genovesa Pump & Spray Balsamic Vinegar & Olive Oil Vinaigrette; *Duchesse:* Classic French Dressing, Classic Italian Dressing, Garlic Dressing & Dip, Luxury Dill Dressing For Salmon, Oil Free Dill & Lemon Dressing; *Florentino Dressing:* Balsamic Vinegar, Sun-dried Tomato; *Just Wicked Dips:* Hot Tomato & Mango, Mango & Cinnamon, Mango & Lime; *Life:* Egg Free Mayonnaise Dressing, Egg Free Salad Cream Dressing; *Salad Light:* Balsamic Vinaigrette, Garlic & Herb, Lemon Provençal; *River Edge:* Balsamic Dressing, Cumin & Jalapeno Salsa, Pesto Caesar Dressing, Serious Garlic Dip, Sun-dried Tomato & Herb Dressing; *Windjammer Sunshine Dressing:* Mango, Passion Fruit, Raspberry

SAFEWAY

Amigo's Salsa Dip: Hot, Mild; *Dressing:* Fresh French, Oil Free Salad, Provençale Vinaigrette, Roast Garlic & Onion, Sun-dried Tomato, Sun-dried Tomato & Basil, Sweet Red Pepper; *Pre-packed Salsa:* Fresh, Fresh Green

SALSA CORDOVERA√

Salsa Especial Picante Cordovera

SAN AMVROSIA HEALTH FOODSπΩ

Salsa; *Dips:* **Artichoke, Aubergine, Spicy Pinto Bean, Tahini**

SARSONS

Sarsons for Salads

SOMERFIELD

Dip: Barbeque, Salsa, Tomato Salsa; *Dressing:* French, Healthy Selection Reduced Calorie, Healthy Selection Reduced Fat Herb & Garlic, Low Fat French

SUMA™§πΩ

Vegannaise (mayonnaise): Plain, w Garlic

TESCO

Salsa Dip; *Salad Dressing:* 95% Oil Free, French, Garlic Vinaigrette, Mustard & Tarragon, Original Fresh Style Vinaigrette, Premium French Vinaigrette, Reduced Calorie Salad Cream, Sun-dried Flavour, Sweet Red Pepper, Tomato & Herb

WAITROSE

Salsa Dip; *Dressings:* French, Lemon Garlic & Chive, Sun-dried; *Vinaigrette:* Fat Free, Sherry

WALKERS

Dippas Salsa Dip: **Cool Tomato, Hot Spicy**

YAKSO

Mayo, Mayo w Garlic

EGG REPLACERS

ALLERGYCARE√øπ

Whole Egg Replacer

ORGRANø

No Egg Egg Replacer

GRAVIES & STOCKS

ALLERGYCARE√øπ

Gravy Mix

APPLEFORDS

Low Salt Gravy Mix

ASDA

Gravy Vegetarian Granules

BESTFOODS

Knorr Cubes: Garlic & Italian Herbs Seasoning for Pasta, Seasoning for Pilau Rice Vegetable Stock; *Knorr Herb Cubes:* Mixed Herbs, Parsley & Garlic

BIOFORCE

Herb Seasoning Salt: Herbamare, Plantaforce, Trocomare

BISTOπΩ

Gravy Powder; *Granules:* Chip Shop Curry, Gravy, Onion Gravy, Vegetarian

CO-OPπΩΔfcd85

Gravy Browning, Rich Brown Gravy Mix

CROSSE & BLACKWELL

Gravy Browning

GR LANEøπΩΔfcd87

Vecon Country Cup, Vecon Stock Paste

JESSUP MARKETINGπΩ

Naturally Good Vegetable Gravy Powder

JUST WHOLEFOODS√πΩ

Vegetarian Stock Powder

KALLO

Organic Liquid Seasoning; *Organic Stock Cubes:* French Onion, Garlic & Herb, Mushroom, Tomato & Herb, Tomato & Peppers, Vegetable; *Stock Cubes:* French Onion, Garlic & Herb, Low Salt Vegetable, Tomato & Herb, Vegetable, Yeast Free Vegetable; *Vegetable:* Gravy Powder, Organic Stock Powder, Stock Granules

McDOUGALLSπΩ

Thickening Granules

MARIGOLD

Swiss Vegetable Bouillon Powder: **Organic, Reduced Salt**

ORGRANø

Vegetarian Gravy Mix

OXOπ

Vegetable Stock Cubes; *Gravy Granules:* Onion, Vegetable; *Herb & Spice Cubes:* Chinese, Indian

RAYNER BURGESSπ

Gravy Browning

SAFEWAY

10 Vegetable Stock Cubes, Vegetable Gravy Granules

SOMERFIELD

Vegetable Gravy Granules

WAITROSE

Gravy Granules, Vegetable Stock Cubes

HAMPERS

GREEN GOURMETø§πΩfcd96

Vegan Hampers

HEALTHY HAMPERSø§π

Vegan Hampers

HEMP UNION

Hemp Foods Hampers: Luxury, Organic

VEGAN SOCIETY√π§Ω

Vegan Starter Hamper

'ICE CREAMS', SORBETS ETC

ALDIπ

Yippee Fruited Ice Lollies

ANGLO AMERICAN ICE CREAM

Fruticool: Caribbean Fruit Mix, Lemon, Lime, Mango, Passion Fruit & Banana, Piña Colada, Pineapple, Raspberry, Strawberry, Watermelon

ASDA

10 Assorted Fruit Juice Lollies, 10 Real Orange Juice Lollies; *Ice Snaps:* 12 Lemon, 12 Orange; *Spiral Lollies:* 4 Cider, 4 Lemonade

BIRDS EYE WALLS

Star Wars, Tricky Licky; *Calippo:* Lemon & Lime, Orange, Pineapple & Grapefruit; *Max Fruit Ice:* Lemonade, Orangeade

BRAKE BROS

Orange Flavour Lolly; *Sorbet:* Lemon, Mango, Orange, Passion Fruit, Raspberry

FAYREFIELD FOODS√

Swedish Glace Iced Non-Dairy Dessert: **Chocolate, Mocha & Chocolate Ripple, Pear, Raspberry, Strawberry, Vanilla**

HALDANE

Ice Delight: Chocolate Swirl, Strawberry Swirl

HEMP UNIONø™§πΩfcd93

Hemp Ice Dessert

MARANELLIS

Ice Supreme: Chocolate, Raspberry Ripple

MARCANTONIO FOODS

Ice Cream Cones; *Little Bear:* Cones, Wafer Cups

MARKS & SPENCER

Fat Free Sorbet: Orange, Passion Fruit, Raspberry & Blackcurrant; *Orange Juice:* Bar, Take Away Bar, Tube; *Wine Sorbet:* Red, White

MENORQUINA

Individual Whole Sorbet: Lemon, Orange

NESTLÉ

Fruit Joy; *Mr Men Water Ice:* Blackcurrant, Orange

PROVAMELπ

Ice Dessert: Chocolate, Strawberry, Vanilla

RAKUSEN'S™

Vanilla Choc Ices; *Flavoured Dessert Ices:* Chocolate Orange, Fruits Of The Forest, Strawberry, Toffee, Vanilla

ROWNTREE'S

Fruit Pastil: Blackcurrant, Orange

SAFEWAY

10 Orange Juice Lollies; *Assorted:* 10 Fruit Lollies, 10 Fruit Splits, Savers Lollies; *Sorbet:* Blackcurrant, Lemon, Orange

SOMERFIELD

10 Double Lickers, Basics 10 Assorted Fruit Lollies; *Sorbet:* Lemon, Mango

SUNRISE√™πΩfcd

Carob Ices; *Ice Dream:* Chocolate, Raspberry Ripple, Strawberry, Vanilla

TESCO

Lollies: Assorted 10 Real Fruit, Orange Juice

TOFUTTI√§π

Chocolate Fudge Treats, Rock & Roll, Teddy Fudge; *Cuties:* all; *Lite Lite [tub]:* all; *Mini Tubs:* all; *Supreme [tub]:* all

WAITROSE

Assorted Lollies; *Sorbet:* Apricot & Amaretto, Blackcurrant, Blueberry, Lemon, Mango, Orange Marnier, Pimms, Pink Gin, Tropical Fruit

MARGARINES, FATS ETC

BROADLANDπ

Vegetable Suet

CO-OPπΩΔfcd85

Soya Spread, Shredded Vegetable Suet

GRANOSE

Diet Half Fat Spread; *Margarine:* Low Salt Vegetable, Olive Grove; *Non-Hydrogenated Margarine:* Soya, Sunflower, Vegetable

GRANOVITAπ

Non Hydrogenated: **Low Fat Spread, Sunflower Margarine, Vegetable Margarine**

LUNN LINKS√øπΩ

Kitchen Garden Sunflower Spread

MATTHEWS FOODS™π

Pure: Organic Spread, Soya Spread, **Sunflower Margarine**

MONKI

Sunflower Spread

ORGRANø

Fat Replacer

RAKUSEN'S™

Tomor Margarine: Block, Sunflower

ST GILES FOODS

Fry Light: Butter Flavoured, Extra Virgin Olive Oil, Garlic, Sunflower Oil

SAFEWAY

Organic Spread, Soya Margarine

SHARWOOD'S

Vegetable Ghee

SMILDE™

Bebo Sunflower Spread [10g pots]

SOMERFIELD

Soya Spread

SPRY CRISP 'N' DRYπ

Solid Vegetable Oil

SUMA™§πΩ

Spread: 100% Sunflower, Low Fat, Organic, Soya

TESCO

Baking Margarine, Soya Spread

VAN DEN BERGH

Cookeen, White Cap

VITAQUELL√™π

Margarine: Cuisine, Extra, Light, Organic

WAITROSE

Soya Spread, Sunflower Margarine, Vegetable Suet

PASTRY

ASDA

Filo, Puff, Shortcrust, Traditional Shortcrust Pastry Mix; *Vol-au-Vents:* 36, 60 Shells

BRAKE BROS

Demi-Puff Lids (oval), Filo, Short; *Puff:* Double Lattice Lids (oval), Double Lattice Sheets, Lids (oval), Pastry, Sheets, Squares; *Vol-au-Vents:* Cocktail, Medium, King Size

CLIVE LOWEøπ

Organic Rough Puff Pastry

HOPPERS FARMHOUSE BAKERY

Mixed Grains *w* Herbs Quiche Base, Wholemeal Pastry Shell

ORGRAN√πΩ

Pizza & Pastry Mix

PILLSBURYπ

Jus-Rol: Cheddapuffs, Filo Pastry, Puff Pastry Blocks, Puff Pastry Sheets, Shortcrust Pastry Blocks, Shortcrust Pastry Sheets; *Jus-Rol Vol-au-Vents:* Medium, Party

PICKLES, SAUCES, VINEGARS ETC

ALDIπ

Bramwells: English Mustard, Mint Sauce; *Colway:* Brown Sauce, Malt Vinegar, Tomato Ketchup; *Newland:* Baby Beetroot in Sweet Vinegar, Pickled Red Cabbage, Pickled Sliced Beetroot, Sweet Pickle, Sweet Pickled Onions; *Sauce:* Masterchef Chilli Con Carne Mix, Romana Pasta, Worldwide Sweet & Sour

ASDA

Mango Chutney, Pickled Red Cabbage, Tomato Ketchup; *Beetroot:* Baby in Sweet Vinegar, Crinkle Cut in Sweet Vinegar, Sliced in Malt Vinegar; *Farm Stores:* Bolognese Sauce, Brown Sauce, Pickled Sweet Onions, Sliced Beetroot in Malt Vinegar, Sweet & Sour Sauce, Tomato & Herb Sauce, Tomato Ketchup; *Gherkins:* Baby, Crinkle Cut, Pickled; *Healthy Choice:* Original Pasta Sauce, Rogan Josh Cooking Sauce; *Marinade:* Citrus Chilli, Hoi Sin, Spicy Barbecue; *Mustard:* Coarse Grain, Dijon, English, French; *Onions:* Hot & Spicy Chilli,

Mild Curry Korma, Pickled in Dark Vinegar, Pickled Silverskin, Sweet, Tikka Masal Balti; *Pasta Sauce:* Farm Stores Tomato & Herb, Mediterranean Vegetable, Original Tomato, Smokey Barbecue, Spicy Tomato, Tomato & Mushroom, Tomato w Garlic; *Piccalilli:* Mustard, Sweet; *Pickle:* Harvest, Lime, Mixed; *Relish:* Gherkin, Hamburger, Onion, Sweetcorn; *Sauce:* Apple, Brown [glass, squeezy], Cranberry, Jalfrezi Cooking, Mexican Chilli Cooking, Mint, Sweet & Sour, Sweet & Sour Cook In; *Vinegar:* Cider, Garlic Wine, Red Wine

BATCHELORSπ

Chicken Tonight Sauce: Barbecue, Oriental Sweet & Sour, Spanish Chicken

BAXTERS

Beetroot in Redcurrant; *Chutney:* Albert's Victorian, Ena's Mulled Plum, Mango w Ginger, Mediterranean, Spiced Fruit, Tomato w Red Pepper; *Jelly:* Cranberry, Mint, Redcurrant, Wild Rowan; *Sauce:* Apple, Cranberry, Mint, Rich Mediterranean Pour Over

BESTFOODS

Knorr Marinades in Minutes Flavours: Cajun, Tikka; *Napolina Pizzeria Pizza Topping:* Spicy Tomato Pepper & Herbs, Traditional Tomato Herbs & Spices; *Napolina Recipe Chopped Tomatoes:* w Bolognese Seasoning, w Herbs, w Onion & Herbs Seasoning

BIOFORCE

Kelpamare

BIONOVA

Sauerkraut; *Gherkins:* **Sour, Sweet & Sour Vegan;** *Vinegar:* **Red Wine, White Wine**

BLUE DRAGON

Rice Vinegar; *Curry Sauce:* Dayung, Redang

BRAKE BROS

Frozen Sauce: Create Your Own Pizza Spicy Tomato, Peanut, Tomato Italian Style Pasta

CLEARSPRING√ø§π

Brown Rice Vinegar, Mikawa Mirin, **Natto Miso Chutney,** Red Plum Seasoning, Takuan Daikon Pickle; *Japanese Soya Sauce:* **Shoyu, Tamari**

COLMAN'Sπ

Cooking Sauce [jar]: Country Beef, Spicy Pork; *Sauce:* Bramley Apple, Classic Mint, Cranberry & Orange, Redcurrant, Rich Pepper & Tomato, Sweet & Sour Pour Over Dry Mix; *Mint:* Fresh Garden in Vinegar, Sweet Jelly; *Mustard:* Dijon Shop, English, English Powder, French, French [squeezy], Garlic, Herb & Tomato, Horseradish, Peppercorn

CO-OPπΩΔfcd85

Brown Sauce, English Mustard, Mango Chutney, Mint Jelly, Piccalilli, Sweet Piccalilli, Sweet Pickle, Tomato Ketchup; *Brown Sauce:* Everyday, Squeezy Bottle; *Cook In Sauce Mix:* Beef Bourgignon, Chicken Provençale, Chilli Con Carne, Farmhouse Sausage Casserole, Lamb Ragout, Madras Curry; *Pasta Sauce:* Classico, Crunchy Vegetables, Hot &

Spicy, Lite, Mushroom, Red & Green Peppers; *Relish:* Barbeque, Hamburger, Onion, Sweetcorn; *Sauce:* Apple, Fruity, Fruity [squeezy], Mint; *Tomato Ketchup:* Everyday, Low Sugar/Salt, Squeezy; *Malt Vinegar:* Brown, Distilled

CROSSE & BLACKWELL

Branston Rich & Fruity Sauce; *Bonne Cuisine Sauce:* à l'Orange, de Paris; *Branston Pickle:* Original, Sandwich, Tomato & Chilli; *Classic Creations:* Chicken Chasseur, Country Pork Casserole, Lamb Ragout, Sausage & Tomato, Shepherd's Pie, Turkey Casserole; *Indian Creations:* Chicken Balti, Chicken Curry, Chicken Korma; *Mexican Creations:* Chicken Fajitas, Chilli Con Carne; *Pasta Creations:* Sausage & Herb Pasta, Tuna & Tomato Bake; *Stir Fry Creation:* Black Bean Stir Fry, Lemon Chicken, Oriental Beef, Oriental Chicken, Sizzling Black Bean, Sweet & Sour Pork; *Vegetable Creations:* Balti, Chilli

DE RIT ORGANIC PRODUCTS

Coarse Mustard

DOLMIO

Delizio Two Step Sauce: Garlic Onion & Basil, Sweet Pepper, Vegetable Primavera, Wild Mushroom; *Sauce For Bolognese:* Extra Garlic, Extra Mushrooms, Extra Spicy, Original; *Sauce For Pasta:* Chianti, Classico, Piccanti, Toscana, Vegetale; *Stir In Sauce:* Roasted Vegetable, Sun-dried Tomato, Sweet Pepper

DUFRAIS

Bistro Chef; *Vinegars:* all

FULL OF BEANSπΩ

Celebration Wholegrain Mustard, Lime Pickle

GO ORGANIC§π

Organic Pasta Sauce: Tomato, *w* Tomatoes & Aubergine, *w* Tomatoes & Basil, *w* Tomatoes & Olive, *w* Tomatoes & Sweet Pepper

GRANOVITAπ

Grannie's Traditional Brown Sauce; *Organic:* Tomato Ketchup, Tomato Sauce for Pasta

GREEN CITY WHOLEFOODSøπ

Shoyu Soya Sauce

HAMBLEDEN HERBSøπΩfcd82

Organic Vinegar: Dill & Fennel, Mint, Red Basil, Provençal, Spice, Tarragon

HEINZ

Apple Sauce [can, jar], Ploughman's Pickle, Smokey Barbecue Sauce, Tomato Frito, Tomato Ketchup; *Speciality Pickle:* Mild Mustard, Piccalilli, Tangy Sandwich, Tangy Tomato; *Weight Watchers Cooking Sauce:* Chinese Szechuan, Italian Pasta, Mexican Chilli, Oriental Sweet & Sour

HENDERSONS√øπΩ

Desperate Dan Spicy Tomato Splash, Relish

JAMES WHITE√øπ

Fruit Coulis Dessert Sauce: 3 Red Fruits, Apricot, Blackcurrant, Raspberry, Strawberry

JETHRO'Søπ

Marinade: Ginger & Soy, Hot Cajun, Lemon & Coriander, Lime & Chilli, Pineapple & Chilli, Red Wine & Juniper, Red Wine & Thyme, Rosemary & Bay; *Stir Fry Sauce:* Five Spice, Hot & Sour, Orange Spice

JIFπ

Juice: Lemon, Lime

KALLO

Organic Stock Cubes: French Onion, Garlic & Herb, Mushroom, Tomato & Herb, Vegetable

MARKALø

Mustard: Dijon, Traditional French

MARKS & SPENCER

Aubergine Pesto, Cocktail Gherkins, Piccalilli, Redcurrant Jelly, Sweet Pickle, Tomato Ketchup; *Beetroot:* Crinkle, Organic Crinkle Cut, Whole; *Chutney:* Mango, Spicy Fruit, Spicy Mango, Sweet Mango, Tomato, Traditional Fruit; *Marinade:* Garlic & Rosemary, Lime & Coriander, Tomato & Basil; *Mustard:* Dijon, English, Wholegrain, Wholegrain Ale; *Olives:* Green *w* Dressing [deli], Kalamata, Queen Green; *Pasta Sauce:* Mixed Peppers, Mushroom, Olive, Peppers & Tomato, Sun-dried Tomato, Tomato & Herb; *Pickled:* Cucumbers, Onions, Organic Onions, Silverskin Onions; *Relish:* Onion, Sweetcorn, Tomato; *Sauce:* 95% Fat Free Tomato Sauce, Apple, Arrabbiata, Bori Mild, Brown, Cranberry, Dark Soy, Madras, Mint, Roasted Vegetable, Spicy Tomato BBQ, Tomato & Basil Sauce; *Vinegar:* Balsamic, Italian

Balsamic

MARTLETπ

Cider Vinegar; *Organic Preserves:* all

MERIDIANøπ

Tomato Ketchup; *Cooking Sauce:* Balti, Rogan Josh; *Japanese Sauce:* Shoyu, Tamari; *Organic Pasta Sauce:* Mushroom, Olive, Tomato & Herb

MITOKUø

Sushi Pickle: Cucumber, Daikon, Ginger, Ginger *w* Ume

MR BEAN

Aubergine Vegetable Caviar; *Cooking Sauce:* Chinese, Italian, Korma; *Organic Mediterranean Sauce:* Aubergine in Tomato, Ratatouille, Tomato *w* Aromatic Herbs, Tomato *w* Basil

NORFOLK LAVENDERΩfcd84

Lavender Mustard

ORGANICO

Pasta Sauce: w Basil, *w* Capers, *w* Mushrooms

ORGRANø

Vegetarian Bolognese Sauce

PAN YAN

Bramley Apple Sauce, Original Pickle

PATAK'Sπ

Cooking Sauce: Dopaza, Jalfrezi, Madras, Rogan Josh; *Mango Chutney:* Hot, Major Grey, Sweet; *Pickle:* Brinjal, Chilli, Extra Hot Mango, Hot Mango, Major Grey Mango, Mild Lime, Mild

Mango, Mixed, Sweet Lime, Sweet Mango, Tomato; *Sauce:* Balti Medium, Delhi Mild, Madras, Rogan Josh, Vindaloo

RAGUπ

Pasta Sauce: Basil & Oregano, Bolognese, Country Mushroom, Green & Red Peppers, Italian Vegetable, Onions & Garlic, Original for Lasagne, Red Wine & Herbs, Traditional Recipe

RAYNER BURGESSπ

Mushroom Ketchup, Sweet Pickle; *Chutney:* **Economy Mango, Goodfayre, Mango;** *Cocktail:* **Capers, Gherkins, Olives, Onions;** *Jelly:* **Mint, Redcurrant;** *Mustard:* **English, French;** *Relish:* **Barbecue, Hamburger;** *Sauce:* **Barbecue, Brown, Cranberry, Mint, Tomato**

ST GILES FOODS

La Genovesa Pump & Spray Balsamic Vinegar; *Florentino:* Balsamic Vinegar, Basil Pesto *w* Extra Virgin Olive Oil, Crushed Sun-dried Tomatoes *w* Extra Virgin Olive Oil, Dairy Free Basil Pesto *w* Extra Virgin Olive Oil, Garlic & Walnut Pesto, Garlic Bread Spread (Dairy Free), Neapolitan Pesto Hot & Garlicky, Red Pesto *w* Basil Sun-dried Tomatoes & Extra Virgin Olive Oil, Sicilian Pesto *w* Olives Sun-dried Tomatoes Olive Oil & Herbs, Sun-dried Tomato Halves in Olive & Sunflower Oil Blend, Tomato & Basil Sauce; *Life:* English Mustard, French Mustard, Fruity Brown Sauce, Horseradish Sauce, Tartare Sauce, Tomato Ketchup, Worcester Sauce; *Old Dakota:* Habanero Hot Pepper Sauce & Baste, Hickory BBQ Sauce & Baste, Huckleber-ry Sauce & Baste, Jalapeno Sauce & Baste, Liquid Smoke Barbecue Marinade, Maple Glaze; *River Edge Mustard:* Roast Onion, Smoked Dijon; *Tropic Isle:* Barbados Chicken & Pork Marinade, Caribbean Lime Curry Marinade, Garlic Chilli & Herb Marinade, Jamaican Chicken Marinade, Trinidad Lime & Ginger Cooking Sauce

SAFEWAY

Healthy Choice Salad Cream, Hot Sun-dried Tomato Marinade, Traditional Mixed Pickles; *Chutney:* Curried Fruit, Delicatessen Mango, Drayman's, Farmhouse, Fig & Date, Mango, Peach, Spiced Plum, Tomato; *Jelly:* Mint, Redcurrant; *Ketchup:* Savers Tomato, Tomato; *Marinade:* Hickory Smoke Flavour, Hot Sun-dried Tomato; *Mustard:* Dijon, English, French, German, Wholegrain; *Olives:* Black Pitted, Black Sliced, Green Pitted, Green Pitted & Stuffed *w* Almonds, Green Pitted & Stuffed *w* Pimento, Spicy Garlic Green, Whole Green, Whole Queen Green; *Pickle:* Sandwich, Sweet; *Pickled:* Crinkle Cut Beetroot, Dark Onions, Dill Cucumbers, Mexican Style Chilli Onions, Red Cabbage in Sweet Vinegar, Shallots, Silverskin Onions *w* Turmeric & Mustard Oil, Sliced Beetroot, Strong Onions, Sweet Sliced Beetroot, Sweetened Baby Beetroot, Sweetened Silverskin Onions, Unsweetened Baby Beetroot, Unsweetened Silverskin Onions, Unsweetened Sliced Beetroot; *Sauce:* Apple, Black Bean, Black Bean Stir Fry, Bramley Apple, Cranberry, Cranberry & Port, Dhansak, Fresh Garden Mint, Fruity Brown, Healthy Choice Napolitana, Healthy Choice

Sweet & Sour, Jalfrezi, Lemon Stir Fry, Mint, Piri Piri, Red Wine & Mushroom, Redcurrant, Savers Brown, Spiced Wild Cranberry, Spicy Brown, Spicy Creole, Sweet & Sour, Tomato Onion & Herb, Wild Cranberry w Port & Orange; *Sauce For Pasta:* Basilio, Healthy Choice Italian, Italian Mushroom, Italian Onion & Garlic, Italian Peppers, Primavera, Puttanesca, Traditional Italian; *Sauce Mix:* Casserole Chilli Con Carne, Casserole Spaghetti Bolognese, Simmer White

SANCHIØ

Mirin, Pickled Ginger; *Sesame Oil:* Hot Toasted, Toasted; *Soy Sauce:* Organic Shoyu, Organic Tamari, Shoyu, Tamari; *Vinegar:* Organic Brown Rice, Umi Su Plum

SARSONS

Soy Sauce; *Vinegars:* all

SEEDS OF CHANGE

Organic Tomato Ketchup; *Organic Pasta Sauce:* Mushroom & Onion, Spicy Roasted Garlic, Tomato & Basil

SHARWOOD'S

Lime Pickle; *Fruit Chutney:* Apricot, Caribbean Tropical Fruit, Indian Curried Fruit, Peach; *Green Label Chutney:* Bengal Hot, Major Grey, Mango, Mango & Apple, Mango & Lime; *Indian Cooking Sauce [jar]:* Balti Rajmahal, Hot Jalfrezi, Jalfrezi Fruity Hot, Madras Spicy Hot, Mild Jalfrezi, Rezala, Vindaloo Extra Hot; *Standard Indian Cooking Sauce [can]:* Dhansak, Madras, Rogan Josh

SIMPLY ORGANICπ

***Fresh Organic Pasta Sauce:* Tomato & Basil (Napoletana), Tomato w Olives & Capers (Puttanesca)**

SOMERFIELD

English Mustard, Malt Vinegar, Piccalilli, Sweet Piccalilli, Sweet Pickle, Tomato Ketchup; *Healthy Selection:* Pickled Onions In Light Vinegar, Pickled Red Cabbage In Vinegar, Pickled Silverskin Onions, Sweet Pickled Crinkle Cut Beetroot, Sweet Pickled Onions, Sweet Pickled Sliced Beetroot, Sweet Pickled Whole Baby Beetroot, Tomato Ketchup; *Olives:* Pimiento Stuffed Green, Pitted Black, Pitted Green; *Culinary Sauce:* Chilli, Rogan Josh Curry Culinary, Sweet & Sour; *Pasta Sauce:* Traditional, w Chunky Vegetables, w Mushrooms, w Onion & Garlic, w Peppers; *Sauce:* Apple, Basics Brown, Brown, Cranberry, Fruit, Mediterranean Vegetable, Mint, Tomato & Herb

SUMA™§πΩ

Tomato Ketchup

TESCO

Cocktail Cherries, Cornichons, Crinkle Cut Gherkins, Piccalilli, Pickled Red Cabbage, Red Cabbage Mulled Wine, Sandwich Piccalilli, Sweet Piccalilli; *Beetroot in Vinegar:* Crinkle Cut Sweet, Pickled Sliced, Whole Baby, Whole Baby Sweet; *Chinese Cooking Sauce:* Stirfry Szechuan, Taste of Orient Hoi Sin; *Chutney:* Curried Fruit, Finest Apple & Flame Roasted Tomato/Garlic, Finest Apricot & Fig, Finest Spiced Plum & Apple, Mango, Peach; *Mustard:* Dijon, English, Finest Horseradish, Wholegrain; *Olives:* Black, Black Sliced, Finest, Pimento & Tomato Stuffed, Pitted Black, Pitted Green, Queen, Salad Mix, Whole Green; *Pasta Sauce:* Chunky Vegetable, Healthy Eating, Mushroom, Onion & Garlic, Original, Original Better Value, Red/Green Peppers, Spicy; *Pickled Onions:* Dark Spiced, Hot & Spicy, Hot & Spicy Shallots, Mild, Sharp Silverskin, Sweet Silverskin; *Premium Pasta Sauce:* Basilico, Olive, Piccante, Vegetale; *Relish:* Sweetcorn, Tomato/Chilli; *Sauce:* BBQ [squeezy], Bramley Apple, Brown, Cranberry, Festive Cranberry, Finest Cumberland, Finest Dill, Fruity Brown [bottle, squeezy], Jalfrezi Indian Cooking, Mint, Ready to Serve Mint [squeezy], Value Brown, Value Tomato [bottle], Wild Logonberry; *Vinegar:* Chip Shop, Finest Balsamic

TILDA MADHUR JAFFREYπ

Sauce: **Balti, Green Lime Masala, Madras**

UNCLE BEN'S

Sweet & Sour Sauce· Cantonese Extra Fruity, Hong Kong Spicy, Peking Original, Shanghai Light; *Two Step Sizzle & Stir Sauce:* Cantonese, Rogan Josh, Sweet & Sour, Szechwan

VILLAGE BAKERYøπΩ

Green Tomato Chutney

VINCEREMOSøπ

Aceto Balsamico di Modena

VINTAGE ROOTSøπ

Vinegar: Balsamic, French Wine, Raspberry Wine, Red Wine, Shallot Wine, Tarragon, White Wine

WAITROSE

Artichoke Hearts, Chilli Oil; *Beetroot:* Baby, Pickled Baby, Pickled Sliced, Sliced Beets, Sliced in Vinegar, Sweet Baby, w Apple & Onion; *Chutney:* Apple & Walnut, Apricot Ginger & Garlic, Curried Fruit, Date Apricot & Orange, Hot Mango, Mango, Spiced Peach; *Gherkins:* Cocktail, Crinkle Cut, In Brine, Spears in Brine; *In Brine:* Cornichons, Cucumbers; *Jelly:* Cider & Sage, Lemon Dill, Mint, Redcurrant w Port, Rosé Wine, Savoury Blackberry, Spiced Apple; *Ketchup:* Reduced Sugar Tomato, Tomato, Tomato [squeezy]; *Mustard:* Dijon, English, French, Wholegrain; *Olives:* À la Grecque in Brine, Almond Stuffed, Black & Green, Black Smoked, Black w Orange, Gaeta, Green in Brine, Kalamata, Large Black w Tomatoes, Large Green, Large Green & Black w Lemon, Marinated Black, Mixed Marinated, Mixed Stuffed in Brine, Pimento Stuffed Green, Pimento Stuffed Queen, Pitted Black in Brine, Pitted Green in Brine, Riviera, Spanish Black, Stuffed Greek, Stuffed Green, w Garlic & Chilli, w Oregano; *Onions:* Caram Borettane, Pickled, Pickled Silverskin, Sweet Pickled, w Tumeric & Mustard, w Mustard & Peppercorns; *Piccalilli:* Mustard, Sandwich, Sweet; *Pickle:* Sandwich, Spiced Cucumber, Sweet; *Pickled:* Damsons, Red Cabbage, Shallots, Sweet Red Cabbage; *Relish:* Pepper

Olive & Herb, Salsa, Tomato Apple & Tarragon, Tomato Onion & Garlic; *Sauce:* Apple, Arrabbiatta, Caribbean Creole, Chilli, Chilli & Coriander, Chilli Masala, Chinese Dan Dan, Cranberry, Fruity, Gooseberry in Wine, Hot & Fruity, Italian Arrabbiata, Italian Funghi Pasta, Italian Napolitana, Japanese Sweet & Sour, Mediterranean, Mint, Orange *w* Ginger, Plum & Ginger *w* Balsamic Vinegar, Redcurrant in Port, Singapore Spicy, Spicy, Spicy Brown, Sweet & Sour Cooking, Thai Lemongrass; *Soy Sauce:* Dark, Japanese, Light, Teriyaki; *Spanish:* Caper Berries, Capers, Capers Capute; *Sun-dried:* Antipasta Tomatoes, Aubergines, Courgettes, Crushed Tomatoes, Green Peppers, Red Peppers, Tomatoes; *Tapenade:* Green Olive & Coriander, Sun-dried Tomato; *Vinegar:* Garlic Wine, Malt, Mixed Herb Wine, Mixed Spice, Rosé Wine, Speciality Gift, Tarragon Wine, White Wine

WHOLE EARTHø§π

Kensington Sauce; *Organic:* **Italiano Mushroom Sauce, Italiano Spaghetti Sauce, No Added Sugar Tomato Ketchup, Romana Pasta Sauce**

YAKSO

Ketjap Manis Indonesian Sweet Shoyu, **Shoyu, Tamari**

ZEST™π

Vegan Pesto Basil Sauce

PIES & PASTIES

AMBROSIAN VEGETARIAN FOODS√ø™§π

Porkless Pie; *Pasties:* Cheez 'N' Chive, Cheezy Baked Bean, Pesto

BRAKE BROS

Vegetable Pasties

CLIVE LOWEøπ

Clive's Wonderful Pies: **Aloo Gobi, Arabian Chickpea, Chestnut Cassoulet, Cream of Mushroom, Hungarian Goulash, Mexican Sweetcorn, Vegetable Ensemble**

GET REAL ORGANIC FOODSπ

Sutaki Pie

GOBBLINπΩfcd86

Pies: Aduki Shepherds, Pinto, Vegetable Tofu; *Pasties:* Curry, Savoury Vegetable

SKINNY LIZZIE'S

Jumbo Sos Roll, Onion Bhaji, Porkless Pie, Sos Roll, Vegemince Cornish Pasty, Vegetable Samosa

SOY FOODSø™π

Mushroom & Tofu Pie; *Pasties:* Arame, Vegetable

SAVOURIES — CANNED/BOTTLED

ALDIπ

Corale Baked Beans in Tomato Sauce;

Carlini: Spaghetti Hoops in Tomato Sauce, Spaghetti in Tomato Sauce

ASDA

Healthy Choice Chick Pea Dahl, Ratatouille; *Beans In Tomato Sauce:* Baked, Farm Stores Baked, Healthy Choice Baked, Mixed; *Spaghetti In Tomato Sauce:* Farm Stores, Healthy Choice, Spaghetti

BIONOVA

Baked Beans in Tomato Sauce

BUITONI

Ratatouille

CO-OPπΩΔfcd85

Ratatouille Provençale; *Baked Beans:* Everyday, in Tomato Sauce, Reduced Sugar & Salt; *Spaghetti:* Everyday, in Tomato Sauce, Numbers in Tomato Sauce, Reduced Sugar & Salt, Rings in Tomato Sauce

GO ORGANIC§π

Organic Curry [jar]: **Spicy Chickpeas & Spinach, Sweet & Sour Spicy Vegetables**

GRANOSE

Lentil & Vegetable Casserole, Nuttolene, Sausalatas; *Meatless:* Bolognese, Chilli, Mince & Onion

GRANOVITAπ

Nut Luncheon, Vegetable Hotpot

HPπ

Vegetable Lasagnetti; *In Tomato Sauce:* Baked Beans, Beans, Healthy Beans, Organic Beans

HARTLEYπ

Mixed Bean Salad In A Spicy Sauce, Red Kidney Beans In Chilli Sauce, Vegetable Ravioli In Tomato Sauce; *In Tomato Sauce:* Baked Beans, Beans, Numbers, Spaghetti, Spaghetti Rings, Wholewheat Rings

HEINZ

Meat Free Spaghetti Bolognese, Rigatoni Pomodora; *Beans:* Barbecue, Curried, Mixed Chilli; *Beans In Tomato Sauce:* Baked, Healthy Balance Baked; *Pasta Shapes In Tomato Sauce:* Action Man, Barbie, Noddy, Sooty, Teletubbies, Thomas the Tank Engine; *Spaghetti In Tomato Sauce:* Hoops, Spaghetti; *Weight Watchers:* Baked Beans In Tomato Sauce w No Added Sugar, Italiana Vegetable Ravioli In Tomato Sauce, Spaghetti In Tomato Sauce w Parsley

MARKS & SPENCER

Baked Beans, Indian Rice, Long Grain Rice, Vegetable Tomato Dahl

MORTONπ

Chunky Vegetable Curry; *Casserole:* Pasta & Vegetable, Spicy Bean & Rice

ORGANIC VALLEY LTD√ø™π

Baked Beans, Spaghetti Hoops

ORGRANø

Gluten-Free Spaghetti in Tomato Sauce

PATAK'Sπ

Allo Mattar Sabzi Potato & Pea Curry,

Kabli Dahl, Lobhia Dahl, Masala Sabzi Vegetable Curry, Sabzi Tarkari Vegetable Curry, Tarka Dhal

PLAMIL√™§π

Pease Pudding w Mace

RAKUSEN'S™

Baked Beans

REALLY INTERESTING FOOD CO√π Ωfcd

Ready Meal: **Colombo Curry, Gado Gado, Moorish Garbanzos, Satu, Thai Green Curry, Thai Temple Curry**

SAFEWAY

Salad Bean Mix; *Beans In Tomato Sauce:* Baked, Healthy Choice Baked, Savers Baked; *Spaghetti In Tomato Sauce:* Rings, Short Cut

SOMERFIELD

Ratatouille; *Beans In Tomato Sauce:* Baked, Basics Baked, Healthy Selection Baked; *In Tomato Sauce:* Basics Spaghetti, Rings, Spaghetti, Wholewheat Spaghetti

SUMA™§πΩ

Brown Lentils in Tomato Sauce

TESCO

Bubble & Squeak, Mixed Bean Salad, Mixed Bean Salad Vinaigrette, Ratatouille Provençale, Saag Aloo, Taco Mixed Beans & Mex Sauce; *Baked Beans:* Curry, in Tomato Sauce, 50% Less Sugar & Salt, Reduced Sugar & Salt, Value; *Spaghetti:* 50% Less Sugar & Salt, in Tomato Sauce, Letters, Rings in Tomato

Sauce

WAITROSE

Ratatouille, Spaghetti, Spaghetti Rings; *Beans:* Baked, Baked w Reduced Sugar/Salt, Organic Baked in Tomato Sauce; *Mixed Beans:* Curry Sauce, in Tomato Sauce, Salad, Spicy Saucy, Sweet & Sour

WESTLER FOODSπ

Ready Meal: **Balti, Chilli Con Carne, Vegetable Casserole & Dumplings, Vegetable Curry**

WHOLE EARTHø§π

Organic: **Baked Beans, Campfire Baked Beans, Ready Rice**

SAVOURIES — CHILLED/FRESH

ASDA

4 Vegetable Samosa, 6 Onion Bhaji, 8 Onion Pakora w Sweet Chilli Dip, 12 Mini Onion Bhaji, Bombay Potato, Caribbean Vegetable Stew, Indian Meal For One (Vegetarian), Indian Pilau Rice, Indian Selection, Mini Vegetable Spring Rolls, Mushroom Dopiaza, Pakora Selection w Sweet Chilli Dip, Spicy Rice; *Salad:* Couscous Roasted Vegetable & Mixed Bean Salad, Healthy Choice Couscous, Italian Bean & Roasted Red Pepper, Italian Pasta [Pre-packed/Deli], Middle Eastern Bulgar Wheat, Spicy Rice, Sweet & Sour Pasta; *Stir Fry w Chinese Style Sauce:* Fresh Chinese, Fresh Chow Mein; *Tex Mex:* Mardi Gras Rice, Mexican Rice,

Mexican Vegetable (Tomato)

CLIVE LOWEøπ

Readymeal: Arabian Chickpea, Chestnut Cassoulet, Hungarian Goulash, Mexican Chilli

CO-OPπΩΔfcd85

Indian Selection Pack, Jacket Potato w Beans, Mini Onion Bhajis, Onion Bhajis, Onion Pakora w Chilli Sauce, Pilau Rice, Ratatouille, Salad Splits Mediterranean Style Pasta Salad, Vegetable Samosas, Vegetable Spring Rolls

EVERNATπ

Organic Sandwiches: Hummus & Leaf Salad, Roasted Vegetables

GOBBLINπΩfcd86

Samosa, Savoury Roll; *Baked Potato Filling:* Chilli, Spicy Vegetable, Three Bean Hotpot

MACSWEENøπ

Vegetarian Haggis

MARKS & SPENCER

Café Frites, Chargrilled Café Veg, Lite Vegetable Casserole, Mushroom Provençale, Onion Bhaji, Ratatouille, Seasoned Potato Wedges, Vegetable Curry, Vegetable Pakora; *Potatoes:* Hassleback, Mediterranean Style New, Roast, Rosemary & Garlic; *Salad:* Bean, Beetroot, Connoisseur Caesar, Couscous & Vegetable Pot, Fruity Coleslaw, Green, Organic Beetroot, Organic Sweetcorn, Tomato & Basil; *Stir Fry:* Mushroom, Oriental

MULTICULTURAL SANDWICHES™π

Sandwiches: Crunchy Peanut Butter w Fresh Cucumber, Crunchy Peanut Butter w Sliced Peach, Herb & Mushroom Pâté w Iceberg Lettuce, Hummus w Couscous Roast Courgette & Iceberg Lettuce, Hummus w Sweetcorn Fresh Cucumber & Iceberg Lettuce, Mixed Salad w Asparagus, Mushroom Pâté w Crispy Fried Onions & Fresh Watercress, Roast Aubergine w Bulgar Wheat Mango Chutney & Lettuce, Roast Vegetables w Mango Chutney & Iceberg Lettuce, Smooth Peanut Butter w Jelly, Special Lentil Pâté w Iceberg Lettuce

SAFEWAY

Carrot Dipper w Barbecue Flavour Dip, Couscous & Grilled Vegetable Duo, Mediterranean Style Vegetables, Mexican Style Pan Fry, Potato Wedges For Roasting w Herb Flavoured Oil; *Coffee Shop:* Maharajah Vegetable Curry, Vegetarian Chilli; *Delicatessen:* Bombay Potato, Chana Dal, Grilled Onions w Roasted Garlic, Marinated Sun-dried Tomatoes, Mixed Antipasto, Mushroom À La Grecque, Onion Bhaji, Onion Pakora, Palum Pakora, Pea & Mushroom Bhajee, Roasted Vegetables, Seasoned Artichokes; *Delicatessen Olives:* Green, Kalamata, Mexican Style, Mixed w Roasted Vegetables, Pitted Black, Pitted Green & Black; *Delicatessen Rice:* Basmati, Mexican, Mild Curry, Pilau; *Delicatessen Salad:* Braised Rice & Wild Rice, Carrot Nut & Sultana, Crispy Vegetable, Economy Tomato Pasta, Indian Rice, Italienne Pasta, Spanish Style Potato, Spicy Bean; *Delicatessen Vegetable:* Bhaji, Curry, Mini Samosa, Rogan Josh,

Samosa, Spring Roll; *Pre-packed Delicatessen:* Gobi Aloo Saag, Indian Snack Selection, Mustard Bombay Potato, Onion Bhaji, Onion Pakoras *w* Sweet Chilli Sauce, Pilau Rice, Roasted Vegetables *w* Couscous, Thai Style Fragrant Rice, Vegetable Chilli, Vegetable Curry, Vegetable Samosas, Vegetable Spring Rolls; *Stir Fry:* Aromatic, Beansprout, Italian Style Pasta, Japanese Style, Mix, Mushroom, Oriental Style, Sweet & Sour, Thai Style, Vegetable; *Pre-packed Healthy Choice Salad:* Beetroot, Carrot & Sultana, Couscous, Fruity Rice, Mixed Bean, Tomato & Pasta; *Pre-packed Salad:* Beetroot, Couscous & Pan Fried Vegetables Snack, Italian Style Pasta, Mexican Style Corn, Premium Pasta & Roasted Vegetable

SOMERFIELD

4 Vegetable Spring Rolls, 6 Onion Bhajis, Healthy Selection Salad Selection — Reduced Fat Italian Style Pasta Salad, Vegetable Samosas, White Pudding Links; *Celebration:* Fresh American Dips Chilli Flavour Tortilla & Bean Salsa, Fresh Dip Selection Salsa & Breadsticks, Mini Indian Selection, Spicy Potato Wedges; *Delicatessen:* Beetroot & Orange Salad, Onion Bhaji, Vegetable Samosa, Vegetable Spring Roll; *Rice:* Cantonese Vegetable Bowl, Pilau

SOY FOODSø™π

Ganmodoki Tofu Mock Duck, Mushroom & Nut Parcels, Organic Nut Roast, Vegetable & Tofu Samosa

SPECIALITY BRANDS™

Stir Fry Veggie Wrap

TESCO

Baked Potato & Ratatouille, Couscous Salad, Crispy Seaweed, Gobi Aloo Saag, Houmous & Green Salad Sandwich, Indian Selection, Onion Bhajis, Potato Wedges, Saffron Rice, Tex Mex Style Vegetable Chilli, Vegetable Dhal; *Mini:* Aloo Saag Bhaji, Assorted Indian Snacks, Onion Bhaji, Vegetable Spring Rolls

THE SPICE VILLAGEø™

Spice Trail [frozen on request]: Bihari Rajma, Rajasthani Kumbhi Subzi

WAITROSE

6 Vegetable Pakoras, Bombay Potatoes, Mixed Anti-Pasti, Mushrooms À La Grecque, Rosti; *Couscous:* Mediterranean, *w* Roast Vegetables, Wrap *w* Roast Vegetables; *Grilled:* Red & Yellow Peppers, Sliced Aubergines; *Masala:* Dal, Dal *w* Rajma; *Pilau:* Carrot, Lemon, Saffron, Spinach & Carrot; *Rice:* Curried, Fragrant, Lemon, Thai Fragrant; *Roast:* Aubergines *w* Herbs, Peppers, Potatoes & Peppers in Balsamic Vinegar, Onions *w* Herbs; *Salad:* Carrot & Nut, Carrot & Poppy Seed, Indonesian, Layered Oriental, Layered Tuscan, Mediterranean, Mediterranean Pasta, Mediterranean Style Orzo, Pasta, Potato & Mint, Potato & Spring Onion, Roast Vegetable Ratatouille, Spicy Pasta, Sweet & Sour Pasta, Tapas 3 Bean, Tapas Couscous, Three Bean & Pasta, Tomato Pepper & Pasta, Tuscan Bean; *Tabouleh: w* Sultanas, *w* Tomatoes; *Vegetable:* Casserole, Curry, Samosa

WHAT ON EARTHøπ

Vegetali: Calzone, Pizza

SAVOURIES — DRIED

ASDA

Savoury Rice: Golden Vegetable, Sweet & Sour

BATCHELORSπ

Tomato Onion & Herbs Pasta 'N' Sauce; *Beanfeast:* Bolognese Style, Mexican Chilli; *Delicately Flavoured Rice:* Coriander & Herbs, Mild Chilli & Lime, Pilau, Toasted Almond & Ginger; *Original Savoury Rice:* Mild Curry, Mushroom, Sweetcorn & Peppers; *Rices of the World:* Chinese, Indian, Spanish, Sweet & Sour, Thai; *Supernoodles:* Mild Curry, Mushroom, Sweet & Sour

BESTFOODS

Chinese Chicken Pot Light; *Fun Pot Noodle:* Burger, Nice 'N Spicy; *Knorr Micro:* Chow Mein Noodle, Golden Savoury Rice; *Pot Noodle:* Beef & Tomato, Chow Mein, Nice 'N Spicy, Sweet & Sour

BLUE DRAGON

Rice Noodles: Stir Fry, Thick

CO-OPπΩΔfcd85

Savoury Rice: Beef, Mixed Vegetable, Mushroom

DIRECT FOODS

Bake: Chicken Style, Lentil; *Protoveg:* Beef Style Chunky, Beef Style Mince, Menu Minced Soya & Onion Mix, Natural Unflavoured Chunks, Natural Unflavoured Mince, Smokey Snaps

FIRST QUALITY FOODS√øπ

Couscous Snack Pot: Chinese, Indian, Mexican; *Sammy's Couscous:* Indian, Middle Eastern, Sun-dried Tomato, Wild Mushroom; *Sammy's Organic Couscous:* French Provençale, Italian Pesto

GRANOSE

Roast: Brazil, Cashew, Lentil, Nut, Sunflower & Sesame

GRANOVITAπ

Vegetarian Mix: Onion Bhaji, Pakora

JUST WHOLEFOODS

Organic Textured Vegetable Protein; *Organic Vegetarian Meals Mix:* Couscous w Lentils, Falafel, Hummus, Vegetable Biriyani, Vegetable Chow Mein, Vegetable Pilau Rice; *Vegetarian Stuffing Mix:* Chestnut, Country Style, Organic Apple & Sage, Sage & Onion

ORGRANø

Mix: Falafel, Tabouli Salad

SAFEWAY

Bubble & Squeak, Curry Flavour Super Quick Noodles, Tomato Onion & Herb Pasta Pronto; *Savoury Rice:* Curry Style, Pilau, Spanish Style

SANCHIø

Organic Ramen Noodles: Brown Rice, Mung Bean, Mushroom, Seaweed;

Ramen Noodles: Brown Rice, Buckwheat, Mushroom, Seaweed; *Soba Noodles:* 40% Buckwheat, 100% Buckwheat; *Udon Noodles:* 100% Wholewheat, Brown Rice, Quinoa

SHARWOOD'S

Pilau Rice

SOMERFIELD

Sun-dried Tomato Couscous; *Rice:* Curry Savoury, Delicately Flavoured Pilau

TESCO

Special Byriani Savoury Rice

TRUFREE™

Quick Snack: Potato/Vegetable, Rice/Lentil

WAITROSE

Noodles: Japan Thin, Mixed Udon, Singapore Thin

SAVOURIES — FROZEN

AMBROSIAN VEGETARIAN FOODS√ø™§π

Satay Spring Rolls; *Grills:* Corn, Smokey Barbeque

ASDA

12 Potato Waffles, Garlic & Rosemary Roast Potatoes, Onion Rings (Battered/Breaded); *Southern Fried:* Flavour Chips, Potato Wedge

BIRDS EYE WALLS

Alphabites, Hungry Joes, Potato Croquettes, Potato Waffles, Vegetable Curry w Rice

BRAKE BROS

Baked Jacket Potatoes, Carrot & Coriander Goujons, Chinese Pancakes, Crispy Coated Cajun Onion Rings, Crispy Vegetable Parcels, Hash Browns, Jacket Wedges, Jawsome Potato Bites, Long Boat Potato Shells (baked), Mini Indian Savoury Selection, Mini Vegetable Samosas, Oven Chips, Pommes Duchesse, Potato Dice, Potato Skins (pre-fried), Sauté Potatoes, Spicy Bean & Mango Topper, Straight Cut Chips, Traditional Roast Potatoes, VegeMince, Vegetable Pakora, Vegetable Samosas; *Fries:* Beefsteak Freeze-Chill French, Freeze-Chill French (3/8, 7/16 & 9/16), Julienne Freeze-Chill French, Spicy Lattice, Spicy Spiral, Spicy Wedge, Stay Crisp 3/8, Stay Crisp Julienne; *Individual Recipe Dish:* Mushroom Balti, Raj Vegetable Curry, Savoury Bean Casserole, Vegetable Chilli; *Multi Portion Recipe Dish:* Nutty Vegetable Crumble, Savoury Bean Casserole, Vegetable Chilli; *Stir Fry Mix:* Chinese Vegetable, Indian, Mexican Vegetable, Oriental Vegetable

CALEDONIAN CURRY COø™π

Vegan Indian Ready Meal: **Aubergine Baigan Nariyal, Aubergine Baigan Tamatar, Caledonian Chickpea, Chickpea & Spinach Palak Choley, Lentil Channa Dhal Masala, Lentil Tarka Dhal, Moong Dhal, Mushroom Do Piaza Khumb, Okra Bhindi Mirchiwal,**

Potato & Chickpea Aloo Choley, Pulao Rice, Rajmah, Spinach & Potato Saag Aloo

CAULDRON FOODS LTD√π

Falafel, Nut Cutlets

CO-OPπΩ∆fcd85

Hash Browns; *Onion Rings:* Battered, Breaded; *Waffles:* Mini Potato, Potato

DALOONπ

Onion Bhajis [catering only]; *Samosas:* Mini Vegetable [catering only], Vegetable

DIPAK√™

Mixed Vegetable Spring Rolls, Spinach Bhaji; *Curry:* Soya Chunks, Soya Mince; *Samosa:* Mixed Vegetable, Soya

FINDUS

Spaghetti Napolitan

GOODLIFEπ

Falafel, Nut Cutlets

GRANOSE

Nut Roast

HEINZ

Weight Watchers Frozen Ready Meals Vegetable Hotpot

MCCAINπ

Baby Corn Fire Sticks, Bubble & Squeak, Hash Brown Nuggets, Hash Browns, Hash Rounds, Jacket Wedges, Lemon Pepper Onions Rings, Potato & Onion Hoops, Savoury Herb Dice, Savoury Straight Cut Southern Fries,

Seasoned Roasties; *Chips:* Beefeater, Caterpac Beefeater, Caterpac Straight Cut, Crinkle Cut, Freeze-Chill (7/16 & 9/16), Shoe String Julienne), Straight Cut; *Jacket Potatoes:* Large, Regular; *Potato Skins:* 1/4 Cut, 1/2 Cut; *Potatoes:* Baby Roast, Country Style Diced, Croquettes, Roast, Sauté; *Spicy Fries:* Lattice, Spicy, Wedge

MARKS & SPENCER

Baby Rosti, Mediterranean Style Potatoes, Rice & Vegetable Mix; *Chips:* Crinkle Cut, Low Fat Just Bake, Microwave; *Fries:* American Style, Crispy Coated

MEAL MARTS

Mon Cuisine Vegetarian Food Service: Vegan Beef Steak in Cherry Sauce, Vegan Bologna Style Chub, Vegan Breaded Cutlet, Vegan Breaded Nuggets *w* Sesame, Vegan Burger, Vegan Chinese Beef & Broccoli, Vegan Egg Roll (meatless ginger chicken), Vegan Hawaiian Nuggets in Pineapple Sauce, Vegan Stuffed Shell Pasta IGF, Vegan Turkey Roll Style Chub, Vegan Vegetable Patty

RAKUSEN'S™

Oven Chips, Roast Potatoes; *Latkes:* Mini, Potato

SAFEWAY

Stuffing Balls, Microwavable White Rice, Mini Waffles, Savoury Wedges; *6 Mini:* Spring Rolls, Vegetable Samosas; *Breaded:* Garlic Mushrooms, Red Pepper Strips

SOMERFIELD

Rice & Vegetable Mix, Roast Potatoes; *3*

Way Cook Chips: American Fries, American Style, Crinkle Cut, Steak Cut, Straight Cut; *Chips:* Basics Deep Fry Straight Cut, Basics Frying, Steak Cut, Straight Cut; *Onion Rings:* Battered, In Crispy Breadcrumbs; *Oven Chips:* Basics, Healthy Selection Straight Cut; *Rice:* Golden, Microwaveable White, White

TASTEE FOODS√™

Soya Samosas; *Vegetable:* Samosas, Spring Rolls

TESCO

Hash Browns, Onion Bhajis, Oven Crunchies, Ratatouille

WAITROSE

Jacket Scallops; *Fry Chips:* Straight Cut, Thin Cut; *Oven Chips:* American Style Fries, Crinkle Cut, Steak Cut, Straight Cut; *Potato:* Croquettes, Crunchies

SEASONAL FOODS

ALDIπ

Holly Lane Christmas Pudding

ALLINSON

Wholemeal Hot Cross Buns

ASDA

4 Reduced Fat Hot Cross Buns, Farm Stores Mincemeat, Traditional Christmas Pudding

BRAKE BROS

Baked Mince Pies [frozen]

COLES TRADITIONAL FOODSø§π

Christmas Pudding: Alcohol Free, *w* Beer [keg], *w* Brandy Port & Walnuts, *w* Cider [keg], *w* Cider & Brandy [keg]

CO-OPπΩΔfcd85

Hot Cross Buns, Mincemeat, Mini Hot Cross Buns

CULPEPERøπΩ

Vegetarian Christmas Pudding

D&D CHOCOLATESø

Eggs: 2 Small Carob *w* 'animal' inside, Easter, Mini

DOVES FARMøπ

Mince Pies

EVERFRESH NATURAL FOODS√øπ

Organic Rich Plum Pudding: Gluten Free, Standard

GREEN & BLACK'Sø§π

Maya Gold Easter Egg

HAMBLEDEN HERBSøπΩfcd82

Frankincense & Myrrh, Mulling Spices, Orange Pomander Mix

HOUSE OF DORCHESTERø§π

Plain Chocolate: Assortment, Easter Egg *w* Assorted Plain Chocolates, Easter Egg *w* Plain Chocolate Disc Filling

LEAF

Elizabeth Shaw Easter Egg

LINDT & SPRUNGLI

Excellence 70% Cocoa Plain Chocolate Egg & 9 Mini-eggs

LYONS CAKES

Mince Pies

MACSWEENS

Vegetarian Haggis

MARKS & SPENCER

9 Mini Hot Cross Buns, Christmas Chutney, Luxury Mincemeat; *95% Fat Free Hot Cross Buns:* 4, 9; *Xmas:* Conserve Collection, Marmalade Collection, Strawberry Conserve

MARTLETπ

Organic Mincemeat

MR KIPLING

Glazed Mince Tartlets, Mince Parcels, Mince Pies Selection — Mince Slices; *Mince Pies:* Luxury, Millennium, Mince Pies

MRS PEEKSπ

Christmas Pudding: Cider & Sherry, Rum & Brandy

ROBERTSONSπ

Traditional Mincemeat

ROCOCO CHOCOLATESøπΩ

Dark Chocolate Easter Egg: Hollow w selection of chocolates inside, Solid

SAFEWAY

Christmas Pretzels, Instore Mini Hot Cross Buns, Mincemeat; *Mince Pies:* Deep Filled, Puff Pastry; *Pre-packed:* Hot Cross Bun Cluster, Hot Cross Buns, White Hot Cross Buns, Wholemeal Hot Cross Buns

SAINSBURY'SΩfcd88

Deliciously Dark Vegan Easter Egg

SOMERFIELD

6 Basic Mince Pies; *Bakery:* Hot Cross Buns, Mini Hot Cross Buns, Wholemeal Hot Cross Buns; *Mincemeat:* Luxury, Traditional

SOYFOODSø™π

Organic: Christmas Cake, Christmas Pudding, Gluten Free Christmas Cake, Gluten Free Christmas Pudding, Gluten Free Mince Pies, Gluten Free Mince Pies w Miso & Kuzu, Hot X Buns, Mince Pies w Miso & Kuzu

SUNBLEST

Hot Cross Buns

TESCO

4 Wholemeal Hot Cross Buns, Luxury Fruit & Nut Mix/Belgian Chocolate, Luxury Mincemeat, Mincemeat, Value Christmas Pudding

VEGAN SOCIETY√ø§Ω

Plum Pudding

VILLAGE BAKERYøπΩ

Family Mince, Mincemeat, Vegan Christmas Pudding

WAITROSE

12 Mini Mince Pies; *Hot Cross Buns:* Mini, Reduced Fat, Wholemeal; *Mincemeat:* Special, Traditional; *Pudding:* Luxury Christmas, Original Plum, Tradition-

al Luxury

WILLIAM JACKSON

Plain Hot Cross Buns

XVø§πΩ

Organic Vegan Christmas Pudding

SNACKS — SAVOURY

ALDIπ

Acapulco Tortilla Chips; *Forresters Peanuts:* Dry Roast, Salted & Roasted; *Sprinters Ready Salted Multipack Crisps:* 6 Pack, 24 Pack

ASDA

Bombay Mix, Dry Roasted Peanuts, Loops Ready Salted, Ready Salted Pan Cooked Potato Chips, Ready Salted Pretzels, Roasted & Salted Cashew Nuts; *Crisps:* BBQ, Ready Salted

BUXTON FOODS LTDøπ

The Stamp Collection Chips: Sweet Potato, Vegetable

CO-OPπΩΔfcd85

Ready Salted Potato Rings, Salt & Vinegar Chipsnacks, Salt & Vinegar Multipack; *Crisps:* Chilli Flavour Tortilla Chips, Ready Salted Multipack, Ready Salted Potato Chips; *Roasted Peanuts:* Dry, Salted

COUNTRY ORGANICS√πΩfcd

Mini Pretzels

GOOD FOOD DISTRIBUTORSøπΩfcd74

Bombay Mix: Coarse, Fine, Hot

JORDANS

Tomato & Herb Oven Crisped Chips

KP

Brannigans Delicrisps Sprinkled *w* Sea Salt, Original "Hard Nuts", Spicy Tomato KP Space Raiders; *Hula Hoops:* Original, Salt & Vinegar; *KP Discos:* Pickled Onion, Salt & Vinegar; *KP Frisps:* Ready Salted, Salt & Vinegar; *KP Mini Chips:* Beef, Ready Salted, Salt & Vinegar; *KP Nuts:* Brannigans Beer, Dry Roasted Salt & Vinegar Peanuts, Nutsters Savoury Crunchy Ready Salted Peanuts, Tobago Chilli Roasted Peanuts; *KP Standard Crisps:* Beef, Ready Salted, Salt & Vinegar, Tomato Sauce, Worcester Sauce; *McCoys Thick & Crunchy Potato Chips:* Original, Wild Chilli; *Salted Roasted Nuts:* Almonds, Cashews, Pecans, Pistachios

KETTLE§π

Baked Potato Chips Sea Salt *w* Olive Oil, Poppins Lightly Sea Salted; *Chips:* Kansas, Lightly Salted, Salsa *w* Mesquite; *Tortillas:* Blue Corn, Yellow Corn *w* Sesame Seeds

McVITIES

Go Ahead Crinkled Potato Chips: Ready Salted, Salt & Vinegar

MARKS & SPENCER

Marmite Nibbles, Potato & Onion Slices, Salt & Pepper Pretzel, Salted Tortilla; *Crisps:* Baked Potato Sea Salt, Carrot Parsnip & Celeriac, Chicken & Chips,

Hand Cooked Ready Salted, Potato Rings, Ready Salted, Squares, Sticks, Waffles; *Organic Crisps:* Salt, Salt & Pepper, Sea Salt; *Reduced Fat Crisps:* Cheese & Onion Flat, Chicken & Chips, Ready Salted, Ready Salted Crinkle, Ready Salted Flat, Spring Onion; *Peanuts:* Jumbo, Organic; *Snacks:* Fusilli Pasta, Millennium Bug, Scary

NATURAL CRISPS§πfcd93

Jonathan Crisp: **Jalapeno Pepper, Lightly Salted, Sea Salt & Black Pepper, Sea Salt & Malt Vinegar**

SAFEWAY

Bombay Mix, Cardamom & Black Pepper Poppadoms, Dry Roast Peanuts, Hot & Spicy Snack Selection, Potato Sticks, Pretzel Assortment, Pretzels, Spicy Mix, Tortilla Chips Chilli Flavour, Vegetable Crackers; *Amigo's:* 6 Pack, Sizzling Bacon; *Luxury:* Fruit & Nut Mix *w* Belgian Chocolate, Tropical Fruit & Nut Mix; *Mini:* Garlic Bread, Poppadoms; *Ready Salted:* Crisps, Handcooked Chips, Savers Crisps; *Rings:* Onion, Potato; *Roasted & Salted:* American Peanuts, Large American Peanuts, Peanuts; *Roasted & Salted Nuts:* Cashew, Jumbo Cashew, Jumbo Pistachio, Mixed, Pistachio; *Snack Mix:* American Style, Oriental Style

SANCHIø

Chips: Hot & Spicy Wasabi, Sea Vegetable, Vegetable

SEABROOKøπ

Original Potato Crisps: **Crinkle Cut, Ripples, Straight Cut**

SOMERFIELD

Potato Rings, Ready Salted Crisps; *Roasted Peanuts:* Dry, Large Salted, Salted, Salted Jumbo; *Roast Salted Nuts:* Cashew, Mixed, Pistachio; *Traditional Hand-cooked Crisps:* Lightly Salted, Spring Onion

TESCO

Large Extra Roasted Peanuts, Luxury Almonds Oak Smoke Flavour, Mixed Roasted Luxury Salted Nuts, Onion Rings, Salt & Vinegar Crunchy Sticks, Salted Pretzels, Select Ready Salted Crisps; *Bombay:* Mix, Mix Bowl; *Potato:* Chips, Rings, Triangles; *Tortilla Chips:* Chilli & Lime, Lightly Salted

TRA'FO

Organic Crisps: **Chilli, No Salt, Paprika, Provençale, Salt & Vinegar, Salted**

WAITROSE

Lightly Salted Tortilla, Lower Fat Crinkles, Luxury Roasted Mixed Nuts, Onion Rings, Oven Baked Potato Chips, Paquitos Original, Pretzel; *Cashews:* Korma, Natural Roast, Salted; *Peanuts:* Dry Roast, Large Salted, Natural Roast, Organic Roast Salted, Roast Salted, Roast Salted Large, Sweet & Sour; *Potato Crisps:* 35% Less Fat Low Salt, Assorted, Lightly Salted, Low Fat Crinkle, Ready Salted; *Ready Salted Potato:* Rings, Sticks; *Roasted Salted Nuts:* Almonds, Cashew, Luxury, Luxury Mixed, Macadamia, Mixed, Organic Cashew, Pecans, Pistachios

WALKERS

Doritos Dippas Dipping Chips, Ready Salted Chipsticks, Ready Salted French

Fries; *Smiths Crisps:* Beefy, Prawn Cocktail, Ready Salted, Salt 'N' Shake Original, Salt 'N' Vinegar; *Walkers Crisps:* Beef & Onion, Prawn Cocktail, Ready Salted, Salt & Vinegar, Salt & Vinegar MAX, Tomato Ketchup; *Walkers Lites:* Ready Salted, Salt & Vinegar

SOUPS

ALDIπ

Soupreme: Fresh Tomato & Basil, Vegetable

ASDA

Vegetable

BATCHELORSπ

Packet: Crofters Tomato & Lentil, Highland Lentil; *Slim A Soup:* Minestrone, Tomato & Lentil

BAXTERS

Vegetarian Carrot & Butter Bean; *Healthy Choice:* Carrot Onion & Chick Pea, Italian Bean & Pasta; *Organic:* Carrot *w* Parsnip & Nutmeg, Tomato & Vegetable; *Traditional:* French Onion, Minestrone

BESTFOODS

Knorr Soups of the World Provençale Vegetable 1pt, Tastebreaks Dry Italian Tomato & Basil

BIONOVA

Concentrated Lentil & Pumpkin

CLEARSPRING

Instant Miso: Red (seaweed), White

(tofu)

CO-OPπΩΔfcd85

[can]: Everyday Vegetable, Potato & Leek, Thick Farmhouse Vegetable, Tomato & Lentil, Vegetable; *[dried pkt]:* Minestrone Simmer, Spring Vegetable Simmer

GO ORGANIC§π

Organic Tomato & Basil

HEINZ

Canned Condensed: Vegetable, Vegetable As Served; *Canned Ready-to-Serve:* Country Vegetable, Lentil, Tomato & Lentil, Vegetable, Winter Vegetable; *Weight Watchers [can]:* Carrot & Lentil, Carrot Potato & Coriander, Country Vegetable, Mediterranean Tomato & Vegetable, Split Pea & Lentil, Vegetable, Winter Vegetable

JUST WHOLEFOODS

Organic Instant Mix: Carrot & Coriander, Couscous, Leek & Potato, Minestrone, Tomato, Vegetable

MARKS & SPENCER

Tomato & Lentil; *Fresh:* Country Vegetable, Gazpacho, Organic Tomato & Basil, Spiced Lentil & Vegetable, Tomato & Basil

ORGANIC VALLEY√ø™π

Cream of Mushroom, Cream of Tomato, Leek & Potato, Tomato & Basil, Vegetable

ORGRANø

Vegetable Minestrone

PATAK'Sπ

Chawal Palak, Sabzi Mulligatawny

QUIET REVOLUTION™π

Organic Vegan Fresh: Gazpacho, Polska Tomato

RAKUSEN'S™

Beef & Tomato Flavour, Carrot & Lentil, Chicken & Mushroom Flavour, Thick Pea, Thick Veg

SAFEWAY

Slim Choice Minestrone, Vegetable

SANCHIø

Instant Miso: Organic, Organic w Mushroom, w Seaweed

SEEDS OF CHANGE

Organic: Three Bean, Tomato & Basil

SIMPLY ORGANICπ

Fresh Organic: Lentil & Parsley, Mediterranean Tomato, Yellow Split Pea

SOMERFIELD

Homestyle Chunky Vegetable & Lentil, Vegetable

SOURCE FOODSø

Organic Instant Miso

SUMA™§πΩ

Organic: Carrot & Coriander, Minestrone, Pea, Spicy Lentil, Swede & Orange, Tomato, Tomato & Red Pepper

TESCO

Fresh Sweet Pepper & Chilli; [tin]: Extra Thick Vegetable, Potato & Leek, Tomato & Lentil, Vegetable & Brown Lentil

WAITROSE

Chickpea, French Onion, Gazpacho, Mediterranean & Vegetable, Minestrone, Roast Pepper & Tomato, Spicy Lentil, Tomato & Basil, Vegetable

WESTBRAE

Organic Instant Miso: Red Seaweed, White Tofu

SOYA & OTHER 'MILKS'

ALLERGYCARE√øπ

Alternative Milk Powder: Rice, Soya

ASDA

Soya Milk: Sweetened, Unsweetened

BREWHURST

Evernat Organic: Almond Drink, Hazelnut Drink, Soya Powder

CLEARSPRING

Rice Dream: Calcium Enriched, Carob, Chocolate, **Organic Original**, **Organic Vanilla**, Original, Vanilla

CO-OPπΩΔfcd85

Long Life UHT Soya Drink: Sweetened, Unsweetened; *Soya Drink:* Sweetened, Unsweetened

GRANOSE

Organic Non-Dairy Shake: Banana, Chocolate, Strawberry; *Soya Alternative to Dairy Milk:* Calcium Enriched No Added Sugar, Calcium Enriched Sweetened w Apple Juice, Organic No Added Sugar

GRANOVITAπ

Soya Drink: Calcium Enriched, Organic Sugar Free

MARKALø

Organic Natural Soya Milk

MITOKUø

Sake

PLAMIL√™§π

Calcium & Vitamin Enriched Non-Dairy Alternative to Milk (Soya): **Concentrated Sugar Free, Sugar Free, Sweetened w Apple;** *Sunflower White-Sun Non-Dairy Alternative to Milk w Calcium & Vitamins (Pea):* **No Added Sugar, Sweetened w Apple**

PROSOYA

So Nice Fresh: Chocolate, Original; *So Nice UHT:* Capuccino, Chocolate, Original, Sweetened, Unsweetened, Vanilla

PROVAMELπ

Rice Drink; *Organic Soya Alternative To Milk:* **Cereal w Hazelnuts, No Sug-** ar No Salt, Sweetened w Wheat Syrup; *Soya Alternative To Milk:* Banana, Calcium Enriched Sweetened w Apple Juice, Chocolate, Strawberry, Unsweetened w Calcium & Vitamins, Vanilla

SAFEWAY

Soya Alternative to Dairy Milk: Sweetened, Unsweetened

SKANE FARMERS

Mill Milk Oat Drink: Chocolate, Organic Classic, Organic Fibre, Vanilla

SUNRISE√™πΩfcd

Soya Drink, Soya Drink No Added Sugar, Soya Drink w Calcium & Vitamins

UNISOY

Whitewave: Calcium Enriched Sweetened, No Added Sugar

WAITROSE

Soya Milk: Calcium Enriched, Calcium Enriched Sweetened, Unsweetened

SPICES ETC

ASDA

Tikka Masala Medium Paste

BLUE DRAGON

Paste: Magic, Red Curry

CHIMANSøπ

Spice Blend for Indian Dishes: Aloo Gobi, Bean Curry, Bombay Potatoes, Cauliflower & Spinach Bhaji, Dal, Spicy

THE

Vegan

SOCIETY

Promoting ways of living which
are free of animal products – for
the benefit of people, animals
and the environment

WHERE THERE'S A WILL THERE'S A WAY

There must be many readers who would like to offer
financial support to the Vegan Society's unique work
but have limited means at their disposal. There is,
however, an easy way of helping regardless of present
circumstances – by including a legacy to the Society
in your will. Great or small, such legacies can make a
real and enduring contribution to the promotion of
vegan ideals.

*If you would like to make a bequest to the Society
please request a Legacy Pack*

Contact Vegan Society, Donald Watson House,
7 Battle Road, St Leonards-on-Sea, E Sussex TN37 7AA
t 01424 427 393 **f** 01424 717 064
e fund@vegansociety.com **w** www.vegansociety.com

THANK YOU

Chick Peas, Spicy Mushroom & Peas, Vegetable Soup

MARKS & SPENCER

Curry Paste: Medium, Mild

PATAK'Sπ

Paste: Bhuna, Biryani, Extra Hot Curry, Garam Masala, Kashmiri, Korma, Madras, Mild Curry, Rogan Josh, Tandoori, Tikka, Vindaloo

SAFEWAY

Curry Powders: all; *Spices:* all

SHARWOOD'S

Balti Curry Paste: Hot, Medium, Mild; *Curry Paste:* Extra Hot, Hot, Medium, Mild, Tandoori, Tikka

SPREADS — SAVOURY

ALDIπ

Harvest Spread Crunchy Peanut Butter

ASDA

Vegetable Extract; *Peanut Butter:* Crunchy, Smooth

BESTFOODS

Marmite [jar, portion pk]

BIONA

Yeast Pâté: Gourmet, Green Pepper, Herb, Mushroom

CAULDRON FOODS LTD√π

Chickpea & Black Olive Pâté; *Vegetable Pâté:* w Herbs, w Mushrooms, w Tomato & Red Pepper

CO-OPπΩΔfcd85

Houmous, Vegetable Pâté, Yeast Extract; *Peanut Butter:* Crunchy, Smooth

DUERRS

Peanut Butter: all

EQUAL EXCHANGEπ

Organic Cashew Butter; *Crunchy Peanut Butter:* Salted, Unsalted; *Tahini:* Dark, Light

GR LANEøπΩΔfcd87

*Tartex Organic Pâté; *Natex:* Yeast Extract, Yeast Extract Reduced Salt; *Tartex Vegetarian Pâtés:* all; *Vessen Pâtés:* all*

GOBBLINπΩfcd86

Hummus

GRANOVITAπ

Organic Tofu Pâté Tomato Yeast Free [tube], Red Kidney Spicy Spread; *Organic Vegetarian Pâté [pot]:* Herb, Mushroom, Paprika & Gherkin; *Vegetarian Yeast Pâté [tube]:* Herb Provence, Original, Paprika, Wild Mushroom; *Vegetarian Pâté [pot]:* Herb, Mushroom; *Vegetarian Yeast Spread [bombe]:* Herb Provençal, Mushroom, Olive

KRAFT JACOBS SUCHARD

Vegemite

LUNN LINKS√øπΩ

Kitchen Garden Organic: Peanut Butter, Tahini

MAPLETONS

Vitamin-R Yeast Extract

MARKALø

Vegetable Pâté: Herb, Mushroom, Quinoa

MARKS & SPENCER

Humous, Reduced Fat Humous; *Peanut Butter:* Crunchy, Smooth

MERIDIANøπ

Almond Butter, Cashew Butter, Hazel Butter, Low Salt Yeast Extract, Yeast Extract; *Peanut Butter:* Crunchy, Crunchy No Salt, Organic Crunchy, Organic Crunchy No Salt, Smooth, Smooth No Salt; *Tahini:* Dark, Light

MONKI

Almond Butter, Cashew Nut Spread, Hazelnut Butter, Peanut Butter, Sunflower Spread

NATEX

Yeast Extract Spread: Low Salt Savoury, Savoury

PLAMIL√™§π

Organic Sandwich Spread: w Paprika, *w* Tofu Curry & Pineapple, *w* Vegetables

REDWOOD√ø§π

Cheatin Pâté: Campagne, Forestier, Provençal

ST GILES FOODS

Duchesse Egg Free Sandwich Spread, River Edge Luxury Sandwich Spread

SAFEWAY

Yeast Extract; *Houmous:* Delicatessen, Pre-packed, Reduced Fat Pre-packed; *Peanut Butter:* Crunchy, Smooth; *Spread:* Mexican Chilli Bean, Savoury, Spicy Vegetable, Tomato & Onion

SAN AMVROSIA HEALTH FOODSπΩ

Houmous; *Houmous:* Avocado, *w* Peppers

SOMERFIELD

Houmous; *Peanut Butter:* Basic Crunchy, Basic Smooth, Crunchy, Smooth

SUMA™§πΩ

Organic Sunflower Spread; *Organic Peanut Butter:* Crunchy *w* Salt, Crunchy without Salt, Smooth *w* Salt, Smooth without Salt; *Peanut Butter:* Crunchy *w* Salt, Crunchy without Salt, Smooth *w* Salt, Smooth without Salt; *Pâté:* Herb, Mushroom, Organic Herb, Organic Mushroom, Vegetable

SUN PAT

Peanut Butter: American Style, Crunchy, Smooth, Wholenut

SUNITA

Tahini: Dark, Light

TESCO

Houmous, Houmous *w* Red Pepper, Roasted Vegetable & Caponata Sauce Sandwich Filling, Yeast Extract

food

WAITROSE

Houmous, Reduced Fat Houmous; *Peanut Butter:* Crunchy, Organic Crunch, Organic Smooth, Smooth, Wholenut

WHOLE EARTHø§π

3 Nut Butter, Hummus, Organic Hummus; *Peanut Butter:* Organic Crunchy, Organic Smooth, Original Crunchy, Original Smooth, USA Style Crunchy, USA Style Smooth

YAKSO

Chick Pea Spread

SPREADS — SWEET

ALLERGYCARE√øπ

Dairy Free Real Chocolate Spread

BIORGANIC√ø§π

Special Recipe Seville Orange Marmalade: w Brandy, w Rum, w Whisky

MARKS & SPENCER

New Marmalade & Whisky; *Conserve:* Black Cherry & Kirsch, Raspberry & Cassis

MERIDIAN

No Added Sugar All Fruit Spread: Apricot, Banana & Mango, Black Cherry, Blackberry & Apple, Blackcurrant, Blueberry, Breakfast Grapefruit, Morello Cherry, Peach & Passion, Pineapple & Ginger, Raspberry, Seville Orange, Strawberry, Summer Fruits; *Organic No Added Sugar All Fruit Spread:* Apricot, Blackcurrant, Morello, Raspberry, Seville Orange, Strawberry, Wild Blueberry

MONKI

Carob Nut Spread

PLAMIL√™§π

Carob Spread: Sugar Free, Sweetened

SUMA

Fruit Spread: Apricot, Blackcurrant, Blueberry, Cranberry, Forest Berry, Morello Cherry, Orange, Strawberry

SUNWHEEL NATURAL FOODS

No Added Sugar Fruit Spread: Pear 'n' Apple, Pear 'n' Apricot, Pear 'n' Raspberry

TESCO

Conserve: Black Cherry & Amaretto, Finest Apricot & Brandy, Finest Strawberry & Champagne; *Marmalade:* Bucks Fizz, Finest w Whisky

WAITROSE

Grapefruit Lemon & Lime w Gin Marmalade, Soft Set Peach & Passionfruit w Continental Extra Jam; *Conserve:* Apricot & Almond w Amaretto, Pear Lemon & Ginger w Walnuts; *No Added Sugar Spread:* Apricot, Blackcurrant, Orange, Strawberry; *Preserve:* Blackcurrant & Rum, Strawberry & Champagne

WHOLE EARTH

Pure Fruit Spread: Apricot, Blackcurrant, Strawberry, Wild Blueberry, Wild Hedgerow

TOFU, TEMPEH, MISO ETC

CAULDRON FOODS LTD√π

Tofu: Marinated, Marinated Pieces, Naturally Smoked, Organic, Organic Smoked, Original

CLEAR SPOT

Tofu: Organic, Organic Smokey, Regular

CLEARSPRING√ø§π

Miso: Barley (Onozaki), Brown Rice (Johsen), Hatcho, Sweet White

DANIVALø

Tempeh; *Miso:* Barley, Brown Rice; *Seitan:* Bolognese, Ravioli; *Tofu:* Bolognese, Ravioli

DRAGONFLY FOODSøπ

Organic Tofu: Deep Fried, Natural, Smoked

FULL OF BEANSπΩ

Japanese Style Tofu, Savoury Seitan; *Tempeh:* Frozen, Garlic & Coriander, Marinated, Sesame

LEAFCYCLE√™

Greenleaf Curd, Leafu

MARIGOLD HEALTH FOODSπ

Braised Tofu [can]

MARKALø

Organic Seitan

MITOKUø

Snow Dried Tofu

MURPHY & SONø

Tempeh Starter Culture

PHYTOFOODS√§π

Tempeh Kits

RR TOFU√§π

Tofu: Marinated, Organic, Regular, Sea Cakes, Sesame Rissole, Smoky

SANCHIø

Organic Firm Long Life Tofu; *Miso:* Genmai, Hatcho, Mugi, Organic Mugi, Shiro

SOY FOODSø™π

Tempeh Fingers; *Tofu:* Abura Age Marinated, *w* Nigari

SUNRISE√™πΩfcd

Organic Tofu

TERRASANAø

Seitan in Tamari

WATERFRONT√§πΩ

Organic Tofu

WESTBRAE

Miso: Barley, Brown Rice

YAKSO

Tempeh; *Seitan:* Goulash, in Tamari

'YOGHURTS'

GRANOSE

Yogert: Apricot, Blackcurrant & Apple, Peach Melba, Raspberry, Strawberry

GRANOVITAπ

Deluxe Soyage: **Black Cherry, Peach & Apricot, Plain, Raspberry, Strawberry; *Organic Soyage:* Fruits of the Forest, Peach & Apricot, Strawberry**

HALDANE

Yoga: Blueberry, Peach & Apricot, Plain, Strawberry

PLAMIL√™§π

White-Sun Alternative to Yogurt w Added Fibre: **Black Cherry, Peach & Passion, Strawberry**

PROSOYA

SoYog: Fruits of the Forest, Natural, Peach, Raspberry, Strawberry

PROVAMELπ

Junior Yofu: **Banana, Peach, Pear, Strawberry; *Yofu:* Black Cherry, Organic Peach & Mango, Organic Red Cherry, Peach, Peach & Mango, Plain Organic, Red Cherry, Strawberry, Vanilla**

SO GOOD

Yogert: Black Cherry, Natural, Peach & Passion Fruit, Pineapple, Strawberry

YOSAπ

Yosa Oat Probiotic: Apple & Banana Fortified w Calcium, Fruits Of The Forest, Peach & Passion, Pineapple

notes

- **banana chips** May be dipped in honey.

- **bread** A few pre-packed loaves contain either skimmed milk powder or vitamin D_3. Most large producers use vegetable-based emulsifiers (E471, E472 etc). Check with local bakers re. ingredients and type of fat used to grease tins.

- **cereals** The vitamin D in fortified cereals is commonly the animal-derived D_3.

- **chocolate** Do not assume that plain chocolate is always animal-free. For UK-produced chocolate, reading the ingredients listing is not always sufficient. Continental plain chocolate is less likely to contain animal substances.
  Cadbury, Leaf, Lindt & Sprungli, Marks & Spencer, and Thorntons chocolate products listed here have been made without animal-derived ingredients or processing aids. However, they have been produced on the same lines as milk chocolate products, so although machines are cleaned thoroughly between different products (to meet health and hygiene, and product quality, requirements), there is a very slight, theoretical, risk of contamination, meaning that they may not be suitable for dairy intolerants. Note that this is the case for *all* products except those made by companies which produce nothing but vegan products.

- **crisps** Whey, lactose or other animal-derived processing aids may be used as a flavour carrier. There is no statutory requirement for them to be listed as an ingredient.

- **di-calcium phosphate** May be sourced from bone and may be used as a growth medium for yeast used to manufacture bread. However, the most common yeast food used in the UK baking industry is calcium sulphate (animal-free).

- **fruit** May be glazed with animal (commonly beeswax or shellac), vegetable (usually carnauba — cheaper than shellac) or mineral waxes. Contact manufacturers for further details as information changes regularly (according to season, supplier etc).

- **gelatine carrier** Beta-carotene & vitamin D_2 may be 'carried' in gelatine to maintain stability. As a *general* rule powdered forms of these vitamins are gelatine-derived. In the case of beta-carotene, vegetable oil carriers are available and are generally animal-free, however, when sold as a supplement it is typically encased in capsules made of gelatine.

- **jams, jellies, conserves, marmalade and preserves** Have been omitted as being obviously vegan unless they contain additional ingredients eg alcohol.

- **Patak's** State that they have evidence from suppliers that all stocks are GM free, but believe that no company can honestly claim this unless they have visited original sources.

- **poppadums** Sharwood's contain shellac but this is not listed in the ingredients.

- **processing aids** May be animal derived. There is no statutory requirement for these to be listed on products.

- **salt** Most salt is vegan except some low salts which contain a milk derivative. Bisto produce a variety of different types of salt which are vegan including Iodised Salt which would be useful for the vegan diet (which *may* be low in iodine).

- **sugar** Bone char is sometimes used as a decolourant in sugar production. However, the largest suppliers of sugar to companies in the UK — British Sugar, Tate & Lyle and Billington — do not use any animal-derived ingredients (except for Tate & Lyle Traditional Royal Icing which contains dried egg white powder). Billington supplies Sainsbury's, Tesco, Safeway and Waitrose with their own label unrefined sugars. Whitworths no longer use animal derivatives in the processing of their sugars. Merryfield supplies Aldi supermarkets and its demerara and granulated sugars are suitable for vegans.

- **vinegar** Although malt and spirit vinegars (mainly used in pickles, relishes etc) are generally animal-free, the production of wine, cider and sherry vinegars may involve the use of a fining agent of animal origin.

- **whiteners** Snowcrest say their coffee whitener is vegan, but will not confirm this in writing.

"So what <u>do</u> you eat?"

A practical guide to healthy animal-free nutrition and healthy family meals. By Liz Cook. £12.95 + p&p

This isn't just a cookery book it's a work of art! Seventy large, glossy pages of vegan recipes, all hand-written and beautifully illustrated by Liz in the same style as her famous nutrition wallcharts.

Vegan Nutrition Chart

Nutrient information at a glance. Wipe clean. 18cm by 88cm. £2.75 + p&p.

Special Offer!
Buy the book and the wallchart together for £12.70 + p&p

Vegan Confectionery

Fine mint chocolates
16 essential oil of mint chocolates - distinctively packaged with the Vegan Society logo in gold
£4.99 + p&p

Organic Gourmet Chocolate Truffles
A truly luxurious box of 18 organic, gourmet truffles, dusted with cocoa powder
£9.99 + p&p

Vegan Macadamia Bliss Nougat
With pistachio. The first totally animal-free nougat.
40g bar
£4.95 + p&p

Plum Pudding
Delicious, rich plum pudding made from natural and mainly organic ingredients. Not just for Xmas! 400g
£4.95 + p&p

drink

alcopops   92
beers   92
champagne   94
ciders & perries   95
'hot'   96
low & non-alcoholic   96
soft   97
spirits & apéritifs   102
wines   104

notes   *116*

ALCOPOPS

ASDA

Alcoholic: Dandelion & Burdock, Pineapple & Grapefruit; *Bite:* Apple, Grapefruit, Lemon, Orange

BEERS

ALDIπ

Lager: Galahad Premium, Steinbrau; *Saracen:* Lager, Pilsner Lager, Strong Lager

ASDA

Best Bitter, Bière de Luxe, German Pilsener Lager, Lager; *[bottled & keg made by Shepherd Neame]:* Gentleman Jack, Rusty Rivet, Whitechapel Porter; *Farm Stores:* Bitter, Lager

BASS

Grolsch, Staropraman [bottle]

BATEMANS

[bottle]: Sainsbury Premium Ale, Valiant Special Bitter, Victory Ale, XXXB Special Bitter

BLACK SHEEPπ

Ale: Black Sheep, Riggwelter Strong Yorkshire, Yorkshire Square

BORVE BREW HOUSE√øπ

Borve Ale [bottle, draught], Strong Ale [bottle], Tall Ships [bottle, draught]

BRAKSPEAR™

Naturale, V Bottled Ale

BROUGHTON ALESπ

Black Douglas, Border Gold, Old Izaak, Scottish Oatmeal Stout, The Ghillie; *Ale:* Greenmantle, Merlin's, Old Jock

CALEDONIAN BREWING CO√øπΩ

Golden Promise Organic Beer (Scotland)

CARLSBERG-TETLEYπ

Carlsberg: Export 5.0% [bottle, can, keg], Ice 5.0% [bottle, can], Lager 3.8% [bottle, keg], Lager 4.1% [bottle, can], Special Brew 9.0% [bottle, can]

CHARLES WELLSø§π

[can, bottle, keg]: Bombardier, Cobra (own factory production only), Crest, Eagle Bitter, Fargo, Josephine Grimsley, Red Stripe (own factory production only), Super Crest

CROPTON BREWERYπ

[bottle conditioned beers]: Backwoods, King Billy, Monkmans Slaughter, Scoresby Stout, Two Pints, Uncle Sam's

DUBLIN BREWING CO√π

1798 Revolution Red Ale, Beckett's Gold, D'Arcy's Dublin Stout, Maeve's Crystal Wheat

FULLER, SMITH & TURNERπΩ

[bottle]: 1845, Extra Special Bitter, Golden Pride, India Pale Ale, London Porter, London Pride, Pale Ale, Vintage Ale

JOSEPH HOLTπ

Brown Stout

KELHAM ISLAND√π

Pale Rider Ale [bottle]

LINFIT™π

English Guineas Stout [bottle, draught], Linfit Dark Mild

M&Mø

Jade Bière (France)

PITFIELD BREWERYø™§πΩ

Duke's Spring Ale, Eco Warrior

ST PETER'S BREWERYø

Organic Vegan Ale

SAMUEL SMITH™π

Ale [bottle]: India, Nut Brown Old Brewery Pale, Organic Best; *[bottle]:* Imperial Stout, Oatmeal Stout, Pure Brewed Lager, Taddy Porter

SCOTTISH COURAGE BREWINGπΩ

[bottle, can, keg]: Beck's, Holsten Pils

SEDLESCOMBE VINEYARD√ø™π

Bucher Pilsner

SHEPHERD NEAMEøπ

[bottle & keg]: 1698 Celebration Ale, Bishops Finger, Brown Ale, Christmas Ale, Early Bird, Goldings Ale, Harry Half-yard, Late Red, Light Ale, Masterbrew, Spitfire

SOMERFIELD

Bière de Belgique, French Premier Lager, German Pilsner

VINCEREMOSøπ

Organic Case: Beer, Lager; *Pinkus Muller Brauerei (Munster):* Gambrinus (Czech Republic), Original Flag Porter (UK), Pinkus Alt Obergarrig (Germany), Pinkus Hefe Weizen (Germany), Pinkus Pils (Germany), Pinkus Special Lager (Germany)

VINTAGE ROOTSøπ

Belgium: Moinette Dupont, Saison Dupont; *Germany:* Bucher Organic Pilsner, Oko Krone Pilsner, Riedenburger Organic Lager (Helles), Riedenburger Weisse 'Michaeli Dunkel', Riedenburger Weisse Wheatbeer

VIVA!√ø§π

Clausthaler Low Alcohol Lager, Cobra, Gambrinus, Viva, Zwiec

WAITROSE

Bavarian Pils, Danish Export, Hofmark Beer; *Ale:* India Pale, Pale, Scotch, Traditional Pale; *Bitter:* Midland, Organic, Wessex; *Lager:* Czech, Dutch, French, German Pilsner, Italian, Strong German; *West Country:* Bitter, Stout

WHITBREADπ

Heineken Export, Kaltenberg, Rolling Rock

CHAMPAGNE

ASDA

Brut, Vintage

ORGANIC WINE COMPANYø

Carte d'Or Brut José Ardinat

VEGAN SOCIETY√ø§Ω

Champagne & Wine Case

VINCEREMOSø𝜋

José Ardinat: Carte d'Or Brut Cuvée Spéciale, Demi Sec Carte d'Or, Rosé Carte d'Or

VIVA!√ø§𝜋

Champagne: Brut, Brut Cuvée Spéciale, Demi Sec, Rosé; *Champagne Method:* Clairette de Die Brut Achard Vincent AC, Clairette de Die Tradition Achard Vincent AC

WAITROSE

Champagne: all

CIDERS & PERRIES

ALDI𝜋

Strong White Cider, Taurus Dry Cider 2l

ASDA

Perry

AVALON VINEYARDø𝜋

Traditional Somerset Cider [draught in plastic jars]: Dry, Medium, Sweet

BIDDENDEN√ø𝜋

Cider: Special Reserve, Strong Traditional Kentish

DUNKERTON'S√ø𝜋

Perry [bottle]: Dry, Medium Sweet;

Sparking Cider [bottle]: 33cl, 75cl, 500ml; *Still Cider [bottle]:* Breakwells Seedling, Court Royal, Kingston Black; *Traditional Still Cider [bottle]:* Dry, Medium Dry, Medium Sweet, Sweet

HP BULMER

Ciders: all

MERRYDOWN

Cider: Pulsate White, Pulse White, Vintage Dry, Vintage Medium

SAFEWAY𝜋Ω

Sweet Cider

SEDLESCOMBE VINEYARD√ø™

Farmhouse Cider: Dry, Reserve

VINTAGE ROOTSø𝜋

Cider: Normandy, Westons Organic

WAITROSE

Mousseux, Strong Scrumpy; *Cider:* Extra Strong, White; *Traditional Cider:* Low Alcohol, Medium Dry, Strong Dry; *Vintage:* Cider, Perry

WESTON & SONSø𝜋

Cider & Ginger Pinch, Cider & Lemongrass, Perry & Blackcurrant; *Cider:* Classic Vintage, First Quality Draught, LA, Organic, Special Vintage, Strong Medium Dry; *Marcles:* Medium Sweet, Millennium; *Oak Conditioned:* Collection Pack, Henry Westons Vintage Reserve, Strong Medium Dry, Strong Medium Sweet; *Perry:* Classic, Herefordshire Country; *Scrumpy:* Bounds Bran, Extra Strong, Old Rosie, Supreme, Traditional; *Stowford Press:* Dry, Medium Dry, Medium Sweet

'HOT'

A.▨

Drinking Chocolate

BIOFORCE

Bambu Instant

CADBURY

Drinking Chocolate

CITRESSE

Instant Lemon Tea

CO-OPπΩΔfcd85

Drinking Chocolate, Instant Coffee & Chicory Powder

COUNTRY ORGANICS√πΩfc

Barley Coffee

GREEN & BLACK'Sø§π

Nocaf, Organic Hot Chocolate, Wake-cup

HAMBLEDEN HERBSøπΩfcd82

Organic Carob

LIMAø

Yannoh: Ground, Instant

NESTLÉ

Caro

PAYNES

Lift Tea: Apple, Original Lemon, Peach,

Reduced Sweetness Lemon

PREWETT'S

Chicory Drink: Instant, Organic Instant

RIDPATH PEKπ

Barleycup

ST GILES FOODS

Café Roma Coffee Enhancer Syrup: Amaretto Liqueur, Irish Whiskey Liqueur, Roasted Hazelnut, Vanilla Creme; *Café Roma Liqueur Coffee Concentrate:* Amaretto, Caribbean, Cherry Brandy, Crème de Menthe, Irish

SAFEWAY

Drinking Chocolate

TESCO

Instant Lemon Tea Granules

WAITROSE

Organic Drinking Chocolate

LOW & NON-ALCOHOLIC

GREENE KING

Lowes Low Alcohol Bitter

ORCHID DRINKSπΩ

Amé: Dry, Original, Red, Rosé, White

SHEPHERD NEAMEøπ

Pilgrims Low Alcohol Beer [bottle & keg]

VINCEREMOSøπ

Clausthaler Low Alcohol Lager (Germany), Pétillant de Raisin Château Bousquette

SOFT

ALDIπ

Ameristar Diet Cola, Hyberry Blackcurrant High Juice Drink; *Maceys:* 12 Pack Cup Drinks, Sugar Free Sparkling Strawberry Flavour Cream Soda; *Solesta Juice Drinks:* Blackcurrant, Orange, Tropical Fruit; *Sunquen:* Apple & Blackcurrant, Low Calorie Orange, Whole Orange; *Topstar:* Bitter Lemon, Cola, Diet Cola, Diet Indian Tonic Water, Diet Lemonade, Ginger Ale, Lemonade, Soda Water, Sugar Free Cherryade, Sugar Free Orangeade *w* Sweeteners

ALLERGYCARE√øπ

Soya Alternative Milk Shake Powder: Banana, Coconut, Strawberry, Vanilla

ASDA

Diet Lemonade, Regular Cola; *Farm Stores:* Cola, Lemonade, Low Calorie Cola, Low Calorie Lemonade, Low Calorie Orangeade; *Flavoured Spring Water:* No Added Sugar Peach, Raspberry & Strawberry; *Flavoured Water:* Cranberry, Elderflower, Pink Grapefruit; *Juice Drink:* Cranberry & Blueberry, Cranberry & Raspberry, Cranberry & Redcurrant, Melon; *No Added Sugar Crush:* Apple, Blackcurrant, Mandarin & Mango, Orange, Pineapple & Grapefruit, Pink Grapefruit; *No Added Sugar Drink:* Apple & Blackcurrant, Orange, Three Fruit; *No Added Sugar Juice Drink:* Apple, Cranberry, Fruit Salad, Peach Melba, Pear Drops, Sherbet Lemon, Strawberries & Cream, Strawberry; *No Added Sugar Squash:* Apple, Apple & Blackcurrant, Orange, Orange & Apricot, Orange & Pineapple, Pear & Blueberry, Pink Grapefruit, Tropical; *Squash:* Lemon, Lemon & Lime, Orange, Orange & Pineapple

ASPALL

Juice: Apple, Organic Apple

BIONA

Juice: Apple, Carrot, Orange, Red Grape, Tomato, Vegetable

BIONOVA

Squash: **Grapefruit, Lime, Orange**

BIOTTA

Organic Juice: Beetroot, Breuss, Carrot, Celery, Tomato, Vegetable Cocktail

BRITVIC

Bass Shandy Lemon Flavour Soft Drink *w* Beer, Quosh Apple & Blackcurrant Drink; *Britvic:* American Ginger Ale, Bitter Lemon Drink, Blackcurrant Flavour Cordial, Draught Concentrated Orange Juice, English Apple Juice, Grapefruit Juice, Indian Tonic Water, Irn Bru, Lime Juice Cordial, Low Calorie Bitter Lemon Drink, Low Calorie Indian Tonic Water, Orange Juice, Orange Squash, Peppermint Flavour Soft Drink, Pineapple Juice, Pink Grapefruit Juice, Quencher Orange Drink, Soda Water, Tomato Juice, Tomato Juice Cocktail; *Britvic 55 Juice Drink:* Apple, Apple Soft, Orange, Orange Soft, Pineapple, Pineapple Soft, Tropical; *Britvic Citrus Spring Drink:*

Lemon, Lime, Orange; *Britvic J2O Juice Soft Drink:* Apple & Mango, Apple & Melon, Orange & Passionfruit; *Britivic Ruby's Soda:* Cranberry & Blueberry, Cranberry & Orange, Cranberry & Raspberry; *Corona:* Cherryade, Lemonade, Limeade, Low Calorie Lemonade, Orangeade; *Idris Traditional Style:* Cream Soda, Dandelion & Burdock, Ginger Beer; *R White's:* Lemonade, Low Calorie Premium Lemonade, Premium Lemonade; *Robinson's Fruit & Barley Soft Drink w Barley:* Apple, Blackcurrant, Citrus Juice, Peach, Pear, Pink Grapefruit, Summer Fruits; *Robinson's Fruit Break Low Calorie Soft Drink:* Citrus Fruits & Barley, Peach Fruit & Barley, Pink Grapefruit & Barley, Summer Fruits & Barley; *Robinson's High Juice Drink:* Blackcurrant, Forest Fruits, No Added Sugar Pink Grapefruit, Orange, Pink Grapefruit, Summer Fruits; *Robinson's Soft Drink:* Apple, Apple & Blackcurrant High Juice w Spice Lemon & Wine Flavours, Blackcurrant, Lemon Barley, Orange; *Robinson's Special R Low Calorie Drink:* Apple & Blackcurrant Soft, Apple Soft, Blackcurrant Juice, Orange Soft, Summer Fruit Soft, Tropical Soft; *Tango Drink:* Apple, Low Calorie Apple; *Tango Low Calorie Soft Drink:* Apple, Cherry, Lemon, Tropical; *Tango Soft Drink:* Apple, Blackcurrant, Cherry, Lemon, Tropical; *Tango Still Drink:* Apple, Blackcurrant, Lemon Juice Soft; *Top Deck:* Cherryade, Dandelion & Burdock, Lemonade, Orangeade

CADBURY

Choc-A-Shake

CALYPSO

Vimto Cups; *Calypso Cups:* all; *Calypso Flavoured Spring Water:* all; *Calypso Pure Juice:* all; *Cuplets:* Pure Orange Juice, Spring Water; *Flintstones Juice Drinks:* all; *Flintstones Light Juice Drinks:* all; *Kwenchy Kups:* all; *Rugrats Flavour Drinks:* all; *Sparkling Calypso:* all; *Tom & Jerry Cups:* all; *Tom & Jerry Flavour Drinks:* all

CO-OPπΩΔfcd85

Cola, Cream Soda, Dandelion & Burdock, Diet Iron Brew, Ginger Beer, Iron Brew, Lager & Lime Flavoured Soft Drink w Beer, Limeade, Orangeade, Raspberryade, Sparkling Apple Juice; *Cola:* Diet, Everyday, No Added Sugar, Premium, Premium Diet; *Concentrate:* Apple & Blackcurrant, Lemon Barley Water, Lime Cordial, Orange High Juice Squash, Orange Lemon & Pineapple, Whole Lemon, Whole Orange; *Concentrated No Added Sugar:* Apple & Blackcurrant, Apple Low Calorie, Everyday Low Calorie Orange Drink, Lemon, Lemon & Lime Drink, Lemon Barley Water, Mixed Fruit Low Calorie, Orange, Orange Lemon & Pineapple, Peach Barley Water, Pear & Blueberry Drink, Strawberry Low Calorie; *Crush:* Apple, Pineapple & Grapefruit; *Gently Sparkling Flavoured Water:* Apple, Grapefruit, Peach, Raspberry; *Lemonade:* Diet, Everyday, Lemonade, Lemonade Shandy, Peach, Pink; *No Added Sugar:* Orangeade, Strawberryade; *Mixers:* American Dry Ginger Ale, Bitter Lemon, Indian Tonic Water, Indian Tonic Water w Lime, Low Calorie American Dry Ginger Ale, Low Calorie Bitter Lemon, Low Calorie Indian Tonic Water, Soda Water, Tonic Water w Lime;

Ready-to-Drink: Everyday Sugar Free Raspberry & Orange Cup, No Added Sugar Tropical Juice, Sun Up Orange, Sun Up Tropical Whole Fruit; *Sugar Free Mini-Pop:* Blackcurrant, Cherryade, Cola, Limeade, Orangeade; *Tangy:* Blackcurrant, Lemon Drink, Orangeade

COPELLA

Sparkling Apple

CULPEPERøπΩ

Ginger Beer; *Elderflower:* Cordial, Fizz; *Juice:* Apple, Ginger

ELLA DRINKS LTD√øπ

Bouvrage Raspberry Juice Drink

FRESH√§πΩ

Innocent Fruit Smoothie: Bananas & Oranges, Cranberries & Raspberries, Mangoes Passion Fruit & Pineapples, Strawberries

GREEN & BLACK'Sø§π

Aloe Lemon, Cola w Guarana, Orange Soda, Real Lemonade

GUSTO√ø§π

Herbal Drink: Ginkola, Goddess, Gusto, Lemonade

JAMES WHITE√øπ

Big Tom Bloody Mary Mix, Great Uncle Cornelius' Finest Spiced Ginger; *Juice:* Bramley, Cox, Organic Apple, Organic Pear, Russet

LA VERJA

Juice: Apple, Orange, Orange & Banana, Peach & Apple, Pear & Pineap-ple, Pineapple, Tomato, Tropical Fruit

LIBBY'S

Juicy Juice Orange, Tomato Juice; *C:* Apple, Berry, Grapefruit, Orange; *Drink:* Um Bongo, Um Ognob; *Organic Juice:* Apple, Grapefruit, Orange, Tomato

MARKS & SPENCER

Cola, Freshly Squeezed Lemonade, Pamplemousse, Peach Still Water, Reduced Sugar Blackcurrant Dilute, Revitalise Cranberry & Passionfruit, Symphony Elderflower Sparkling Water w Lemon; *Diet:* Cola, Lemon Sparkle, Pineapple & Grapefruit Sparkle; *Freshly Squeezed Juice:* Clementine, Orange, Orange & Banana, Orange & Raspberry, Pink Grapefruit; *Juice:* 3 Pack Thomas Apple, Apple, Apple & Mango, English Cox Apple, Florida Grapefruit, Florida Orange, Florida Squeezed Orange, Jaffa Orange, Organic Apple, Organic Orange, Pineapple & Lime, Pineapple Mango & Passion Fruit, Sweet & Smooth Orange; *Nectar:* Fraise, Frambois; *Quest:* Diet Mango & Lemon, Grapefruit & Lime; *Pouch Drink:* Orange, Tropical; *Supreme Juice Drink:* Apple, Orange; *Water:* Elderflower Spring, Lemon & Lime Flower, Lemon & Lime Still, Mixed Berry, Pear Sparkling, Sparkling, Still

MERIDIAN

Fruit Juice Concentrates: Apple, Apple & Apricot, Apple & Blackcurrant, Apple & Cherry, Apple & Exotic Fruits, Apple & Lemon, Apple & Strawberry, Organic Apple, Organic Apple & Apricot, Organic Apple & Cherry, Pear

drink

MERRYDOWN

Schloer: Original Apple, Peach, White/Red Grape; *Schloer To Go:* Apple, Orange/Lemon

NESTLÉ

Nesquik: all

NUTRICIA

Concentrated Cranberry Juice *w* Vitamin C

O+

Lime & Cactus, Mandarin & Lemongrass

ORCHID DRINKSπΩ

Aqua Libra: Berry, Dry [750ml only], Original

ORGANIC WINE COMPANYø

Juice: Jus de Raisin l'Arbre aux Soleils, Nectar d'Abricot Mas de Gourgonnier

PLJπ

Lemon, Lime Juice

RAYNER BURGESSπ

Crusha Milk Shake Syrup: Banana, Black Cherry, Chocolate, Lime, Pineapple, Raspberry, Strawberry

RED BULL CO LTD

Red Bull

ROCK'S ORGANIC CORDIALS√π

Organic Cordial: Blackcurrant, Christmas, Elderflower, Ginger, Lemon, Lime, Summer Fruit, Tangerine, Tropical Fruit; *Organic Squash:* Lemon, Lime, Orange

SAFEWAY

Soft Drinks & Carbonates: all

SEDLESCOMBE VINEYARD√ø™π

1066 Country Juice: Apple, Pear

SOMERFIELD

American Ginger Ale, Basics Lemonade, Bitter Lemon, Cherryade, Cola, Diet Lemonade, Diet Traditional Lemonade, High Juice Orange Squash, Lemonade, Limeade, Low Calorie American Ginger Ale, Orangeade, Soda Water, Still Lemonade, Strathglen Spring Carbonated Natural Mineral Water, Strathglen Spring Still Natural Mineral Water, Sugar Free Diet Lemonade, Traditional Lemonade, Traditional Style Cream Soda, Traditional Style Ginger Beer; *Cola:* Basics, Diet Caffeine Free Original, Diet Original, Original; *Drink:* Apple & Blackcurrant, Basics Cola Flavour, Citrus Fruit, Lemon, Lemon & Lime, Orange, Orange & Mango Fruit, Orange & Peach, Orange Fruit, Orange Lemon & Pineapple, Pineapple Fruit *w* Coconut Flavour; *Juice:* Apple, Basics Pure Orange, English Apple, English Pressed Apple, Grapefruit, Jaffa Orange, Lime Cordial, Pressed English Apple, Pure Apple, Pure Florida Orange, Pure Florida Squeezed Orange, Pure Grapefruit, Pure Orange, Pure Pineapple, Pure Premium Orange, Spanish Orange, Sparkling Apple, Sparkling Red Grape, Sparkling White Grape, Tomato; *Juice Drink:* Apple & Blackcurrant Fruit & Barley, Apple & Grapefruit, Cranberry, Florida Pink Grapefruit, High Blackcurrant, Lemon Fruit & Barley, Orange & Peach, Peach & Apricot Fruit & Barley, Pink Grapefruit Fruit & Barley, Tropical Fruit; *Juice Drink w Sweeteners:* Apple, Apple & Blackcurrant, Basics Orange, Blackcurrant, Cranberry, Cranberry & Blueberry, Orange, Strawberry, Tropical Fruit; *No Added Sugar:* Apple & Blackcurrant Drink, Apple Crush, Apple Drink, Blackcurrant Crush, Cherryade, Lemon Drink, Limeade, Orange Crush, Orange Drink, Orangeade, Pineapple & Grapefruit Crush, Strawberry Drink; *Slightly Sparkling Spring Water w A Hint Of Flavour:* Grapefruit, Peach, Raspberry; *Tonic Water:* Indian, Low Calorie Indian, Low Calorie w A Dash Of Lemon, w A Dash Of Lemon

STELLE

Carrot Juice

TESCO

Diet Lemonade, Iron Brew, Lemonade, Lemonade Shandy, Lime Juice Cordial, Orangeade (no added sugar), Sparkling Diet Lemonade, Sparkling Lemonade, Traditional Style Ginger Beer; *Cola [large bottle]:* Best Ever, Best Ever Diet, Sparkling; *Cola Multi Packs [can]:* Best Ever, Best Ever Diet; *Drink:* Blackcurrant & Redcurrant, Lemonade & Cranberry, Light Grape & Cranberry, Light Lemon & Grapefruit, Light Orange & Pineapple, Lime & Banana, Orange & Raspberry, Tropical; *Flavoured Spring Water:* Apricot & Fruit, Blackberry & Grape, Mandarin, Peach; *Hint Flavoured Spring Water:* Blackberry & Grape, Elderflower & Lemon, Peach; *Hi Juice:* Apple Squash, Apricot, Blackcurrant, Cloudy Apple, Cranberry & Raspberry, No Added Sugar Blackcurrant, No Added Sugar Orange, Orange Squash, Pink Grapefruit, Pink Grapefruit Squash; *Juice Drink [long life/cartons]:* Apple & Elderflower, Cherry, Cranberry, No Added Sugar Cranberry, Raspberry, Still Lemonade; *Lemonade [large bottle]:* Diet, Diet Lemonade, Diet Lemon & Lime, Lemonade, Sparkling Lemon & Lime; *Mixers [bottle]:* American Ginger Ale, Bitter Lemon, Cola w Twist of Lemon, Dry Ginger Ale, Indian Low Calorie Tonic Water, Lemonade w Twist of Lemon, Low Calorie Tonic Water, Low Calorie Tonic w Lemon, Low Calorie Tonic w Twist of Lime, Tonic w Twist of Lemon; *No Added Sugar Barley Water:* Peach Apricot, Summer Fruits, Tropical; *No Added Sugar Squash:* Apple, Blackcurrant, Grapefruit, Lemon, Mixed Fruit, Orange, Orange & Apricot, Orange Lemon & Pineapple, Peach, Pear & Blueberry, Summer Fruit; *Old Fashioned Style:* Dandelion & Burdock, Orange & Barley; *Sportz Drinks:* Lime & Lemon, Orange; *Squash:* Apple & Blackcurrant, Blackcurrant, Lemon & Lime; *Sugar Free Drinks:* Blue Bubblegum, Candy Floss, Fruit Salad, Limeade, Rhubarb & Custard, Strawberry; *Value:* Low Calorie Orange, Low Sugar Cola, Low Sugar Lemonade; *Vita Esprit:* Apple Cranberry & Blackberry Leaf

THORNCROFT VINEYARD

Cordial: Elderflower, Nettle, Pink Ginger, Rosehip; *Sparkling:* Elderflower, Nettle Ale, Pink Ginger

drink

V8

V8 Vegetable Juice

VINCEREMOSøπ

Fruit Extravaganza Case; *Juice:* Apple '1066 Country', Orange Vitalia, Pear '1066 Country', Red Grape Ferme des Arnaud, White Grape Clos St Martin

VIRGIN COLA§π

Lips: **Lemon Lime, Orange;** *Virgin:* **Big Orange, Caffeine Free Cola, Cola, Diet Cola, Ginger Beer, Hi-Energy, Lemon Lime**

VITALLA

Juice: Apple, Grapefruit, Orange, Prune, Red Grape, Red Grapefruit, White Grape

VOLONTE

Juice: Apple, Grapefruit, Orange, Pineapple, Red Grape, Tomato

VOLVIC

Natural Mineral Water

WAITROSE

Bitter Lemon, Cola, Ginger Beer, Lemonade, Traditional Cream Soda, Traditional Ginger Beer; *Chilled Iced Tea:* Lemon, Peach; *Cola:* American Style, American Style Diet, Diet, Diet American, Diet Premium, Original American, Premium; *Cordial:* Elderflower, Lime Juice; *Crush:* Pineapple, Raspberry & Blackcurrant, Summerfruit, Tropical; *Drink:* Apple & Blackcurrant, Apple & Elderflower, Apple & Strawberry, Apple Cranberry & Blueberry, Blackcurrant, Citrus, Lemon & Lime, Orange, Orange & Mango, Orange Lemon & Pineapple, Pear, Summer Fruit, Tropical, Whole Apple & Blackcurrant, Whole Lemon, Whole Orange; *Ginger Ale:* American, Dry; *Juice:* Carrot & Orange, Reduced Sugar Blackcurrant; *Juice Drink:* Apple & Cranberry, Apple Cranberry & Blueberry, Apple Lime & Kiwi, Cranberry, Frizzante Sparkling Red Grape, Frizzante Sparkling White Grape, Grape, Grape Apple & Guava, Organic Apple; *Lemonade:* Diet w Juice, Low Calorie, Old Fashioned, Sparkling, Still, Traditional; *Low Calorie:* American Ginger, Bitter Lemon, Lemonade, Tonic Water; *No Added Sugar Drinks:* Apple, Apple & Blackcurrant, Grapefruit, Lemon, Orange, Orange & Apricot, Orange Juice, Strawberry, Tropical; *Refresher:* Apple & Rhubarb, Gooseberry & Elderflower; *Smoothie:* Apple Banana Blackcurrant & Cranberry, Peach & Banana, Strawberry & Banana; *Squash:* Grapefruit & Pineapple, High Juice Lemon, High Juice Orange, Lemon; *Sugar Free:* Appleade, Cherryade, Lemonade, Orangeade; *Tonic Water:* Diet, Diet Lemon, Mandarin, Tonic Water, w Lemon; *Water:* Carbonated & Lemon, Elderflower Spring, Fiz Mineral & Lime, Soda, Tonic

SPIRITS & APÉRITIFS

ALDIπ

Bodegas Peninsular Cream Sherry, Cognac Carrière Croizet, Cromwell Gin, Highland Earl Scotch Whisky, Napolean Brandy, Southern Belle, Tamova Vodka, White Rum

ASDA

3 Star Cognac, Deep South The American Classic, Gin, Napolean French Brandy, Peach Schnapps, Vodka, White Rum; *Premium:* Gin, Vodka; *Rum:* Dark, White, Windward Caribbean White *w* Coconut; *Sherry:* Amontillado, Cream, Fino, Pale Cream; *Vodka:* Blackcurrant, Citrus, Premium; *Whisky:* 3 Year Old, 10 Year Old Single Malt, 12 Year Single Highland Malt, 12 Year Single Speyside Malt, Oak Cash Matured Scotch, Old Glenn 10 Year Islay Malt, Old Kilkenny Irish

CARMEL

Brandies: all; *Vodka:* all

ORGANIC WINE COMPANYø

Alain Verdet Crème: de Cassis de Bourgogne, de Framboise, de Mure, de Pèche; *Cognac:* Foussignac Napoleon Guy & Georges Pinard, Foussignac VSOP Guy & Georges Pinard, Three Star Jacques & Dany Brard Blanchard, VSOP Jacques & Dany Brard Blanchard; *Pineau des Charentes Jacques & Dany Brard Blanchard:* Blanc, Rosé; *Spanish Port Sierra Morena Vino Seco Gabriel Gomez:* Dorado, Palido

SAFEWAYπΩ

Fonseca Guimaraens Vintage Port; *Spirits:* all

UNITED DISTILLERS & VINTNERS

Amaretto di Saronno, Archers Peach County Schnapps, Croft Vintage Port, Gilbeys Gin, J & B Whisky, Jack Daniels, José Cuervo Tequila, Malibu, Singleton Whisky, South Comfort Liqueur Spirit; *Croft Sherries:* all; *Smirnoff:* Mule, Vodka

VINCEREMOSøπ

Calvados VSOP Domaine de Cinq Autels, Da Mhile Millennium Scottish Malt Whisky, Estonian Vodka Viru Valge, Polish Vodka Wisniowska; *Cuban Rum Havana Club:* Anejo Reserva, Extra Aged Reserva 7 Year, White 3 Year Seco; *Fortified Wines & Port:* Organic Vintage Character Port Quinta do Infantado, Sierra Morena Seco Vino Dorado, Sierra Morena Seco Vino Palido; *French Cognac (Guy Lhéraud):* Edouard III 3 Year, Pineau des Charentes, Spéciale Trois Étoiles 3 Year; *French Fruit Liqueurs:* Abricot au Cognac, Cassis au Cognac, Framboise au Cognac, Orange au Cognac; *Russian Vodka:* Krepkaya 56%, Limonnaya, Moskovskaya, Okhotnichya, Pertsovka, Starka, Zubrovka

VINTAGE ROOTSøπ

Fortified Wines & Ports: AOC Muscat de Rivesaltes Clos St Martin, AOC Pineau des Charentes Jacques & Dany Brard Blanchard, Cerise (Cherry) François Clot, Organic Vintage Character Port Quinta do Infantado, Vinoix (Walnut) François Clot; *Liqueurs:* Crème de Cassis (Blackcurrant), Crème de Framboise (Raspberry), Crème de Mure (Blackberry), Crème de Pèche (Peach); *Spirits:* Cognac, Cognac Napoleon, Cognac VSOP, Grappa di Vinacce di Chianti Classico, Vieux Calvados Daufrantas (Apple Brandy)

drink

VIVA!√ø§π

Ararat Ani Brandy; *Cognac (Guy Lhéraud):* Edouard III 3 Year, Pineau des Charentes, Spéciale Trois Étoiles 3 Year; *Fortified Wines & Port:* Organic Vintage Character Port Quinta do Infantado, Sierra Morena Seco Vino Dorado, Sierra Morena Seco Vino Palido; *Fruit Liqueurs:* Abricot au Cognac, Cassis au Cognac, Framboise au Cognac, Orange au Cognac; *Rum:* Havana Club Extra Aged Reserva, Havana Club White; *Vodka:* Krepkaya, Limonnaya, Moskovskaya, Okhotnichya, Pertsovka, Starka 43%, Viru Valge, Wisniowska, Zubrovka

WAITROSE

1994 Late Vintage Port, Armagnac, Bourbon, Canadian Grain, Dunkelweiss, Gin, Grain Gin, Vodka; *Brandy:* French, Spanish; *Cognac:* Cognac, Millennium, Reserve; *Rum:* West Indian, White; *Whisky:* 3 Year Blended Scotch, 5 Year Blended Scotch, 10 Year Old Lowland Single Malt, 12 Year Blended Malt Scotch, Irish, Irish Malt, Island Malt, Islay Malt Scotch, Millennium Malt, Pure Highland Malt Scotch, Speyside Scotch

WESTBAY DISTRIBUTORS

Bacardi Rigo, Bacardi Rum, Limon, Metz; *Bacardi Breezers:* all

WINES

ALDIπ

Budavar: Chardonnay, Merlot; *Vinelli:* Bianco, Extra Dry

ANIMAL AID√ø§πΩΔfcd76

Celebration Fizz Case: Clairette de Die Brut José Ardinat, Prosecco Spumante de Valdobiaddene Perlage, Spumante Brue Tenuta San Vito; *Red Wine Case:* Cabernet Sauvignon, Corbières, Merlot, Syrah-Malbec; *Special Millennium Case:* Cabernet Sauvignon, Champagne, Chardonnay, Domaine de Petit Roubié, Merlot, Sauvignon Blanc, Syrah-Malbec; *White Wine Case:* Chardonnay Sauvignon Blanc, Domaine de Petit Roubié

ASDA

Beaujolais, Beaujolais Villages, Bordeaux Blanc Medium, Cape Merlot, Cape Sauvignon Blanc, Cava, Cava Medium Dry, Cava Rosado, Chablis, Chardonnay Jardin de la France, Châteauneuf de Cape Red Wine, Chenas, Chenin Blanc Demi-Sec, Chilean Chardonnay, Chilean White, Claret, Côtes de Bergerac, Côtes du Rhône, Domaine Pont Pinot Noir, Gargenaga Chardonnay, Gold Seal Liebfraumilch, Hungarian Medium Chardonnay, Lambrusco Lavigna Rosso 4%, Macon Village Blanc, Moulin à Vent Oak Aged, Muscadet, Puglia Toggia, Rosé d'Anjou, St Emilion, Soave, Tramontane Syrah Reserve, Vin de Paye Côte de Gascogne Blanc, Vin de Table Red, Vintage Cava; *Argentina:* Chardonnay, White; *Australia:* Cabernet Sauvignon, Chardonnay; *Oaked:* Côtes de Rhône Red, Soave, Viura; *Romania:* Cabernet Merlot, Chardonnay; *South Africa:* Cabernet Sauvignon, Pinotage

AVALON VINEYARDøπ

Medium Sweet Raspberry, Sweet Tayberry; *Gooseberry:* **Dry, Red Medium Sweet;** *Organic English:* **Dry, Medium Dry**

BIDDENDEN√øπ

White, Red, Rosé, Sparkling

CARMEL

Dessert & Apéritif: all; *Private Collection:* all; *Sparkling:* all; *Sweet:* all; *Valley:* all; *Vineyard Selection:* all

CO-OPπΩΔfcd85

Australia White Chardonnay, English White Table, Hungarian White, Italy Red Chianti Classico Otto Santi, Sparkling Cava Moscato Spumante, USA White California Colombard; *France White & Rosé:* Bergerac Blanc, Blanc de Blancs, Bordeaux Medium Sweet, Chardonnay Fleur de Moulin, Muscadet, Premières Côtes de Bordeaux, Rosé d'Anjou, Sancerre Domaine Raimbault, Vouvray Domaine les Perruches; *France Red:* Beaujolais, Châteauneuf du Pape Cellier des Princes, Côtes de Ventoux, Côtes du Rhône Villages Domaine de Hauterive, Côtes du Rousillon, Louis Mousset Crozes Hermitage, Valreas Domaine de la Grande Bellane, Vin de Pays de l'Hérault Rouge; *Germany White:* Bernkasteler Kurfustlay, Hock, Kabinett, Liebfraumilch, Niersteiner Gutes Domtal

DISOS√øπ

Pure French: **Red, White**

HARBOURNE VINEYARD√øπΩ

English White: **Dry 1993, Medium Dry 1992, Rosé 1994, Seyval Blanc 1993**

ORGANIC WINE COMPANYø

English Sparkling Sedlescombe Brut 1994 Traditional Method Roy Cook, English White Sedlescombe Dry EVQW Psr 1996 Roy Cook, French Rosé Domaine de Petit Roubie Vin de Pays de l'Hérault Olivier Azan, New Zealand Red Nelson Pinot Noir 1998 Richmond Plains; *Australian Red:* Cabernet Sauvignon 1993 Thistle Hill, Clare Valley Red 1997/9 Penfolds, Shiraz 1997 Botobolar Vineyard Keving & Trina Karstrom; *Australian White:* Chardonnay 1993 Thistle Hill, Chardonnay 1997 Botobolar Vineyard Kevin & Trina Karstrom, Clare Valley Chardonnay Sauvignon Blanc 1997/8; *French Red:* Albaric Vin de Pays du Gard Hoirie Albaric, Château Côtes des Caris Bordeaux AC 1998 Christian Guichard, Château Côtes des Caris Bordeaux Superieur AC 1997 Christian Guichard, Château Moulin St Magne Côtes de Castillon AC 1997 Jean-Gabriel Yon, Clos de la Perichère Graves AC 1995 Gabriel Guerin, Clos du Joncuas Gigondas AC 1995 "Esprit de Grenache" Fernand Chastan, Clos du Joncuas Gigondas AC 1995 Fernand Chastan, Clos du Joncuas Gigondas AC 1997 Fernand Chastan, Domaine de la Grangette Vin de Pays d'Oc 1996/7 Syrah Emmanuelle Mur, Domaine de la Grangette Vin de Pays d'Oc Tradition Robert Mur, Domaine de Petit Roubié Vin de Pays de l'Hérault Olivier Azan, Domaine St Apollinaire Côtes du Rhône AC 1995 "La Quintessence" SCA Daumas, Domaine St Apollinaire Côtes du Rhône AC 1995/7 "Cuvée d'Apolline" SCA Daumas, Domaine St Apollinaire Côtes du Rhône AC 1995/7 "Cuvée Prestige" SCA Daumas, Le Petit Roubié Vin de Pays de l'Hérault 10 litre box, Le Petit Roubié Vin de Pays de l'Hérault Merlot 10 litre box, Pinot Noir AAC 1998 André Stentz, Vacqueyras AC 1997 "La Font de Papier" Fernand Chastan, Vin de Pays du Jardin de France Cepage Cabernet Guy Bossard; *French Sparkling:* Blanquette de Limoux AC Bernard Delmas, Clairette de Die AC Brut Méthode Traditionelle GAEC Archard Vincent, Clairette de Die AC Demi Sec "Tradition" GAEC Archard Vincent, Cremant d'Alsace AAC André Stentz, Cuvée Ludwig Hahn Vin Mousseux Méthode Traditionelle Guy Bossard, Saumur Brut AC 1989 Gerard Leroux; *French White:* Château Côtes des Caris Bordeaux Blanc Sec AC 1996 Christian Guichard, Château Côtes des Caris Bordeaux Blanc Sec AC 1997 Christian Guichard, Château la Garenne Sauternes AC 1996 Nicole & Christian Ferbos, Château le Barradis Monbazillac AC 1995 Labasse-Gazzini, Château Pech-Latt Corbières AC 1998 SC Pech-Latt, Château Petit Roubié Picpoul de Pinet Coteaux du Languedoc AC 1998 Olivier Azan, Clos de la Perichère Graves AC 1998 Gabriel Guerin, Domaine de la Grangette Vin de Pays d'Oc Sauvignon Emanuelle Mur-Gomar, Domaine de Petit Roubié Vin de Pays de l'Hérault Cepage Marsanne Azan, Domaine de Petit Roubié Vin de Pays de l'Hérault Olivier Azan, Domaine de Petit Roubié Vin de Pays des Côtes de l'Hérault Olivier Azan, Domaine St Apol-

linaire Côtes du Rhône AC 1997 "Blanc de Blancs" Frederic Daumas, Domaine St Apollinaire Côtes du Rhône AC 1997 "l'Exceptionnelle" Viognier Frederic Daumas, Gewurztraminer AAC 1998 André Stentz, Gros Plant du Pays Nantais VDQS 1996 sur Lie Guy Bossard, Le Petit Roubié Vin de Pays de l'Hérault 10 litre box, Muscadet de Sevre et Maine AC 1997 sur Lie "Hermine d'Or" Guy Bossard, Muscadet de Sevre et Maine AC 1998 sur Lie Guy Bossard, Muscadet de Sevre et Maine AC 1999 sur Lie Domaine de la Parentière, Muscat AAC 1998 André Stentz, Riesling AAC 1997 André Stentz, Sancerre AC 1998 Nicole et Christian Dauny, Terres Blanches Les Baux de Provence AC 1998 Noel Michelin, Tokay Pinot Gris AAC 1998 André Stentz; *Italian Red:* Barbera Colline Novarese DOC 1998 Bianchi, Bonarda Colline Novarese DOC 1997 Bianchi, Cabernet Franc Lison Pramaggiore DOC 1998 Arnaldo Savian, Chianti DOCG 1994 Casale, Gattinara DOC 1995 Bianchi, Ghemme DOC 1994 Bianchi, Merlot Lison Pramaggiore DOC 1998 Arnaldo Savian, Natum Rosso Colline Teatine IGT 1998 Agriverde, Nebbiolo "Vigneto Valfre" Colline Novarese DOC 1997 Bianci, Refosco dal Peduncolo Rosso lison Pramaggiore DOC 1998 A Savian, Riseis Montepulciano d'Abruzzo DOC 1997 Agriverde, Sangiovese Rosso dei Colli della Toscana Centrale 1993/4 VdT Casale, Selvato Vino da Tavola 1997 Azienda Agricola "Nuova Murgia", Sizzano DOC 1995 Bianchi, Spanna Nebbiolo Colline Novarese DOC 1997 Bianchi; *Italian Sparkling Spumante Brut:* DOC Erbulace "Incontro"

Guiseppe Bianchi, IGT Arnaldo Savian; *Italian White:* Chardonnay Lison Pramaggiore DOC 1998 Arnaldo Savian, Erbaceo Vino da Tavola 1997 Azienda Agricola "Nuova Murgia", Erbaluce Colline Novarese DOC 1998 Bianchi, Natum Bianco Colline Teatine IGT 1998 Agriverde, Pinot Grigio Lison Pramaggiore DOC 1998, Riseis Trebbiano d'Abruzzo DOC 1997 Agriverde, Tocai Italico Lison Pramaggiore DOC 1998 Arnaldo Savian, Trebbiano Bianco dei Colli Della Toscana Centrale Vino da Tavola 1997 Casale, Tresor Chardonnay Colline Teatine IGT 1998 Agriverde, Verduzzo Lison Pramaggiore DOC 1998 Arnaldo Savian; *New Zealand White:* Millton Vineyard Chenin Blanc Barrel Fermented 1997, Millton Vineyard Gisborne Chardonnay 1998, Millton Vineyard Te Arai River Sauvignon Blanc 1998, Nelson Chardonnay 1998 Richmond Plains, Nelson Sauvignon Blanc 1998 Richmond Plains; *USA White Bonterra Mendocino County Fetzer Winery:* Chardonnay 1996/8, Muscat 1998, Roussanne 1998, Viognier 1996/8

SAFEWAY$\pi\Omega$

Australia Rosé Hardys Stamp Grenache/Shiraz, Eastern Europe Red Dunavar Cabernet Sauvignon, France Rosé (Côtes du Rhône) Côtes du Luberon, Italy Rosé S/W Lambrusco Light 4%, North America Red S/W Californian Oak Aged Cabernet Sauvignon, Portugal Red S/W Stanlake, Spain White S/W Moscatel de Valencia; *Australia Red:* Dawn Ridge Red, Hardys Bankside Shiraz, Hardys Barossa Valley Shiraz, Hardys Nottage Hill Cabernet Sauvignon Shiraz, Hardys Stamp Shiraz Cabernet Sauvignon, Penfolds Bin 389 Cabernet Sauvignon/Shiraz, Penfolds Koonunga Hill Shiraz/Cabernet 1995, Penfolds Rawsons Retreat Bin 35 1997, S/W Australian Red, S/W Oaked Cabernet Sauvignon, S/W Oaked Shiraz, S/W Shiraz, S/W Shiraz/Ruby Cabernet, Wolf Blass Yellow Label Cab Sauvignon 1994; *Australia White:* Hardys Barossa Valley Chardonnay 1994, Hardys Nottage Hill Chardonnay, Hardys Stamp Semillon/Chardonnay, Penfolds 'The Valleys' Clare & Eden Valley 1997, S/W Chardonnay, S/W Chardonnay/Sauvignon 1995 Clare Valley, S/W Dry White, S/W Oak Chardonnay, S/W Semillon/Chardonnay; *Eastern Europe White:* S/W Hungarian Country Wine, S/W Irsai Oliver 1998 Nieszmely, S/W Matra Mountain Sauvignon; *France Red (Bordeaux & Atlantic)* Oak Aged Claret, S/W Margaux; *France Red (Burgundy):* Gevrey Chambertin 1995, Labore-Roi Nuits St Georges 1995, S/W Beaune 1997; *France Red (Côtes du Rhône):* Raison d'Être, S/W Dom Manoir de Maransan; *France Red (Midi):* S/W Fitou, S/W Organic Vin de Table; *France White (Bordeaux & Atlantic):* Mouton Cade 1994, S/W Bergerac Blanc, S/W Bordeaux Blanc Demi-Sec, S/W Bordeaux Blanc Sec 1998, S/W Oak Aged Bordeaux Blanc; *France White (Burgundy):* S/W Macon Villages, S/W Montagny 1ER Cru; *France White (Côtes du Rhône):* Fait Accompli, S/W DOM Manoir de Maransan White, S/W VDP de l'Ardèche Blanc; *France White (Midi):* Colombard Sauvignon VDP de Gers, Dom Brial Muscat de Rivesaltes, S/W

Vin Blanc; *Germany:* Devils Rock Riesling, S/W Hock, St Ursula Morio Muskat 1995; *Italy Red:* D'Istinito Nero d'Avola Nerello Mascalese, S/W Chianti, S/W Chianti Classico, S/W Lambrusco Rosso, S/W Oak Aged Valpolicella; *Italy White:* d'Istinito Trebbiano Insolia, S/W Lambrusco Bianco, S/W Lambrusco Light 4%; *New Zealand White:* Montana Chardonnay Marlborough 1995, Montana Sauvignon Marlborough 1995; *North America White:* Ironstone Chardonnay, S/W Californian Oak Aged Chardonnay 1995; *South Africa White:* Kleinezalze Sauvignon Blanc, S/W South African Chardonnay; *South America White:* S/W Chilean Sauvignon, S/W Chilean White; *Sparkling:* Graham Beck Brut, Hardys Nottage Hill Chardonnay, Lindauer Brut, S/W Cremant de Bourgogne, S/W Sparkling Spumante Brut

SEDLESCOMBE VINEYARD√ø™π

French Claret; *Country:* Black Cherry, Golden Apple, Yellow Plum; *English:* 1066 Country Dry White, 1066 Country Late Harvest, Brut 1996, Dry Red 1997-8, Late Harvest 1998, Millennium Rosé 1996, White Dry Organic 1997

VEGAN SOCIETY√ø§Ω

Champagne & Wine Case: 96 Volcanic Hills Chardonnay, Bianco di Custoza Ottomarzo, Carte d'Or Champ Brut Ardinat, Côtes du Rhône Villages Valreas, Dom St Michel Shrah Malbec, Dominio Los Pinos Tinto, Millton Semillon Chardonnay 96, Perlage Spumante Brut, St Michel Sauvignon Blanc, Vino Bardolino Classico

VINCEREMOSøπ

Italy Rosé Bardolino Chiaretto Ottomarzo DOC 1998, Lebanon Château Musar 1993, New Zealand Rippon Vineyard Pinot Noir 1995/6; *Australia (Glenara):* Cabernet-Merlot 1993/5, Riesling 1996/7; *Australia (Penfolds):* Chardonnay-Sauvignon Blanc 1997/8, Shiraz-Cabernet 1997/8; *Champagne Method:* Clairette de Die Brut Achard Vincent AC, Clairette de Die Tradition Achard Vincent AC; *Country Broughton Pastures (Hertfordshire):* Blackcurrant, Elderberry, Elderflower, Ginger; *England:* Chudleigh Vineyard Kerner 1997, Sedlescombe Vineyard Dry White 1997/8; *France Red:* Beaujolais Supérieur Château de Boisfranc 1998, Burgundy Hautes Côtes de Nuits Bourgogne Rouge Paul Giboulot AC 1997/8; *France Red (Bordeaux):* Bordeaux Supérieur Château Coursou AC 1997/8, Bordeaux Supérieur Château la Blanquirie AC 1996/7, St Emilion Château Barrail des Graves AC 1996/7; *France Red (Domaine Saint Michel):* Cabernet Sauvignon 1997/8, Corbières AC 1996/7, Merlot 1997/8, Syrah-Malbec 1997/8; *France Red (Loire):* Saumur-Champigny Domaine des Frogeres AC 1997, Touraine Gamay Domaine de la Garre Garrelière AC 1997/8; *France Red (Provence):* Côtes de Provence Cabernet Sauvignon Domaine Richeaume, Côtes de Provence Cuvée Columelle Domaine Richeaume AC 1996/7, Côtes de Provence Domaine du Jas d'Esclans Cru Classe AC 1996, Côtes de Provence Syrah Domaine Richeaume AC 1996/7, Côtes de Provence Tradition Domaine Richeaume AC 1996/7; *France Red*

(Rhône): Châteauneuf du Pape Pierre André AC 1994/6, Côtes du Rhône Cave la Vigneronne Villedieu AC 1997, Côtes du Rhône Jacques Frelin AC 1997/8, Côtes du Rhône Vignoble de la Jasse AC 1997, Côtes du Rhône Villages Valreas Domaine de la Grande Bellane AC 1996/7, Crozes Hermitage Jacques Frelin AC 1996/7, Gigondas Vignoble Saint-Frederic Clos du Joncuas AC 1996/7; *France Red (South):* Cabardes Jacques Frelin AC 1998, St Chinian Domaine des Sou Lie AC 1998, Vin de Pays d'Oc Armen Cabernet Boise 1998, Vin de Pays d'Oc Cabernet Sauvignon Domaine de Clairac 1997/8, Vin de Pays d'Oc Jacques Frelin 1997/8, Vin de Pays d'Oc Merlot Domaine de Picheral VDP 1997/8, Vin de Pays de l'Hérault Domaine de Clairac Joubio 1997/8, Vin de Pays de l'Hérault Domaine de Savignac 1997/8, Vin de Pays de l'Hérault French Organic Red 1998, Vin de Pays de l'Hérault Merlot Domaine de Bajac 1998, Vin de Pays de l'Hérault Syrah Domaine de Clairac 1997, Vin de Pays des Coteaux de Cabrerisse Domaine de la Bouletière 1996/7, Vin de Pays du Gard Domaine de Barjac 1997/8, Vin de Pays du Gard Jacques Frelin 1998; *France Rosé:* Touraine Domaine de la Garrelière Rose AC 1998, Vin de Pays d'Oc Domaine de Clairac Cabernet Sauvignon Rosé 1997/8, Vin de Pays de L'Hérault Domaine de Clairac Joubio Rosé 1998, Vin de Pays des Coteaux de Cabrerisse Domaine de la Bouletière Rosé 1997/8, *France White:* Burgundy Chablis Petit Chablis Jean Goulley AC 1997/8, Rhône Châteauneuf du Pape Blanc Pièrre André AC 1997/8; *France*

White (Alsace): Gewurztraminer Eugene Meyer AC 1997, Pinot Blanc Eugene Meyer AC 1996/7, Sylvaner Eugene Meyer AC 1996, Tokay-Pinot Gris Eugene Meyer 1996; *France White (Bordeaux & Bergerac):* Bergerac French Organic Wine 'Les Charmes' AC 1997/8, Bordeaux Château Coursou AC 1997/8, Bordeaux Château Vieux Georget AC 1997/8, Entre Deux Mers Château la Blanquerie AC 1997/8, Entre Deux Mers Domaine du Bourdieu AC 1997/8; *France White (Domaine Saint Michel):* Blanc de Blancs 1997/8, Chardonnay 1997/8, Sauvignon Blanc 1997/8; *France White (Loire):* Gros Plant sur Lie Guy Bossard 1997/8, Muscadet de Sevre et Maine sur Lie Domaine de la Parentière AC 1997/8, Muscadet de Sevre et Maine sur Lie Guy Bossard, Muscadet de Sevre et Maine sur Lie 'Hermine d'Or' 1996/7, Sancerre Christian et Nicole Dauny AC 1998, Touraine Chenin Blanc Domaine de la Garrelière AC 1997/8, Touraine Sauvignon Domaine de la Garrelière AC 1997, Vouvray Le Haut Lieu Sec Huet AC 1996; *France White (South):* Corbières Château de Caraguilhes Blanc AC 1998, Marsanne Jacques Frelin AC 1996/8, Picpoul de Pinet Château Petit Roubié AC 1997/8, Vin de Pays de l'Aude Chardonnay Domaine la Batteuse 1997/8, Vin de Pays de l'Hérault Houbio Blanc Domaine de Clairac 1997/8, Vin de Pays des Côtes de Thau Domaine de Petit Roubié 1998, Vin de Pays des Pyrénées Orientales Muscat Sec Clos St Martin 1997/8; *France White (Sweet):* Monbazillac Château le Barradis AC 1994, Muscadet de Rivesaltes Clos St Martin 1997, Sauternes Château la Garenne AC

1996; *Germany:* Auslese Ortega 1998, Kabinett Scheurebe 1998, Muller Thurgau Qba 1997/8, Spatlese Kerner 1997/8; *Hungary Volcanic Hills:* Gyongyos Dry White Harslevelu 1997/8, Neszmely Irsai Oliver 1996, Neszmely Pinot Grigio 1996, Sopron Sauvignon Blanc 1997/8, Szekszard Dry Red Kekfrankos 1997/8, Tok Chardonnay 1997/8; *Italy Red:* Bardolino Classico Ottomarzo DOC 1998, Cabernet del Veneto Perlage IGT 1997/8, Chianti San Vito DOCG Roberto Drighi 1997/8, Chianti Vigna la Reina Tenuta San Vito DOCG 1996/7, Fior di Selva Barrique DOCG 1995/6, Merlot Perlage DOC 1998, Novello Perlage IGT 1998/9, Regiano Barrique Perlage 1996, Solatio Rosso Perlage 1998, Valpolicella Classico Ottomarzo DOC 1998; *Italy Sparkling:* Prosecco Spumante de Valdobiaddene Perlage, Spumante Brut Tenuta San Vito; *Italy White:* Bianco Colli dell'Etruria Centrale DOC 1997/8, Bianco di Custoza Ottomarzo DOC 1997/8, Chardonnay Perlage DOC 1998, Pinot Grigio Perlage DOC 1998, Soave Superiore Fasoli Gino DO\C 1998, Solatio Bianco Perlage 1998, Tiziano Barrique 1997, Verdiglio Tenuta San Vito IGT 1996, Vin Santo Tenuta San Vito DOCG 1989; *Mixed Case:* Bargain Selection, Organic Taster; *New Zealand (Millton Vineyard):* Chardonnay Gisborne Vineyards 1998, Chenin Blanc Barrel Fermented 1996/7, Opou Riesling 1998, Sauvignon Blanc Te Arai Vineyard 1998, Semillon-Chardonnay 1997/8, Traminer-Riesling 1996; *New Zealand (Richmond Plains):* Nelson Chardonnay 1997/8, Nelson Pinot Noir 1997/8, Nelson Sauvignon Blanc 1998/9; *Spain:* Can Vendrell Blanco Albet i Noya 1997/8, Can Vendrell Tinto Albet i Noya 1997/8, Dominio del Arenal DO Utiel-Requena 1997/8, Dominio los Pinos Blanco 1998, Dominio los Pinos Crianza DO Valencia 1996/7, Dominio los Pinos Tinto DO Valencia 1998, Rioja Noemus DO 1997/8; *USA Fetzer:* Chardonnay Bonterra 1996/7, Zinfandel Bonterra 1996/7

VINTAGE ROOTSøπ

America White Chardonnay Bonterra Mendocino California Fetzer Vineyards 1995/6, England White Seyval Blanc Devon Chudleigh Vineyard 1997, Greece White VQPRD Mantinia 'Orino' Domaine Spiropoulos 1996/7, New Zealand Red Pinot Noir Nelson Richmond Plains 1997; *Australia Red:* Cabernet Sauvignon/Merlot Victoria Robinvale Vineyard 1995, Cabernet Sauvignon Mudgee Thistle Hill Vineyard 1993, Shiraz/Cabernet Clare Valley Penfolds 1996, Shiraz Mudgee Botobolar Vineyard 1996; *Australia White:* Chardonnay Mudgee Botobolar Vineyard 1997, Chardonnay Mudgee Thistle Hill Vineyard 1993, Chardonnay/Sauvignon Clare Valley Penfolds 1996/7, Chenin/Chardonnay/Sauvignon Victoria Robinvale Vineyard 1997/8, Riesling Adelaide Hills Glenara Vineyard 1995, St Gilbert Dry Mudgee Botobolar Vineyard 1996; *Austria White:* Grinzinger Reisenburg Franz Mayer 1996/7, Nussberger Chardonnay Franz Mayer 1997, Sauvignon Blanc Franz Mayer 1997; *France Red (Beaujolais):* AOC Beaujolais Gérard Belaid 1996/7, AOC Morgon Gérard Belaid 1996/7, AOC Régnié Christian

Ducroux 1997; *France Red (Bordeaux & Bergerac):* AOC Bordeaux Supérieur Château Coursou 1996/7, AOC Bordeaux Supérieur Château Le Rait 1996/7, AOC Côtes de Bergerac Château Richard 1995, AOC Côtes de Bourg Château Falfas 1995, AOC Côtes de Bourg 'Le Chevalier' Château Falfas 1995, AOC Fronsac Château La Grave 1996, AOC Pesac Léognan Château Haut-Nouchet 1995, AOC St Emilion Grand Cru 'Cuvée du Maître' Château Jacques Blanc 1995; *France Red (Burgundy):* AOC Bourgogne Passetoutgrain d'Heilly Huberdeau 1996, AOC Saint Romain Guyot et Fils 1996; *France Red (Loire):* AOC Saumur Champigny Domaine des Frogeres 1996, Vin de Pays des Marches de Bretagne Guy Bossard 1997; *France Red (Provence):* AOC Côtes de Provence Cru Classé Domaine du Jas d'Esclans 1993/4, AOC Côtes du Lubéron Château la Canorgue 1996, AOC Les Baux de Provence Château Romanin 1996, AOC Les Baux de Provence Domaine Terres Blanches Cuvée Aurelia 1995; *France Red (Rhône):* AOC Châteauneuf du Pape Domaine de Marcoux 1996, AOC Châteauneuf du Pape Pièrre André 1993/4, AOC Côtes du Rhône 'Cuvée d'Apolline' Domaine St Apollinaire 1994/5, AOC Côtes du Rhône 'Cuvée Prestige' Domaine St Apollinaire 1995, AOC Côtes du Rhône 'La Quintessence' Domaine de Marcoux 1996, AOC Crozes Hermitage Domaine Combier 1997, AOC Gigondas Clos du Joncuas 1993, AOC Vacqueyras Domaine Clos de Caveau 1996; *France Red (South):* AOC Corbières Sélection Vieilles Vignes

Château Pech Latt 1996, AOC Côtes du Roussillon Clos St Martin 1997, AOC Saint Chinian Comte Cathare Château de Combebelle 1995/6, AOC Saint Chinian Comte Cathare Prestige Château de Combebelle 1995/6, VDQS Cabardes Château de Brau 1997, VDQS Cabardes 'Cuvée Exquise' Château de Brau 1997, Vin de Pays d'Oc Cabernet Sauvignon Comte Cathare Prestige Domaine de Combebelle 1996, Vin de Pays d'Oc 'Mediterranean' Comte Cathare Biodynamic 1996, Vin de Pays de l'Aude Domaine de Brau 1997/8, Vin de Pays de l'Aude Domaine Mestre Grotti 1997, Vin de Pays de l'Hérault Les Pradelle 1997/8, Vin de Pays des Côtes de Thongue Cuvée Jacques Dehlon Domaine Bassac 1995, Vin de Pays des Côtes de Thongue Organic Louis Dehlon 1997/8, Vin de Pays du Gard Albaric 1997/8, Vin de Pays du Gard Domaine Costeplane 1997; *France White (Alsace):* AOC Gewurztraminer André Stentz 1996/7, AOC Tokay d'Alsace André Stentz 1997; *France White (Bordeaux & Bergerac):* AOC Bergerac Sec Cuvée Non Filtré Château Large Malartic1997, AOC Bergerac Sec Domaine de Richard 1996/7, AOC Blayais Domaine du Grand Loup 1997/8, AOC Bordeaux Organic Blanc Piroux 1996/7, AOC Bordeaux Sec Château Moulin de Romage 1997/8, AOC Bordeaux Sec Sauvignon Château le Rait 1997/8, AOC Monbazillac Château le Barradis 1995, AOC Pessac-Léognan Château Haut Nouchet 1996, AOC Saussignac Coup de Coeur Château Richard 1995/6, AOC Saussignanc Tradition Château Richard 1995/6; *France White (Burgundy):* AOC Chablis

Domaine Jean Goulley 1997, AOC Chablis Premier Cru Fourchaume Domaine Jean Goulley 1997, AOC Chablis Premier Cru Montmains Domaine Jean Goulley 1996/7, AOC Petit Chablis Domaine Jean Goulley 1997, AOC Saint Romain Guyot et Fils 1996; *France White (Loire):* AOC Muscadet de Sevre et Maine sur Lie Domaine de la Parentière 1997/8, AOC Muscadet de Sevre et Maine sur Lie Guy Bossard 1997/8, AOC Muscadet de Sevre et Maine sur Lie 'Hermine d'Or' Guy Bossard 1996/7, AOC Sancerre Christina Dauny 1997, AOC Vouvray Moelleux Le Haut Lieu Premier Trie Huet 1990, AOC Vouvray Sec Le Mont Huet 1996; *France White (Provence):* AOC Coteaux d'Aix en Provence Domaine Terres Blanches 1996/7, AOC Côtes de Provence Cru Classé Domaine du Jas d'Esclans 1997, AOC Côtes du Lubéron Château la Canorgue 1997; *France White (Rhône):* AOC Châteauneuf du Pape Pièrre André 1995/6, AOC Côtes du Rhône L'Exceptionnelle Viognier Domaine St Apollinaire 1995/6; *France White (South):* Vin de Pays de Catalan Muscat Sec Domaine St Martin 1997/8, Vin de Pays de Gard Chardonnay Domaine Costeplane 1998, Vin de Pays de l'Aude Blac de Brau Domaine de Brau 1997/8, Vin de Pays de l'Aude Chardonnay Domaine de Brau 1997/8, Vin de Pays de l'Aude Domaine Mestre Grotti 1997/8, Vin de Pays des Côtes de Thongue Muscat Moelleux Domaine Basac 1997, Vin de Pays l'Hérault Les Pradelle 1997/8; *Fruit & Speciality:* Sedlescombe Apple, The Granary Blackcurrant; *Germany White:*

Qba St Ursula Organic Weinkellerei 1996/7, Riesling Kabinett Trocken Klaus Knobloch 1996/7, Weisserburgunder Kabinett Trocken Klaus Knobloch 1997; *Italy Red:* DOC Barbera d'Alba Viberti 1996, DOC Bardolino Classico Ottomarzo 1997, DOC Barolo Viberti 1994, DOC Chianti Classico Buodonno 1996, DOCG Chianti Solatio Casciane I 1997, DOC Colli Euganei Cabernet Villa Sceriman 1996/7, DOC Colli Euganei Merlot Villa Sceriman 1996/7, DOC Dolcetto D'Alba Viberti 1996/7, DOC Valpolicella Amarone Classico Ottomarzo 1996, DOC Valpolicella Classico Ottomarzo 1997, Sicilia 'Mistral' Rosso Vasari 1997, Vino da Tavola de Verona 'Serenel' Bettili 1997, Vino da Tavola Rosso dell' Umbria 'Terre di San Nicola' Di Filippo 1996/7, Vino da Tavola Rosso dell'Umbria Villa Conversino di Filippo 1997; *Italy White:* DOC Piemonte Chardonnay Nuova Cappelletta 1997, DOC Piemonte Chardonnay Viberti 1997, DOC Soave Bettili 1997/8, DOC Soave Superiore Fasoli Gino 1997/8, Serenel Frizzante Bettili 1997/8, Sicilia Mistral Bianco Vasari 1997, Vino da Tavola de Verona 'Serenel' Bettili 1997/8, Vino da Tavola del Veneto Chardonnay Fongaro 1997, Vino da Tavola del Veneto Sauvignon Blanc Fongaro 1997; *New Zealand White:* Chardonnay Nelson Richmond Plains 1996/7, Sauvignon Blanc Nelson Richmond Plains 1997/8; *Rosé:* AOC Côtes de Provence Cru Classé Rosé Domaine du Jas d'Esclans 1997, DOC Bardolino Chiaretto Ottomarzo 1997, Vin de Pays de l'Aude Domaine de Brau 1997/8; *South Africa Red (Cape Soleil Paarl District Sonop Wine Farm):* Cabernet Sauvignon 1998, Pinotage 1998; *South Africa White (Cape Soleil Paarl District Sonop Wine Farm):* Chardonnay 1997/8, Sauvignon Blanc 1998; *Spain Red:* DO La Mancha Caballero de Mesarrubias 1997, DO Penedes Can Vendrell Tinto Albet i Noya 1997, DO Priorato Mas Igneus FA206 1997, DO Rioja Vina Urubi 1996, DO Utiel Requena 'Canada Honda' Bodegas Iranzo 1996/7; *Spain White (Albet i Noya):* DO Penedes Can Vendrell 1997/8, DO Penedes Chardonnay Colleccio 1996/7, DO Penedes Macabeu Colleccio 1997, DO Penedes Xarello Colleccio 1996/7, DO Penedes Xarello d'Anyada Albet i Noya 1998; *Sparkling:* AOC Blanquette de Limoux, AOC Clairette de Die 'Tradition', AOC Crémant de Bourgogne, DO Cava Brut Reserva 1995, DO Cava Can Ventrell, DOC Lessini Durello

VIVA!√ø§π

France Dry White (Burgundy) Petit Chablis Jean Goulley AC 1996/7, France Red (Beaujolais) Beaujolais Supérieur Château de Boisfranc 1997, France Red (Burgundy) Hautes Côtes de Nuits Paul Giboulot AC 1995/6, France Red (Provence) Côtes de Provence Domaine du Jas d'Esclans Cru Classé AC 1993, Lebanon Château Musar 1991; *Australia:* Cabernet-Merlot Glenara 1993/4, Chardonnay-Sauvignon Blanc Penfolds 1996/7, Riesling Glenara 1995/6, Shiraz-Cabernet Penfolds 1995/6; *France Dry White (Alsace Pierre Frick):* Gewurztraminer AC 1995/6, Pinot Blanc AC 1996/7, Sylvaner AC 1996/7; *France Dry White (Bordeaux):* Château Coursou AC

1996/7, Château Vieux Georget AC 1996/7, Entre Deux Mers Château la Blanquerie AC 1996/7, Entre Deux Mers Domaine du Bourdieu AC 1996; *France Dry White (Loire):* Gros Plant Sur Lie Guy Bossard 1996/7, Muscadet de Sévre et Maine sur Lie Domaine de la Parentière AC 1996/7, Muscadet de Sevre et Maine sur Lie Guy Bossard AC 1996/7, Sancerre Christian et Nicole Dauny AC 1996/7, Touraine Chenin Blanc Domaine de la Garrelière AC 1996/7, Tourine Sauvignon Domaine de la Garrelière AC 1996/7, VDP de Loire French Organic White 1996/7, VDP de Loire Selection Menager 1996/7; *France Dry White (South):* Château de Caraguilhes Blanc AC 1996, Domaine St Michel Blanc de Blancs 1996/7, Domaine St Michel Chardonnay 1996/7, Domaine St Michel Sauvignon Blanc 1996/7, Vin de Pays des Côtes de Thau Domaine de Petit Roubié 1996/7, Vin de Pays des Pyrenées Orientales Muscat Sec Clos St Martin 1996/7; *France Dry White (Rhône):* Châteauneuf du Pape Blanc Pièrre André AC 1995/6, Vin de Pays de Vaucluse 1996/7; *France Red (Bordeaux):* Bordeaux Supérieur Château Coursou AC 1996, Bordeaux Supérieur Château la Blanquerie AC 1995/6, St Emilion Château Barrail des Graves AC 1995/6; *France Red (Loire):* Touraine Gamay AC 1996, Vin de Pays des Marches de Bretagne Cépage Cabernet Guy Bossard; *France Red (Rhône):* Côtes du Rhône Domaine de la Grande Bellane AC 1994/5, Côtes du Rhône du Peloux AC 1996, Côtes du Rhône Villages Valréas Domaine de la Grande Bellane AC 1996, Crozes Hermitage J Frelin AC 1996; *France Red (South):* Corbières

Domaine Cabrairal AC 1995/6, Domaine St Michel Cabernet Sauvignon 1996/7, Domaine St Michel Corbières AC 1994/5, Domaine St Michel Merlot 1996/7, Domaine St Michel Syrah-Malbec 1996/7, Minervois J Frelin AC 1994/5, Vin de Pays d'Oc J Frelin 1996/7, Vin de Pays de l'Hérault 1996/7, Vin de Pays de l'Hérault Domaine de Savignac 1996/7, Vin de Pays du Gard Domaine de Barjac 1996/7; *France Rosé:* Touraine Domaine de la Garrelière AC 1996/7, VDP des Coteaux de Cabrerisse Domaine de la Bouletiere 1996/7, Vin de Pays d'Oc Cabernet Sauvignon Rosé Dom de Clairac 1997; *France Sweet White:* Monbazillac Château le Barradis AC 1994, Muscat de Rivesaltes Clos St Martin; *Germany:* Auslese Ortega 1994/5, Kabinett Silvaner 1996/7, Muller Thurgau Qba 1996/7, Spatlese Kerner 1996/7; *Hungary (Volcanic Hills):* Gyongyos Dry White Harslevelu 1996, Neszmely Irsai Oliver 1996, Neszmely Pinot Grigio 1996, Sopron Sauvignon Blanc 1996, Szekszard Dry Red Kekfrankos 1996, Szekszard Merlot 1996, TOK Chardonnay 1996, Villany Cabernet Sauvignon 1996; *Italy Red:* Cabernet del Veneto Perlage 1995/6, Chianti San Vito DOCG Roberto Drighi 1996/7, Chianti Vigna la Reina Tenuta San Vito DOCG 1994/5, Fior di Selva Barrique DOCG 1994/5, Merlot Perlage 1995/6, Novello Perlage 1997/8, Regiano Barrique Perlage 1994/5, Solatio Rosso Perlage 1995/6; *Italy Sparkling:* Prosecco Spumante de Valdobiaddene Perlage, Spumante Brut Tenuta San Vita; *Italy White:* Bianco Colli dell'Etruria Centrale DOCG 1996/7, Chardonnay Perlage 1996/7, Pinot Grigio Perlage 1996/7, Solatio Bianco Perlage 1996/7, Verdiglio Tenuta San Vito 1995/6, Vin Santo Tenuto San Vito DOCG 1989; *Mixed Cases:* Bargain, Bronze, Gold, Silver; *New Zealand:* Chardonnay Barrel Fermented Millton 1995, Estate Chardonnay Millton 1996, Nelson Chardonnay Richmond Plains 1996/7, Nelson Sauvignon Blanc 1995/6 Richmond Plains 1995/6, Semillon-Chardonnay Millton 1997, Te Arai Oak Aged Sauvignon Blanc Millton 1996; *Spain:* Can Vendrell Blanco Albet i Noya 1996, Can Vendrell Tinto Albet i Noya 1996, Dominio los Pinos Tinto DO Valencia 1996

WAITROSE

Beaujolais, Bordeaux Sauvignon, Calvados du Pays d'Auge, Côtes du Rhône Rouge, Highland Malt Sherry, Riesling Gewurztraminer, Special Reserve Claret; *Montilla:* Cream, Medium, Pale Dry

WINE RACKπ

Jewel Vineyards Chardonnay; *Bonterra Vineyards Organic:* Barrel Select Viognier, Cabernet Sauvignon, Chardonnay; *Fetzer:* Echo Ridge Sauvignon Blanc, Sundial Chardonnay, Viognier

XVø§πΩ

Italian: Blanco di Custoza, Chardonnay Perlage, Pino Grigio Perlage, Soave Fasoll Gino, Solatioi Blanco Periage, Vernaccia di San Gimignano; *Organic French Red:* Armen Cabernet Bolse 1998, Cabardes J Frelin, Cabernet, Cabernet Sauvignon Domaine de

Clairac, Côte de Rhône, Côtes du Rhône J Frenin 1998, Domaine de Clairac Jublo VDP de l'Hérault, Domaine de Farlet Merlot, Merlot Domaine de Picheral, St Chinlan Domaine des Soulle 1998, Syrah Domaine de Clairac 1997/8; *Organic French Rosé:* Cabernet Sauvignon Rosé Domaine de Clairac, Jouble Rosé Domaine de Clairac, Vin de Pays Rosé; *Organic French Sparkling:* All Méthode Traditionelle Blanc de Blanc Brut, Clairblo Monopole Domaine de Clairac Brut, Clarette de Die Brut; *Organic French White:* Domaine de Farlet Chardonnay, Domaine de Farlet Viognier, Domaine de Petit Roubié, Jouble Blanc Domaine de Clairac, Marsanne J Frelin, Picpoui de Pinet Château Petit Roubié; *Organic Italian Red:* Bardolino Classico Ottomarzo 1998, Cabernet de Veneto 1998, Chianti San Vito, Merlot Perlage 1998, Solatio Rosso Periage 1998, Valpolicella Classico Ottomarzo 1998

notes

- **beers** As a general rule traditional, cask-conditioned beers ('real ales') are usually clarified (cleared) with isinglass finings (see *GLOSSARY OF ANIMAL SUBSTANCES, page 231*). The addition of the finings speeds up a process which would otherwise occur naturally. Keg, canned, beer-sphere and some bottled beers are usually filtered without the use of animal substances. Lagers are generally chill-filtered but a *few* may involve the use of isinglass. Animal-derived finings continue to be used in all Guinness-, Scottish & Newcastle-(except Holsten pils and Beck's) and Bass (except Grolsch and bottled Staropraman) *produced* beers. **Charles Wells** are not the sole producer of Red Stripe, or Cobra and therefore can only guarantee that Red Stripe and Cobra produced at their factory is suitable for vegans. None of their cask conditioned beers are suitable, nor the fresh PET 2L Eagle or Bombardier.

- **soft drinks** Be alert to the possible presence of animal-derived colourants, such as cochineal. Orange coloured drinks may contain beta-carotene held in a gelatine suspension (see *gelatine carrier, page 85*).

- **spirits** The production of spirits does not appear to involve the use of animal substances.

- **water** That supplied by Yorkshire Water to the villages of Marsett, Stalling Busk, Boltby, Buckden, Chapel-le-Dale, Oughtershaw, Scar House, Starbotton, Hawkswick, Airton, Fossdale and Barden House (and possibly Aysgarth, Crumma, Newsholme near Skipton, Coalsgarth and Rudland) has been filtered through carbonised cattle bones. In addition, North West water use carbonised cattle bones as a filter in one site in north east Cumbria which serves around 150 people.

- **wines** Most wines on sale in off-licences and supermarkets have been fined using one of the following: blood, bone marrow, chitin, egg albumen, fish oil, gelatine, isinglass, milk or milk casein. Non-animal alternatives include limestone, bentonite, kaolin and kieslguhr (clays), plant casein, silica gel, and vegetable plaques. Several major off-licences now have vegan lists available so do ask.

toiletries & cosmetics

bath & shower	120	lip products	140
brushes etc	124	nail products	140
conditioners & hair care	125	perfumes etc	141
deodorants & antiperspirants	127	shampoos	142
essential & massage oils	128	shaving products	146
eye products	132	skin care	147
feminine hygiene	133	skin make-up	157
foot/leg care	134	soaps	158
gift boxes & packs	135	sun care	162
hair dyes	136	talcum powders	163
hair removal	137	toothpastes & oral hygiene	164
hair sprays, gels etc	137		
hand care	138	notes	166

BATH & SHOWER

ALADDIN AROMASø$\pi\Omega$**fcd87**

Bubble Bath, Shower Gel; *Bath Oil:* **Dispersing, Refreshing, Soothing**

ANIMAL AID√ø§$\pi\Omega\Delta$**fcd76**

Luxury Vanilla & Passion Flower Foam Bath, Violet & Almond Foaming Bath Oil; *Shower Gel:* English Rose Moisturising, Tropical

AUSTRIAN MOOR√ø§$\pi\Omega\Delta$

Moor Life Bath

BEAUTY THROUGH HERBS√ø$\pi\Omega\Delta$**87**

Fruits of the Forest: Bath Essence, Foam Bath, Shower Gel

BIO-D√ø™$\pi\Omega\Delta$**83**

Aromatherapy Bath Essence: **Relaxing, Stimulating;** *Borage Oil:* **Bath Formula, Shower Gel;** *Hemp Oil:* **Bath Foam, Shower Gel**

BODY REFORM√ø§$\pi\Omega$f**cd85**

Aromatherapy Bath Soak, Skin Friendly Foam Bath; *Bath & Shower Gel:* Tea Tree, White Musk; *Reform Sport:* Invigorating Shower Gel, Pain Relieving Bath Soak; *Shower Gel:* Reform for Men, Reviving, Skin Friendly

BODYLINEø§$\pi\Omega$f**cd84**

Leapfrog Bath Jelly, Silvan Fayre Bath Gel, Stress Relief Bath Soak, Vanilla Foaming Bath Essence, Vanilla Shampoo & Shower Gel, X-Stinked Bath Foam; *Bath & Shower Gel:* Dewberry, Grapefruit & Lemon, Magnolia, Peach & Apricot, Sea Foam, White Musk; *Bath Fizzer:* Great Balls of Fire, Let's Get Fizzy Cool, McBath, Marine Breeze, Musk, Shampagne & Strawberries, Stress Buster, Think Pink Fizz; *Bubble Bath:* Choc's Away, Coming Up Roses, Musk, Plan For All Seasons, Transylvanian, Turkish Dee-Light; *Bubbles Pouch:* Gorgeous, Horny, Kinky, Sexy; *Bubbles Test Tube:* Gorgeous, Horny, Kinky, Sexy; *Fizzer Cello Wrap:* Gorgeous, Horny, Kinky, Sexy; *Foam Bath:* Apple & Gooseberry, Freesia, Grapefruit & Lemon, Lilac, Magnolia Flower, Peach & Apricot, Raspberry & Strawberry, Rose, Shampagne & Strawberries; *Gems Pouch:* Gorgeous, Horny, Kinky, Sexy; *Gems Test Tube:* Gorgeous, Horny, Kinky, Sexy; *Shower Gel:* Aloe Vera, Apple & Gooseberry, Freesia, Grapefruit & Lemon, Ice Coconut, Invigorating, Kool Cranberry, Lilac, Magnolia Flower, Mint Freeze, Musk, Peach & Apricot, Raspberry & Strawberry, Rose, Tea Tree, Tranquillitea; *Shower Gel Toothpaste Tube:* Gorgeous, Horny, Kinky, Sexy

CACHETø$\Omega\Delta$**fcd87**

Moisturising Bath & Shower Gel

CAMILLA HEPPERø$\pi\Omega$f**cd86**

Caribbean Bath Foamer, Lemon Verbena Body Shampoo/Shower Gel; *Bath & Shower Gel:* Jasmine, Rose, Seaweed; *Bath Oil:* Herbal Body, Lemon Mint, Marigold, Relaxing, Soothing; *Body Shampoo:* Lavender, White Musk; *Cocktail Shower Shaker:* No 1, No 2, No 3; *Foam Bath:* Avocado, Fruity Bubble, Orange Blossom

CARE FOR LIFE√ø™πΩfcd76

Moisturising Foam Bath

CARIADøπΩ

Bath & Massage Oil: Aches & Pains, Breathe Easy, Calm, Invigorating, Relaxing, Sleep, Sports; *Bath Milk:* Aches & Pains, Breathe Easy, Calm, Invigorating, Relaxing, Sleep, Sports

CONSCIENCE COSMETICS√ø§πΩ∆86

Pure & Mild Shower Gel (Unfragranced)

CO-OPπΩ∆fcd85

Primrose & Camomile Shower Creme; *Creme Bath:* Lotus Flower & Almond, Peach Blossom & Jasmine, Sea Fennel & Lily, White Lilac & Magnolia; *Foam Bath:* Dewberry, Marine Elements, Meadowsweet; *Shower Gel:* Mankind Invigorate, Mankind Refresh, Marine Elements, Meadowsweet

DOLMA√ø™§πΩfcd76

Aromatic Body Shampoo: Antiseptic & Antiviral, Deep Relaxing, Invigorating, Relaxing, Relaxing & Refreshing, Stimulating

ESCENTIAL BOTANICALS√ø™πΩ∆fcd76

Classic Soothing Foam Bath; *Exotic Foam Bath:* Relaxing, Stimulating; *Fruit:* Bath & Shower Gel, Refreshing Foam Bath

ESSENTIAL OIL CO√øπΩfcd93

Base: Dispersable Bath Oil, Foam Bath/Shower Gel

ESSENTIALLY OILS øπ

Base: Bath Oil, Bubble Bath, Shower Gel

FAITH IN NATUREø

Foam Bath: Aloe Vera & Ylang Ylang, Lavender & Geranium, Tea Tree

FAITH PRODUCTSøπΩ∆88

Foam Bath: Aloe Vera & Ylang Ylang, Essential, Lavender & Geranium, Rosemary & Nettle, Seaweed, Tea Tree & Orange

FANTÔME√§πΩfcd78

Aromatherapy Bath Oil: Refresh & Uplift, Rest & Relax, Sensual & Exotic

FARROW & HUMPHRIES√øΩfcd80

Mini Bath Gel; *Bath & Shower Gel [tube]:* Chamomile & Clover, Elderflower & Primrose, Rose & Cornflower; *Foaming Bath Oil:* Chamomile & Clover, Elderflower & Primrose, Rose & Cornflower; *Moisturising Cream Bath:* Chamomile & Clover, Elderflower & Primrose, Fresh Lavender, Rose & Cornflower

FLEUR AROMATHERAPYø™

Bath Oils: all

GR LANEøπΩ∆fcd87

Olbas Bath

GREEN PEOPLEø™πΩ

Shower Gel: Aloe Vera, Rosemary & Red Clay

HEMP UNIONø™§πΩfcd93

Hemp Oil: Bubble Bath, Foam Bath, Shower Gel

toiletries & cosmetics

HONESTY√ø§πΩ∆76

Essential: Mandarin Ginger & Ylang Ylang Shower Gel, Orange Geranium & Lavender Foam Bath; *Fruit:* Apple & Sandalwood Shower & Bath Gel, Strawberry & Papaya Shower & Bath Gel, Tangerine & Vanilla Foam Bath

HUMANE RESEARCH TRUST√ø§πΩfcd

Berwitz Natural Cosmetics: Bath Foam, Body Shampoo, Hair & Body Lotion

KOBASHI√ø™πΩ∆76

All

LOTHIAN HERBSø∆91

Aromatherapy Shower Gel: Cedarwood & Frankincense, Grapefruit & Palmarosa, Lavender & Geranium; *Essential Bath Oil:* Exotic, Refreshing, Relaxing

LUSHøπΩ

Bath Ballistics: All That Jasmine, Big Blue, Bon Bain Bonnard, Butterball, Ching Ling Soo, Chocolate Melt, Feel Good (in the Southern Hemisphere), Fern Shui, Fizzy o'Therapy, Ickle Baby Baff, Kiss Me Klimt, Luverly, Pooh Stix, Slammer, Summer Blues, Tisty Tosty, Waving Not Drowning; *Bath Foam:* Bathos, Blue Skies; *Bubble Bar Slices:* Amandopondo, Aura Suavis, Bathos, Blue Skies & Fluffy White Clouds, Candy Bar, Ceridwen's Cauldron, Dreamtime, Elixir, Floating Island, Flying Saucers, Phoenix, Pleasure Dough, The Big Strawberry; *Shower Gel:* Aqua Mirabilis, Crush; *Smoothie:* Creamed Coconut & Almond, Gumbo Express, Lush Lime, Scrumptious

MARTHA HILLøπΩ

Mountain Herb Shower Gel; *Bath Oil:* Citrus Foaming, Essence of Rose, Lavender, Rosemary Revitalising

MEADOW SWEET OILS√øπΩfcd92

Bath Base Product: Foam, Oil

MEADOWSWEETø™§πΩ∆86

Herbal Relaxing Bath Soak; *Bath Oil:* Relaxing, Rose Foaming; *Bottled Bath Crystals:* Elegant, Lulie, Pastel Musk, Sharelle, Venome, Wild Dewberry; *Foaming Bath:* Aloe Vera, Alpine Fresh, Comfrey & Chickweed Oil, Easy Breathe, Mixed Fruits, Nature Power Anti-Stress, Oriental Musk, Strawberry Sundae, Tropical Palm, White Musk, Wild Dewberry, Ylang Ylang; *Foaming Bath Seeds:* Atlantic Breeze, Lavender, Mountain Pine, Pastel Musk, Peach Delight, Wild Dewberry; *Nature Power Splash:* Sleepytime, Vitalising; *Shower Gel:* Apple, Cherry, Evening Primrose, Fragrance Free

MICHELINE ARCIERøΩfcd

Bath Oil: Anti-Stress, Aromatica, Elan Vital, Harmony, Kypros, Lavender, Rosemary, Sylvestre

MONTAGNE JEUNESSEøπΩfcd78

Evening Primrose Bath Cream, Invigorating Aroma Therapy Spa Bath Gelee, Invigorating Orange Spice Pulp Shower Gel, Peaches & Cream Moisturising Bath, Pink Musk Foaming Bath Essence, Sea Kelp Foaming Bath Aromatherapy, Seaweed & Mineral Exfoliating Shower Gel, Strawberries & Cream Bath Foam; *Aroma Therapy Spa Moisturising Bath:*

Moisturising, Relaxation; *Aroma Therapy Spa Shower Gel:* Invigorating, Relaxation; *Aromatherapie Gaia Bath Elixir:* Calming, Enlightening, Sensuous, Therapeutic; *Dinosaur Mild & Gentle Bubble Bath:* Apatosaurus Dinosaur, Triceratops, T Rex; *Foam Bath:* Orchid Oil, Seaweed & Mineral, Wild Rose

NEAL'S YARD REMEDIESø

Bath Oil: Base, Exotic, Geranium & Orange, Soothing, Stimulating; *Bath Salts:* Citrus, Dead Sea, Geranium, Lavender

NELSONøπΩ

Cleansing Shower Treatment: Energise, Purify, Refresh; Foaming Bath Treatment: Relax, Sensual, Soothe

NEW SEASONS√øπΩfcd76

Neutral Base: Bath Milk, Foam Bath, Shower Gel

NOIRøΩ∆fcd87

Les Essentiels Moisturising Shower Gel

NORFOLK LAVENDERΩfcd84

Bath & Shower Products: all

POWER HEALTHøπΩ

Biocosmetics Starflower Bath Oil, Comfrey Arnica & Witch Hazel Foam Bath, Nature's Mother Feminine Hygiene Wash, Vita Youth Tea Tree Oil Shampoo & Body Wash; *Nature Knows Best Bath Essence:* Pine, Seaweed

PURE PLANT PRODUCTS√Ωfcd76

Aloe Vera Revitalising Shower Gel,

Peaches & Cream Moisturising Shower Creme

SAINSBURY'SΩfcd88

Economy Bubble Bath, Horse Chestnut Bath Gelee, Lucha Green Tea & Lotus Blossom Bath Foam, Sokei-Jasmine & Ginger Bathing Experience; *Dry Skin:* Bath Creme, Skin Shower Creme; *Foam Bath:* Emerald Herb Garden, Sapphire Ocean Spray; *Foaming Shower Gel:* Boost, Indulge, Sapphire Hair & Body Shampoo; *Moisturising Creme Bath Pearl:* Desert Sun, Pearl Mist, Rain Forest, Sea Breeze; *Sensitive Skin:* Bath Creme, Shower Creme; *Shower Gel:* Active, Invigorate, Moisturise, Refreshing, *w* Microban

SHANTI√øπΩ

Aromatic Bath Oil

SHIRLEY PRICE AROMA. øπΩfcd84

Silky Bath

SUPERDRUGΩfcd87

Aromatherapy Foam Bath: Calming Geranium & Sweet Almond Oil, Revitalising Orange & Cinnamon, Sensuous Frankincense & Patchouli, Soothing Lemon & Comfrey, Uplifting Lemongrass & Ginger; *Aromatherapy Shower Gel:* Elderberry & Pomegranite, Lime & Juniper, Peppermint & Eucalyptus; *Creme Bath:* Aloe Vera, Cocoa Butter, Evening Primrose Oil, Evening Primrose Oil *w* Vitamin E Moisture Rich, Family Camelia, Family Coconut, Family Orchid, Family Peony, Peach Kernel, pH for Dry Skin, Vitamin E Moisture Rich; *Economy Creme Bath:* Coral, Pearl, Petal; *Ele-*

ments *Bath Soak:* Earth, Fire, Moon, Sun, Water; *Elements Shower Gel:* Earth, Fire, Moon, Sun, Water; *Family Shower Creme:* Camelia, Coconut, Orchid, Peony; *Floral Creme Bath:* Lavender, Magnolia, Peach Blossom, Rose; *Floral Shower Creme:* Lavender, Magnolia, Rose; *Foam Bath:* Economy, Economy Forest, Economy Oceanic, Economy Sunset, Ocean Blue, pH for Sensitive Skin; *Foaming Bath Oil:* Coconut, Family Camelia, Family Gardenia, Peony; *Life Sense Foam Bath:* Chill Out, Go Wild, Passion, Pleasures, Spirit; *Life Sense Shower Gel:* Go Wild, Pleasure, Spirit; *Men's Aromatherapy:* Anti-Stress Bath Oil 'AAAH!', Invigorating Shower Gel 'WOAH!', Relaxing Bath Soak 'MMMM!'; *Premium Aromatherapy Foam Bath:* Sensuality, Serenity, Vitality; *Rich Creme:* Cream Bath, Shower Creme; *Secret Weapon Foam Bath:* Desire, Energy, Purity, Temptation; *Secret Weapon Shower Gel w Beads:* Energy, Desire, Temptation; *Shower Cream:* Evening Primrose Oil & Vitamin E, Peach, pH for Dry Skin, Vitamin E Moisture Rich; *Shower Gel:* Aloe Vera, Cocoa Butter, Economy Forest, Economy Oceanic, Economy Sunset, Evening Primrose Oil, pH for Sensitive Skin; *Tropical Bath & Shower Gel:* Blueberry, Coconut, Dewberry, Melon, Passion Fruit, Strawberry, Vanilla; *Tropical Pick & Mix Bubble Bath:* Cool Coconut, Decadent Dewberry, Groovy Grape, Perfect Passion Fruit, Strawberry Delight, Tangerine Dream, Very Vanilla; *Tropical Pick & Mix Shower Gel:* Blueberry, Cool Coconut, Dewberry, Grape, Melon,

Passion Fruit, Pink Grapefruit, Tangerine Dream; *Tropicals Bath Bubbles:* Coconut, Pink Grapefruit

VINDOTCO√ø™§πΩfcd75

Body Shower Gels: all

WELEDAøπΩfcd85

Bath Milk: Citrus, Lavender, Rosemary

XVø§πΩ

Connemara: Seaweed Bath, Seaweed Salts, Shower Gel; *Foaming Bath Essence:* Lavender Geranium & Marjoram, Peppermint Spearmint & Rosemary; *Hemp:* Bubble Bath, Shower Gel

BRUSHES ETC

ESSENTIAL OIL CO√øπΩfcd93

Natural Sisal Body Brush

GREEN PEOPLEø™πΩ

Natural Body Glove, Ultra Micro Fibre Cloth

MEADOWSWEETø™§πΩ△86

Nail Brush: Blue, Peach, Pink, White

NATURAL FLOWø

Skin Brush

NEAL'S YARD REMEDIESø

Body Mitt; *Brush:* Back, Nail

SAINSBURY'SΩfcd88

Nail Brush

CONDITIONERS & HAIR CARE

21st CENTURY HEALTH√ø§πΩfcd

Arcom: all

ALADDIN AROMASøπΩfcd87

Conditioner

ANIMAL AID√ø§πΩ∆fcd76

Coconut Conditioner

AUSTRIAN MOOR√ø§πΩ∆

Moor Life Hair Tonic

BEAUTY THROUGH HERBS√øπΩ∆87

Fruits of the Forest Conditioner

BIO-D√ø™πΩ∆83

Hemp Oil Conditioners: all

BODY REFORM√ø§πΩfcd85

Skin Friendly, Tea Tree, White Musk

BODYLINEø§πΩfcd84

Fresh Salad Hair Pack; *Conditioner:* Cranberry & Corn, Dewberry, Ginger & Beer, Musk, Pear & Carrot, Spinach & Grape, Wizard Of Oz

CAMILLA HEPPERøπΩfcd86

Avocado Treatment Wax; *Conditioner:* Herbal Protein, Natural Orange, Raspberry, Rosemary Scalp, Seaweed

CONSCIENCE COSMETICS√ø§πΩ∆86

Conditioner: Camomile, Camomile Highlights, Coconut, Creamy Banana & Vanilla, Lemon Balm & Kiwi

CO-OPπΩ∆fcd85

Conditioner: Apple & Pear, Avocado & Apple, Lemon & Grapefruit, Peach & Apricot; *Vitamin Plus Conditioner:* Dry/Damaged, Normal

DANIEL FIELD√øΩfcd76

Organic & Mineral Research Institute Replace; *Organic & Mineral Hairdressing:* Mineral Hair Repair Masque, Plant Remoisturising Treatment; *Organic & Mineral Hairdressing Conditioner:* Body Builder Detangling, First Aid, Revitalising Mineral; *Supernaturals Conditioner:* Curl Enhancer, Intensive Therapy 5 Spa, Smooth & Shine, Volumising

DOLMA√ø™§πΩfcd76

Hair Conditioner: Cedarwood & Cypress, Lavender & Jojoba; *Hair Lotion:* Geranium Birch & Aloe Vera, Rosemary Nettle & Marigold

ESCENTIAL BOTANICALS√ø™πΩ∆fcd76

Classic Revitalising Conditioner; *Exotic:* Scalp Conditioning Oil for Dry Skin, Scalp Conditioning Oil for Normal to Oily Skin

ESSENTIAL OIL CO√øπΩfcd93

Conditioner Base

ESSENTIALLY OILSøπ

Conditioner Base

FSCπ

Head High Enriched Herbal Conditioner

FAITH IN NATUREø

Conditioner: Aloe Vera & Ylang Ylang,

Lavender & Geranium, Tea Tree

FAITH PRODUCTSøπΩΔ88

Conditioner: Aloe Vera, Jojoba, Rosemary, Seaweed, Tea Tree

FANTÔME√§πΩfcd78

Tea Tree: Conditioner, Headcare Oil, Headcare Spray

FARROW & HUMPHRIES√øΩfcd80

Mini Conditioner

GR LANEøπΩΔfcd87

Conditioner: Tea Tree, Tiki Country Herb

GREEN PEOPLEø™πΩ

Conditioner: Aloe Vera, Rosemary

HEALTH IMPORTSøπΩfcd95

Thursday Plantation Tea Tree Conditioner

HEMP UNIONø™§πΩfcd93

Hemp Oil Conditioner

HONESTY√ø§πΩΔ76

Fruit Range Conditioner: Coconut & Avocado, Jojoba & Peach

HUMANE RESEARCH TRUST√ø§πΩfcd

Berwitz Natural Cosmetics Conditioner

MARTHA HILLøπΩ

Conditioner: Seaweed & Nettle, Seaweed & Rosemary

MEADOW SWEET OILS√øπΩfcd92

Vegetable Based Conditioners: all

MEADOWSWEETø™§πΩΔ86

Scalp Rejuvenator; *Conditioner:* Banana & Vanilla, Camomile, Coconut Frequency, Comfrey & Cade Intensive, Kiwi & Lemon Balm, Mandarin & Papaya, Mango & Apricot, Men's Cologne All Purpose, Nettle Herbal Care, White Musk, Wild Dewberry All Purpose

MILL CREEKπΩ

Conditioner: Aloe Vera, Biotin, Henna, Jojoba, Protein

NEAL'S YARD REMEDIESø

Rosemary & Cedarwood Hair Treatment

NIRVANA NATURAL√ø™§πΩfcd85

Camomile Conditioner

NORFOLK LAVENDERΩfcd84

Conditioners: all

PURE PLANT PRODUCTS√Ωfcd76

Herbal Conditioner

QUINESSENCE√øπΩΔfcd84

Conditioners: all

SABEL™

Intensive Conditioner

SAINSBURY'SΩfcd88

Almond & Mallow for Dry/Damaged, Colour Safe, Provitamin for Dry/Damaged/Coloured; *Michaeljohn:* 2 Minute Moisture Balm Intensive, 3 Minute Wonder Masque Intensive Colour & Curl Treatment, Anti-Static Detangling, Enriching, Tea Tree

SHANTI√ø𝜋Ω

Hair Oil, Hair Tonic

SHIRLEY PRICE AROMA. ø𝜋Ωfcd84

Scalp Tonic

SUPERDRUGΩfcd87

Hair Solution Thicker Hair, Secret Weapon Deep Conditioning Hair Mask; *Conditioner:* Apple & Mint Frequent Use, Fragrance Free Aloe Vera, Head Gear Active Balance, Peach & Wheat, pH Balance, Swim 'n' Sun Leave In, Wild Cherry; *Naturals Conditioner:* Camomile, Cider, Coconut Oil, Coconut Oil Intensive, Dewberry & Rosehip, Henna, Hops & Barley, Tea Tree Oil; *Vitamin Active:* Dry Damaged Hair, Fine Lifeless Hair, Gentle for Frequent Use, Rejuvenating for Permed/Coloured Hair

TIGIIø Ω

Conditioner: Instant, Leave In, Moisture & Shine, Peppermint, Protein Protective Spray; *Essensual:* Thickening Creme, Thickening Paste Conditioner

WAITROSE

A/P Vitalising Conditioner for Extra Shine

WELEDAAø𝜋Ωfcd85

Rosemary Hair Lotion; *Conditioner [bottle]:* Calendula, Lemon Balm, Rosemary

XVø§𝜋Ω

Hemp Conditioner

YIN YANG BEAUTY CARE√ø𝜋Ωfcd72/81

Scalp: Cream *w* Nettles, Lotion

YOUR BODY√ø™𝜋ΩΔ

Conditioner: Aloe Vera, Anti-Dandruff, Vitamin E

DEODORANTS & ANTIPERSPIRANTS

ANIMAL AID√ø§𝜋ΩΔfcd76

White Musk Roll-On Deodorant

BODY REFORM√ø§𝜋Ωfcd85

Reform for Men Deodorant Body Spray; *Antiperspirant:* Skin Friendly, White Musk

CAMILLA HEPPERø𝜋Ωfcd86

Watercress Deodorant

CO-OP𝜋ΩΔfcd85

Active: Antiperspirant Atlantic Breeze, Pacific Breeze; *Antiperspirant:* Apricot, Cool Blue, Cool Ice, Soft Pink; *Roll-On:* Cool Apricot, Cool Blue, Cool Pink

DESERT ESSENCEøΩfcd

Deodorant: Dry By Nature Stick, Natural Roll-On, Tea Tree *w* Lavender

DOLMA√ø™§𝜋Ωfcd76

Deodorant: Roll-On, Stone

FANTÔME√§𝜋Ωfcd78

Tea Tree 5% Roll-On

GREEN PEOPLEø™𝜋Ω

DeoKrystal Deodorant

toiletries & cosmetics

HEALTH IMPORTSøπΩ**fcd95**

Thursday Plantation Tea Tree: Antiperspirant Floral, Antiperspirant Sport, Roll-On Deodorant

HEMP UNIONø™§πΩ**fcd93**

Hemp Oil Deodorant: Musk, Sport

HOLLYTREESø

Deodorant

HONESTY√ø§πΩ△**76**

Deodorant Stone

INNOXAøΩ△**87**

Free & Easy Roll-On

LUSHøπΩ

Deodorant: Aromaco, Aromarant

MARTHA HILLøπΩ

Herbal Deodorant

MILL CREEKπΩ

Deodorant: Aloe, Herbal, Unscented

NEAL'S YARD REMEDIESø

Deodorant: Lemon & Coriander, Stone

NOIRøΩ△**fcd87**

Les Essentiels: Anti Perspirant Deodorant, Deodorising Body Spray, Intensive ADP Roll-On

PURE PLANT PRODUCTS√Ω**fcd76**

Roll-On Antiperspirant Deodorant: Aloe Vera, Peaches & Creme

SAINSBURY'SΩ**fcd88**

Absolute Roll-On Antiperspirant Deodor-ant: Fresh Jade, Ice Blue, Sensitive Light, Soft Pink, Sport 24 Protection

SUPERDRUGΩ**fcd87**

Roll-On Deodorant: Cool Yellow, Family Fresh Pink, Fresh Lilac, Sport, Unperfumed; *Roll-On 24 Hour:* Antiperspirant Deodorant, Men's Antiperspirant Deodorant; *Roll-On Kind to Your Skin:* Pink Blush, Powder Blue; *Roll-On Nature:* Amber Savanna, Polar Fresh, Tropical Mist

WAITROSE

Premier Deodorant Body Spray

WELEDAøπΩ**fcd85**

Deodorant: Citrus, Herbal

XYNERGYøπΩ

Deodorant: Aloe & Cucumber Roll On, Stone

ESSENTIAL & MASSAGE OILS

21st CENTURY HEALTH√ø§πΩ**fcd**

Earth Solutions: all; *Scent Pens:* all

ABSOLUTE AROMAS√øπΩ

Aromatherapy Starter Kits: all; *Essential Oils & Absolutes:* all; *Carrier Oils:* all

ALADDIN AROMASøπΩ**fcd87**

Body Oil: **Anti-Cellulite, Anti-Stress;** ***Carrier Oils:*** **all;** ***Pure Absolutes & Exotic Oils:*** **all;** ***Pure Essential Oils:*** **all;** ***Pure Organic Essential Oils:*** **all;** ***Speciality & Infused Oils:*** **all**

BEAUTY THROUGH HERBS√øπΩ∆87

Aromatherapy Massage Blend: Menopausal, Mood Lifting, Muscle Relaxing, Pre-Menstrual, Refreshing, Relaxing, Sensual; *Carrier Oils:* all; *Essential Oils:* all

BIOFORCE

Toxeucal Massage Oil; *Body Oil:* Lemon, Orange

BODY REFORM√ø§πΩfcd85

Aromatherapy Massage Oil: Relaxing, Sensual, Stimulating; *Carrier Oil:* all; *Essential Oils:* all

BODYLINEø§πΩfcd84

Relaxing Asleep Oil; *Absolutes:* all; *Carriers:* all; *Essential Oils:* all; *Massage Oil:* Handy Hints Body, Invigorating, Stress Relief

BUTTERFLY EFFECT√ø™

100% Natural Hemp & Flower Massage Oil: Aphrodite's Evening Kiss, Aurora's Awakener, Dr Song's Harmonic Back Rub, Nude

CAMILLA HEPPERøπΩfcd86

Natural Oil: Anti-Wrinkle, Grapeseed, Jojoba, Neroli Body Massage, Sweet Almond, Wheatgerm

CARIADøπΩ

Aromaballs: Calm, Head Ease, Passion, Study, Travel; *Carrier Oils:* all; *Essential Oils:* all; *Essential Oil Starter Pack:* No 1, No 2, No 3; *Teenage Pack:* Stress Ball, Study Aromaball, Tea Tree Gel

COTSWOLD HEALTH PRODUCTS√øπΩfcd

Essential Oils: all

CULPEPERøπΩ

Essential Oils: all; *Massage Oils:* all

DESERT ESSENCEøΩfcd

100% Pure Essential Oil: Jojoba, Kinder to Skin Tea Tree, Tea Tree, Tea Tree & Lavender, Tea Tree Eco Harvest, Vitamin E; *Massage & Body Oil:* Love, Relaxation

DOLMA√ø™§πΩfcd76

Aromatherapy Facial Oil: Dehydrated Skin, De-Luxe, Dry Skin, Mature Skin, Sensitive Skin, Thread Veins; *Aromatic Massage Oil:* Anti-Cellulite, Invigorating, Relaxing, Soothing; *Base Oils:* all; *Pure Essential Oils:* all

ESCENTIAL BOTANICALS√ø™πΩ∆fcd76

Massage Oil; *Exotic:* Essential Replenishing Oil for Dry Skin, Essential Replenishing Oil for Normal to Oily Skin

ESSENTIAL OIL CO√øπΩfcd93

Carrier Oils: all; *Pure Essential Oils:* all

ESSENTIALLY OILSøπ

Kanuka Oil, Massage Oil Base; *Absolutes & Attars:* all; *Blended Luxury Massage & Bath Oils:* all; *Essential Oils:* all; *Rare & Exotic Oils:* all; *Starter Kit:* Advanced, Basic; *Vegetable Oils:* all

FAITH IN NATUREø

Oil: Lavender, Tea Tree

toiletries & cosmetics

FAITH PRODUCTSøπΩΔ88

Essential Body Oil; *Aromatherapy Oil:* Lavender, Tea Tree

FANTÔME√§πΩfcd78

Aromatherapy Massage Oil: Refresh & Uplift, Rest & Relax, Sensual & Exotic; *Austrian Blue Glass Aromatherapy Burning Oil:* Refresh & Uplift, Rest & Relax, Sensual & Exotic; *Carrier Oils:* all; *Essential Oils:* all

FLEUR AROMATHERAPYø™

Blended Oils: all; *Carrier Oils:* all; *Essential Oils:* all; *Massage Oils:* all

GR LANEøπΩΔfcd87

Oil: Tea Tree, Tiki Vitamin E High Potency

HAMBLEDEN HERBSøπΩfcd82

Non-Organic Essential Oils: all; *Oil:* Almond, Coconut, Evening Primrose, Sesame; *Organic Essential Oils:* all; *Organic Macerated Oils:* all

HEALTHY HERBSøπΩfcd96

Essential Oils: all

HEMP UNIONø™§πΩfcd93

Pure Hemp Oil Base

HERMITAGE OILS√øπΩfcd90

Essential Oils: all; *Fixed Oils:* all

HONESTY√ø§πΩΔ76

Fleur Blended Oil: Jasmine, Neroli, Rose; *Fleur Pure Essential Oils:* all; *Unscented Oil:* Grapeseed, Sweet Almond

A comprehensive mail order collection of vegan products from companies with compassionate policies.

Honesty bodycare & sun lotions, BWC colour make-up, Daniel Field hair colours & styling products, Dolma perfumes, household cleaners from Bio D & Little Green Shop, Items from Pure Plant, Fleur & Natracare, soaps, toothpaste, recycled stationary and more

For a free catalogue, please phone
01629 814 888
or write to: Honesty, Lumford Mill, Bakewell, Derbyshire. DE45 1GS
Visit our website at: www.honestycosmetics.co.uk

ID AROMATICSøπfcd

Essential Oils: all – **except** Rose Otto

KOBASHI√ø™πΩΔ76

Blended Oils: all; *Carrier Oils:* all; *Essential Oils:* all

LOTHIAN HERBSøΔ91

Calendula Vegetable Oil; *Aromatherapy Massage Oil:* Cellulite Treatment, Exotic, Facial, Hair & Scalp, Muscle Fatigue, Refreshing, Relaxing; *Aromatherapy Push Up Stick:* Eau de Cologne, Eucalyptus, Lavender, Tea Tree; *Blended Essential Oils:* all; *Cold Pressed Vegetables Oils:* all; *Essential Oils:* all; *Organic Essential Oils:* all; *Special Formula:* Don't Resign Relax, Never Ever Again, Tonight's the Night

LUNN LINKS√øπ

Kitchen Organic Essential Oils: all

LUSHøπΩ

Massage Bar: Bewitched, Ego, Into Thin Air, Snake Oil Scalp, Sore Labours Balm, Therapy, Wiccy Magic Muscles

MAROMA√πΩfcd85

Pure Essential Oil Blend: Clear Thoughts, Happy Heart, Joy, Meditation, New Energy, Pure Air, Quiet Mind, Sweet Dreams, Tranquility

MEADOW SWEET OILS√øπΩfcd92

Essential Oils: all; *Carrier Oils:* all

MEADOWSWEETø™§πΩΔ86

Aromatherapy Oils: all; *Carrier Oils:* all; *Massage Oil:* Body Firming/Contouring, Green Apple, Herbal Aromatic Relaxing, Men's Comfrey After Sports, Oriental Musk, Pastel Musk

MICHELINE ARCIERøΩfcd

Aromatherapy Kit: Anti-Infection, Exotic & Uplifting, Pick-Me-Up, Unwinder Anti-Stress; *Essential Body Oil:* Geranium, Healarome, Health, Joy, Lavender, Vitality; *Essential Oils:* all; *Jojoba Body Oil:* Jasmine, Radiance, Rose; *Jojoba Face Oil:* Aurora, Bois de Rose, Camomile, Dawn, Formula 1, Formula 2, Radiance, Rose, Starlight, Sunrise; *Slimaroma Oil:* Bath, Body, Face

MONTAGNE JEUNESSEøπΩfcd78

Black Grape Relaxing Body Oil

NEAL'S YARD REMEDIESø

Aromatherapy For: Balance, Breathing Easy, Clarity, Energy, Passion, Relaxation; *Essential Oils:* all; *Massage Oil:* Aromatic, Base, Geranium & Orange, Sandalwood; *Oil:* Apricot Kernel, Avocado, Coconut, Jojoba, Organic Almond, Seje Rainforest, Sweet Almond, Tibetan Apricot Kernel

NELSONøπΩ

Nelson & Russell Essential Oils: all; *Nelson & Russell Massage Treatment:* Energist, Purify, Relax, Sensual, Soothe

NEW SEASONS√øπΩfcd76

Absolute Oils: all; *Carrier Oils:* all; *Essential Oils:* all; *Organic Oils:* all

NORFOLK LAVENDERΩfcd84

Essential Oils: all

POTTER'S

Comfrey Oil

POWER HEALTHøπΩ

Romany Aromatherapy Oils: all

PURPLE FLAME AROMA.øπΩ**fcd80**

Absolute Oils: all; *Carrier & Base Oils:* all; *Precious Oils in Jojoba:* all; *Pure Essential Oils:* all; *Ready to Use Massage Blend:* After Sport, Before Sport, Body Contour, La Femme Sensuelle, L'Homme Sensuel, Snuggle Down, Unwind, Wide Awake; *Resinoid Oils:* all

QUINESSENCE√øπΩΔ**fcd84**

Carrier Oils: all; *Essential Oils:* all; *Massage Oils:* all

SCOTTISH HERB. SUPPLIES√ø™§πΩ**fcd89**

Base & Carrier Oils: all; *Essential Oils:* all

SHIRLEY PRICE AROMA.øπΩ**fcd84**

Aromatic Body Oil: Jasmine, Neroli, Rose; *Care For Pure Essential Oil/Ready Mix:* After Flight, Cellulite, Circulation, Fatigue, Head Tension, Joints, Lungs, Muscles, Nose & Throat, Sinuses, Sleep/Rest, Stresses, Stretch Mark, Visible Veins, Women; *Carrier Oils:* all; *Essential Oils:* all

SUPERDRUGΩ**fcd87**

Coconut Oil, Evening Primrose Oil Intensive Body Oil, Natural Vitamin E Skincare Oil, Oil of Evening Primrose, Vitamin E Oil; *Premium Aromatherapy Massage Oil:* Sensuality, Serenity, Vitality; *Premium Aromatherapy Pulse Point Oil:* Sensuality, Serenity, Vitality

XVø§πΩ

Lavender

EYE PRODUCTS

ABSOLUTE AROMAS√øπΩ

Relax Your Eyes, Thermal Eye Mask

AUSTRIAN MOOR√ø§πΩΔ

Moor Life Eye Lotion

BEAUTY THROUGH HERBS√øπΩΔ**87**

Galeno: Eye Shadow, Eyeliner, Marine Eye Freshener

BEAUTY WITHOUT CRUELTY√øπΩ**fcd76**

Eye Defining Pencil: Black, Brown, Grey; *Eye Kohl Pencil:* Black, Navy, Teal, Walnut; *Eye Shadow Duo:* Blue Lagoon, Desert Storm, Drift Wood, Olive Grove, Wine & Roses; *Eye Shadow Solo:* Crocodile Tears, Dove Blue, Ginger Cat, Jade, Lovebird, Magnolia, Shimmer, Shy Seal, Timber Wolf; *Mascara:* Black, Brown, Brown/Black, Navy

BODY REFORM√ø§πΩ**fcd85**

Eye Contour Cream, Night Repair Eye Balm

BODYLINEø§πΩ**fcd84**

Eyebright Eye Gel

CAMILLA HEPPERøπΩ**fcd86**

Cucumber Eye Gel, Herbal Eye Cream; *Eye Make-Up Remover:* Lotion, Oil

DOLMA√ø™§πΩ**fcd76**

Aloe Vera Eye Gel, Camomile & Aloe

Vera Eye Cream, Eye Make-Up Removing Oil; *Eye Make-Up Removers:* Camomile, Fennel

ESCENTIAL BOTANICALS√ø™πΩ∆fcd76

Classic Cleansing Eye Cream

FAITH PRODUCTSøπΩ∆88

Aloe Vera Eye Gel

GREEN PEOPLEø™πΩ

Eye Cream, Eye Gel

INNOXAøΩ∆87

Sensitivity: Eye Contour Gel, Eye Make-Up Remover

MARTHA HILLøπΩ

Elderflower Eye Contour Gel, Eye Contour Balm, Eye Make-Up Remover

MEADOWSWEETø™§πΩ∆86

Eye Make-Up Remover Cream; *Eye Gel:* Comfrey & Cucumber, Elderflower, Fragrance Free

MONTAGNE JEUNESSEøπΩfcd78

Soothing Eye Gel

NELSONøπΩ

Aroma Mask Cooling Eye Compress

POWER HEALTHøπΩ

Danny Bernard Herbal Eye Sachet

SAINSBURY'SΩfcd88

Contact Lens Case; *Contact Lens Care:* One Step Peroxide Solution, Step 1 Disinfecting Solution, Step 2 Neutralising Solution; *Eye Make-Up Remover:* Fragrance Free, Oil of Evening Primrose; *For All Contact Lenses:* Daily Cleaner, Saline Solution

SAUFLON

Contact Lens Products: all

SHIRLEY PRICE AROMA.øπΩfcd84

Chamomile Eyecare

SPECSAVERS

Contact Lens Products: all

SUPERDRUGΩfcd87

Evening Primrose Oil: Eye Cream, Eye Make-Up Remover; *Optimum:* Eye Contour Cream, Eye Make-Up Remover; *Vitamin E:* Eye Contour Gel, Eye Make-Up Remover Lotion

YOUR BODY√ø™πΩ∆

Eye Make-Up Remover: Aloe Vera, Vitamin E

FEMININE HYGIENE

NATRACAREø

100% Certified Organic Cotton Tampons: Regular Applicator, Regular Non-Applicator, Super Applicator, Super Non-Applicator; *100% Pure Cotton Tampons:* Regular Mini Non-Applicator, Regular Non-Applicator, Super Non-Applicator; *Press-On Pads:* Night Times, Panty Shields, Regular Towels, Super Towels, Ultra-Slender Towels

FOOT/LEG CARE

AMBER ESSENCE√ø$\pi\Omega$fcd84

Foot Lotion

AUSTRIAN MOOR√ø§$\pi\Omega\Delta$

Moor Life Foot Bath

BIOFORCE

Juniperosan

BODY REFORM√ø§$\pi\Omega$fcd85

Tea Tree Foot Lotion

BODYLINEø§$\pi\Omega$fcd84

Foot Loose Foot Spray, Sweet Feet Foot Scrub; *Foot Lotion:* Heal Appeal, Relaxing

CAMILLA HEPPERø$\pi\Omega$fcd86

Aloe Vera Foot Lotion

CARABAY√ø$\pi\Omega$fcd

Seaweed Foot Bath

CHRISTYø$\Omega\Delta$87

Feet Treats Foot Sachet: Massage Cream, Revitalising Scrub, Revitalising Soak; *Foot Treats Foot Tube:* Massage Cream, Revitalising Scrub, Revitalising Soak

DOLMA√ø™§$\pi\Omega$fcd76

Peppermint Foot Cream; *Aromatic Foot Shampoo:* Lemongrass & Cypress, Peppermint & Tea Tree

ESCENTIAL BOTANICALS√ø™$\pi\Omega\Delta$fcd76

Exotic Cooling Foot Balm

FAITH PRODUCTSø$\pi\Omega\Delta$88

Essential Foot Lotion

FANTÔME√§$\pi\Omega$fcd78

Tea Tree Foot Powder

GRANDMA VINE'Sø

Foot Balm

HEALTH IMPORTSø$\pi\Omega$fcd95

Thursday Plantation Tea Tree: **Foot Powder, Foot Spray**

LOTHIAN HERBSøΔ91

Peppermint & Cypress Foot Cream

LUSHø$\pi\Omega$

Close Up Pied de Pepper Cream, Ultra Fresh Fridge Volcano Foot Mask

MARTHA HILLø$\pi\Omega$

Foot Treatment Cream, Moisturising Foot Balm

MEADOWSWEETø™§$\pi\Omega\Delta$86

Deodorising Foot Spray, Herbal Foot Soak, Leg & Vein Cream; *Foot Cream:* **Comfrey & Peppermint, Peppermint**

MONTAGNE JEUNESSEø$\pi\Omega$fcd78

Iced Blueberry & Balm Mint Deodorising Foot Cooler, Watermelon & Balm Mint Deodorising Foot Scrub

NEAL'S YARD REMEDIESø

Lavender & Tea Tree Foot Salts

NORFOLK LAVENDERΩfcd84

Foot/Leg Care Products: all

POWER HEALTHøπΩ

Leg & Vein Balm; *Lavinia:* Foot & Leg Lotion, Foot Bath Concentrate, Foot Bath Salts, Foot Powder w Essential Oils, Herbal Foot Cream

SUPERDRUGΩfcd87

Cooling Footspray, Exfoliating Foot Scrub, Moisturising Foot Cream; *Soothing:* Footsoak, Skin Complex Leg & Foot Lotion

YOUR BODY√ø™πΩΔ

Peppermint: Foot Bath, Foot Lotion, Foot Powder, Foot Spray

GIFT BOXES & PACKS

ANIMAL AID√ø§πΩΔfcd76

Gift Box 1: English Rose Moisturising Shower Gel, Violet & Almond Foaming Bath Oil & Sea Spray Shampoo; *Gift Box 2:* English Rose Moisturising Shower Gel, Rose Petal & Violet Soap

CARIADøπΩ

Gifts & Packs: 3 Mini Blends, 5 Mini Blends, Aromastone & Essential Oil, Aromatherapy Gift, Body Care, Foot Fetish Pack, Garden Pack, Gel Pack, Heart Amphora & Ylang Ylang Essential Oil, Lavender Pack, Light Bulb Ring & Lavender, Men's Pack, Pregnancy Pack, Relax & Invigorating Pack, Romantic Rose Pack, Sensual Pack, Teenage, Vaporiser & Orange Oil;

Razor & Shave Oil Packs: Alternative, Original; *Starter Pack:* Face & Body, Milk & Gels, Milk Blends, Oils Blends, Range Pack 1, Range Pack 2, Starter Kit

DROYT√øπΩfcd84

Glycerine Soap Man's Gift Box

FARROW & HUMPHRIES√øΩfcd80

Drawstring Gift Set: Elderflower & Primrose, Rose & Cornflower; *Gift Bath & Shower Gel/Soap/Washcloth:* Chamomile & Clover, Elderflower & Primrose, Rose & Cornflower; *Gift Talc/Soap/Perfumed Sachet:* Elderflower & Primrose, Rose & Cornflower; *Travel Set [assorted fragrances]:* Overnight, Weekend

FLEUR AROMATHERAPYø™

Gift Packs

HONESTY√ø§πΩΔ76

Gift Boxes

HUMANE RESEARCH TRUST√ø§πΩfcd

Berwitz Natural Cosmetics: Coconut Body Care Travel Pack (moisturiser, hand & body lotion, bath foam, vegetarian soap), Coconut Hair Care Travel Pack (shampoo, conditioner, body shampoo, vegetarian soap)

KOBASHI√ø™πΩΔ76

Essential Oils Starter Basket

LOTHIAN HERBSøΩ91

Gift Pack: Bath, Food, Massage, Men's, Shower; *Pack:* Aromatherapy Push-Up Stick Display Starter, Luxury, Starter; *Pot Pourri Gift Packed Bag:* Camellia, Cedarwood, Cottage Garden, Dewberry, Jasmine, Lavender, Mediterranean, Mexican Vanilla, Opium, Red Rose, Sicilian Lemon, Spiced Orange, White Musk, Wild Rose, Yuletide

LUSHøπΩ

French Fancies: All That Jasmine, Bon Bain Bonnard, Favourites, Slammer, Summer Blues, Tisty Tosty; *Gift Pack:* Ballistic Barrel, Bomb Perignon Wrapped, Red Rooster Wrapped

PURPLE FLAME AROMA. øπΩ**fcd80**

NVQ Essential Oil Kit

SUPERDRUGΩ**fcd87**

Florals Peach Blossom Creme Bath for Gifts, Tropical Pick & Mix Gift Bag

HAIR DYES

BEAUTY THROUGH HERBS√øπΩ∆**87**

Cryotermol Hair Anti-Aging Treatment

CAMILLA HEPPERøπΩ**fcd86**

Natural Henna Hair Colour: Black, Chestnut Brown, Copper, Natural Auburn

COLORA HENNA√§πΩ**fcd60**

Henna Hair Color: all

DANIEL FIELD√øΩ**fcd76**

Watercolour: all

HAMBLEDEN HERBSøπΩ**fcd82**

Organic Henna

LA RICHE

Directions Semi Permanent Hair Colour: all

NEAL'S YARD REMEDIESø

Henna

SUPERDRUGΩfcd87

Make Up for Hair: Glam Rock Hair Glitter, Spaceman Glitter Gel; *Make-Up for Hair Glitter Gel:* Firestarter, Glitterbug, Gogogreen, Rockstar; *Make-Up for Hair — Hair Lights:* Flame Flecks, Lemon Fizz, Lilyloves; *Make-Up for Hair Mascara:* Bluebelle, Brandysnap, Daredevil, Giltridden, Hazydaze, P/Rays; *Make-Up for Hairspray:* Coppernob, Goldiva, Got the Blues, Mirrorball, Purplexed, Spaced Out

WORLDS END TRADING√ø§πΩfcd

Henna Powder

HAIR REMOVAL

AQUA NATURAL√øπΩfcd88

Simply Smooth

SUPERDRUGΩfcd87

Hair Removing Creams: all

HAIR SPRAYS, GELS ETC

BODYLINEø§πΩfcd84

Curl-Enhancing Styling Spray

CAMILLA HEPPERøπΩfcd86

Jojoba Hair Gel

CO-OPπΩΔfcd85

Styling Gel: Extra Firm, Firm Hold; *Styling Mousse:* Extra Firm, Firm

DANIEL FIELD

Organic & Mineral Hairdressing: Anti-Frizz Protector Hairspray, Body Builder Spray, Cactus Sap Styling Gel, Curl Hold & Shine, Smooth & Shine Serum, Styling Wax; *Organic & Mineral Research Institute:* Anti-Frizz Miracle Spray, Anti-Frizz Serum, Mirror Shine; *Supernaturals:* Curl Enhancing Spritz, Glossing Gel, Mirror Finish Serum, Polishing Wax, Smooth & Shine Serum, Volumising Air-O-Foam

MILL CREEKπΩ

Extra Hold Conditioning Hairspray w Jojoba & Panthenol,

SABEL™

Gel Spray, Protein Spray, Sculpting Gel, Sculpting Lotion, Serum/Hair Polisher, Spritz, Volumising Spray

SAINSBURY'SΩfcd88

Gel: Extra Firm Hold, Wet Look; *Hairspray:* Extra Firm Hold, Firm Hold, Flexible Hold; *Hairtex:* Air Infused Gel, Lightweight Finishing Spray, Lightweight Gel Spray, Volumising Mousse; *Michaeljohn:* Hair Shaping Gel, Hair Texturising Creme Wax; *Mousse:* Extra Firm Hold, Firm Hold, Flexible Hold, Natural Hold

SUPERDRUGΩfcd87

Men's Basic Forest Fresh Hair Cream; *Hair Art:* Design Gel, Freeze Spritzer,

Hairspray, Mousse, Protect & Shine Serum, Sculpture Gel; *Hair Setting Lotion:* Extra Firm, Firm; *Head Gear:* High Shine Gel, Super Hold Gel

TIGIøΩ

Curl Jam, Molding Gel, Root Boost, Straight Talk Flattening Balm, Style Shine; *Essensual:* Spray Gel, Spray Shine, Texturising Pomade

HAND CARE

AMBER ESSENCE√øπΩfcd84

Hand Lotion

ANIMAL AID√ø§πΩ∆fcd76

Marigold & Marshmallow Handcream

BEAUTY THROUGH HERBS√øπΩ∆87

Fruits of the Forest Hand & Body Lotion

BIO-D√ø™πΩ∆83

Squeaky Hand Cleaner, Working Hands Skin Repair Cream

BODY REFORM√ø§πΩfcd85

Safe Hands Environmental Protection Hand Cream, Strawberry & Papaya Hand & Nail Complex

BODYLINEø§πΩfcd84

Lotion: California Dreaming Hand & Body, Lemon Peel Hand

CAMILLA HEPPERøπΩfcd86

Evening Primrose Hand Cream

CARE FOR LIFE√ø™πΩfcd76

Hand & Body Lotion

CARIADøπΩ

Lavender Hand Cream

DESERT ESSENCEøΩfcd

Anti-Bacterial Hand Sanitiser, Peach Hand & Body Moisturiser

DOLMA√ø™§πΩfcd76

Hand Cream: Lemongrass, Wild Poppy

ECOVER™πΩ

Heavy Duty Hand Cleaner

ESCENTIAL BOTANICALS√ø™πΩ∆fcd76

Classic Hand Cream

FARROW & HUMPHRIES√øΩfcd80

Enriched Hand Cream, Hand & Body Balm

GR LANEøπΩ∆fcd87

Tea Tree Hand Wash

GRANDMA VINE'Sø

Hand Cream

HONESTY√ø§πΩ∆76

Unscented Hand Cream *w* Comfrey

INNOXAøΩ∆87

One & All Hand Cream

LOTHIAN HERBSø∆91

Lavender & Patchouli Hand Cream

MARTHA HILLøπΩ

Gardeners Cream

MEADOWSWEETø™§πΩ∆86

Lemon & Hawthorn Barrier Cream, Nature Power Antiseptic Hand Wash

Cleanser, Rose & Glycerine Hand Lotion, White Musk Hand & Body Lotion; *Hand Cream:* Peach & Apricot, Rich Rose

MICHELINE ARCIERøΩfcd

Hand & Nail Oil

MONTAGNE JEUNESSEøπΩfcd78

Vitamin Hand & Nail Cream; *Hand Cream:* Apricot & Almond, Evening Primrose

NEAL'S YARD REMEDIESø

Citrus Hand Wash

NEW SEASONS√øπΩfcd76

Neutral Base Hand Cream

NORFOLK LAVENDERΩfcd84

Hand & Nail Care Products: all

POWER HEALTHøπΩ

Vita Youth Tea Tree Oil Hand Cream

SAINSBURY'SΩfcd88

Hand & Body Lotion: Aloe Vera, Cocoa Butter, Fragrance Free, Oil of Evening Primrose; *Moisturising Handwash:* Citrus, Ivory, Peach, Pure

SUPERDRUGΩfcd87

Vitamin E Hand & Body Cream; *Floral Hand & Body Lotion:* Camellia, Gardenia, Peony; *Hand & Body Creme Wash:* Camellia, Coconut, Orchid, Peony; *Hand & Body Liquid Wash:* Cold Cream, Soft Peach, Warm Pink; *Hand & Body Lotion:*

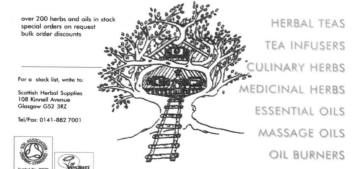

Enriching, pH, Magnolia, Oil of Evening Primrose, Peach; *Hand Wash:* Aloe Vera, Antibacterial Liquid, Cocoa Butter, Evening Primrose Oil, Peach Kernel, pH for Dry Skin, pH for Sensitive Skin

VINDOTCO√ø™§πΩfcd75

Cream Hand Soap; *Hand Cleaner Gels:* all; *Heavy Duty Hand Cleaner:* Abrasive, Non-Abrasive; *Lotion Hand Cleaners:* Abrasive, Non-Hand Cleaners

LIP PRODUCTS

BEAUTY THROUGH HERBS√øπΩΔ87

Galeno Lipsticks

BEAUTY WITHOUT CRUELTY√øπΩfcd76

Lip Defining Pencil: Brown, Pinky Brown, Plum, Rich Red; *Lipstick:* Barely Pink, Brandysnap, Butterscotch, Candy Floss, Caramel Cream, Chilli Red, Clover Pearl, Coppernob, Damson Julep, Foxglove Fever, Iced Melon, In the Pink, Koala, Peach Dream, Perfect Plum, Red Red, Rosewood, Spiced Grape, Sweet Apricot, Tansy Tease, Terracotta, Toffee Apple

CAMILLA HEPPERøπΩfcd86

Lip Smoothie: Banana, Mint, Passion Fruit, Strawberry

DOLMA√ø™§πΩfcd76

Lip Salve: Fennel, Mandarin, Spearmint

HEALTH IMPORTSøπΩfcd95

Thursday Plantation Tea Tree Lipfix

Cream

HEMP UNIONø™§πΩfcd93

Hemp Oil Lip Balm

HONESTY√ø§πΩΔ76

Unscented Lip Balm

MARTHA HILLøπΩ

Clear Moisturising Lip Gloss; *Sheer Moisturising Lip Colour:* Blueberry, Cherry, Soft Rose, Terracotta, True Red, Wine

MEADOWSWEETø™§πΩΔ86

Lip Balm: **Apricot & Peach, Banana, Coconut, Green Apple, Mandarin Orange, Peppermint, Red Cherry, Rich Plum, Strawberry, Wild Dewberry**

POWER HEALTHøπΩ

Biocosmetics Starflower Lip Balm

SUPERDRUGΩfcd87

Lip Balm: Blackberry, Cappuccino, Chocolate Orange, Lemon, Orange, Pineapple; *Lip Gloss:* Candy, Milk Chocolate, Peppermint, Tutti Fruitti

YOUR BODY√ø™πΩΔ

Lip Balm: **Apricot, Banana, Kiwi, Mint, Morello Cherry, Orange, Strawberry**

NAIL PRODUCTS

BEAUTY WITHOUT CRUELTY√øπΩfcd76

Nail Colour: Barely Pink, Butterscotch Cream, Neutral, Poppyshock, Rich Red, Rosewood, Tansy Tease, Vanilla

DOLMA√ø™§πΩfcd76

Nail & Cuticle Cream

MARTHA HILLøπΩ

Cuticle Cream

MONTAGNE JEUNESSEøπΩfcd78

Vitamin Hand & Nail Treatment

SUPERDRUGΩfcd87

Vitamin E Hand & Nail Treatment; *Secret Weapon Nail Varnish:* Desire, Energy, Purity, Temptation

PERFUMES ETC

BODY REFORM√ø§πΩfcd85

Eau de Parfum Natural Sprays: all; *Fragrance Perfume Oils:* all; *Men's Fragrances:* all; *White Musk:* Body Spray, Perfume Oil

BODYLINEø§πΩfcd84

Body Spray: Dewberry, Fragrance Free, Men's Antiperspirant, Musk; *Eau de Toilette:* Ginger, Magnolia, Men's, Musk, Vanilla; *Perfume Oil:* Dewberry, Ginger, Magnolia, Musk, Vanilla

BUTTERFLY EFFECT√ø™

Organic Hemp & Flower Body Spray Mist: Camomile, Citrus, Linden & Eucalyptus, Ylang Ylang

CACHETøΩ∆87

Spray: Eau de Toilette, Perfumed Body

CAMILLA HEPPERøπΩfcd86

Teaza Splash Cologne; *Perfume Oil:* Coel-Na-Mara, Honeysuckle, Hyacinth, Jasmine, Lavender, Lemon Verbena, Lily of Valley, Orange Blossom, Pot-Pourri, Rose, Sandalwood, White Musk

CO-OPπΩ∆fcd85

Body Spray: Citrus Fresh, Floral Pleasures, Fruity Vanilla, Oriental Musk; *Mankind Body Spray:* Invigorate, Refresh

CULPEPERøπΩ

Toilet Waters: all

DOLMA√ø™§πΩfcd76

Vegan Perfume: **Amethyst Mist, Cushie B, Opus in Pastels, Prelude, Quintet, Raga, Rondo, Sarabande, Sonata, Vegamusk**

ESSENTIALLY OILSøπ

Fragrance: Coconut, Dewberry, Freesia, Gardenia, Green Apple, Honeysuckle, Hyacinth, Jasmine, Lavender, Lilac, Lily of the Valley, Magnolia, Musk, Neroli, Night Scented Stock, Peach, Rose, Sandalwood, Strawberry, Tiare, Violet, Ylang Ylang

FANTÔME√§πΩfcd78

Perfume Simmer Pots; *Memories of... Feminine Fragrance:* Allure, Ananya No 5, Eternity, Giorgio, Loulou, Obsession, Opium, Paris, Tommy Girl, Tresor, Ysatis; *Memories of... Masculine Fragrance:* Aramis, Cool Water, Fahrenheit, Jazz; *Memories of... Unisex Fragrance:*

toiletries & cosmetics

CK Be, CK One

FARROW & HUMPHRIES√ø𝛀fcd80

Perfumed Stick: Fresh Lavender, Rose & Cornflower

FLEUR AROMATHERAPYø™

Perfumes: all

HERMITAGE OILS√øπ𝛀fcd90

Perfume Oils: all

INDRAø

Aromatherapy Perfume: Energy, Peace, Unity

KENT COSMETICS√øπ𝛀∆88

Apple Blossom Fragrance

LUSHøπ𝛀

Fragrance: Flower Market, Icon, Karma

MAROMA√π𝛀fcd85

Parfum d'Auroville (alcohol free): Blue Amber, Into the Night, Ocean Breeze, Opium Flowers, Patchouli, Rajasthan, Sweet Sandalwood, Vanilla, White Musk, Wild Rose

MEADOWSWEETø™§π𝛀∆86

Body Spray: Dewberry, White Musk; *Perfume... similar to:* Anais Anais, Armani, Beautiful, Chanel No 5, Giorgio, Joy, Lou Lou, Obsession Musk, Opium, Paris, Passion, Rive Gauche, White Linen, White Musk, Ystasis, Youth Dew

MICHELINE ARCIERø𝛀fcd

Arabimou, Feuilles de Rose

NEAL'S YARD REMEDIESø

Aromatic Cologne

NORFOLK LAVENDER𝛀fcd84

Perfumes etc: all

PERFUMERS GUILDø§π𝛀∆81

Compassion Eau de Parfum, Sample Coffret, Signature Scents; *Classic Collection Fragrance for women:* Alice, Amber, Ann-Marie, Bella, Camilla, Christina, Diana, Gabriella, Hannah, JB Club, Joanna, Laura, Lily of the Valley, Louisa, Margaret, Margot, Pollyanna, Province Lavender, Sophie, Trisha, Twenty One, White Musk; *Classic Collection Eau de Toilette for men:* JB Club, JWB, Kensington, St John, Twenty-One

SAINSBURY'S𝛀fcd88

Bodyspray: Best of the Zest, Musk Madness, Pleasure Zone, Silver Mist, Tickled Pink, Walking on Air

SUPERDRUG𝛀fcd87

Shapers Refreshing Body Mist; *Body Spray:* Magnolia, Peach Blossom; *Floral Decanter:* Lavender, Magnolia; *Secret Weapon Body Spray:* Desire, Energy, Purity, Temptation; *Secret Weapon Solid Perfume:* Desire, Energy, Purity, Temptation; *Tropical Body Spray:* Blue Berry, Melon, Passion Fruit

SHAMPOOS

21st CENTURY HEALTH√ø§π𝛀fcd

Shi Kai: all

ALADDIN AROMASø$\pi\Omega$**fcd87**

Shampoo

ANIMAL AID√ø§$\pi\Omega\Delta$**fcd76**

Sea Spray, Tea Tree & Coconut

AUSTRIAN MOOR√ø§$\pi\Omega\Delta$

Moor Life

BEAUTY THROUGH HERBS√ø$\pi\Omega\Delta$**87**

Fruits of the Forest, Galeno Marine Shampoo & Conditioner

BIO-D√ø™$\pi\Omega\Delta$**83**

Borage Oil, Hemp Oil; *Citrus Scalp Conditioning:* Grapefruit & Ylang Ylang, Lemon & Peppermint, Lime & Evening Primrose, Orange & Aloe Vera; *Hemp Oil Solid Bar:* Lavender & Nettle, Rosemary & Lime, Sandalwood & Wheatgerm, Thyme & Juniper

BODY REFORM√ø§$\pi\Omega$**fcd85**

Reform for Men, Skin Friendly, Tea Tree, White Musk

BODYLINEø§$\pi\Omega$**fcd84**

Anti-Chlorine Protective, Anti-Dandruff Frequent, Anti-Tangle, Apple & Gooseberry, Cranberry & Corn, Dewberry, Grapefruit & Lemon, Magnolia, Northern Exposure, Peach & Apricot, Pear & Carrot, Raspberry & Strawberry, Spinach & Grape; *2 in 1 Shampoo & Conditioner:* Coco Cabana, Men's; *3 in 1:* Aloe Vera, Tea Tree; *Bar:* Barrel Of Beer, Butter, Men's, Muddy Buddy, Shampagne & Strawberries, Tea Tree

CAMILLA HEPPERø$\pi\Omega$**fcd86**

Camomile, Coconut Oil, Herbal, Jojoba Oil, Lavender & Sesame Oil, Men's Conditioning, Natural Orange, Rosemary, Seaweed, Ti-Tree & Thyme, Watercress

CONSCIENCE COSMETICS√ø§$\pi\Omega\Delta$**86**

Birch & Henna All In One, Camomile Highlights, Coconut Oil, Creamy Banana & Vanilla, Fruits of the Sea Conditioning, Lemon Balm & Kiwi, Mild, Wild Thyme & Mint

CO-OP$\pi\Omega\Delta$**fcd85**

2 in 1 Dry/Damaged, Apple & Pear, Avocado & Apple, Enriching/Extra Shine, Frequent Wash, Lemon & Grapefruit, Mild/Frequent, Peach & Apricot; *Anti-Dandruff:* Greasy, Normal; *Conditioning:* Avocado & Apple, Extra Body, Peach & Apricot; *Shampoo & Conditioner:* 2 in 1, Dewberry, Frequent Use; *Vitamin Plus:* Dry/Damaged, Normal

DANIEL FIELD√øΩ**fcd76**

Remove; *Organic & Mineral Hairdressing:* Body Builder Therapy, Dandruff Scalp Therapy, First Aid Therapy, Plant Remoisturising, Revitalising Detox, Spring Water Everyday; *Supernaturals:* Curl Enhancing, Dandruff Scalp Therapy, Intensive Therapy 5 Spa, Smooth & Shine, Volumising

DESERT ESSENCEøΩ**fcd**

Body Boosting, Daily Replenishing; *Moisture Manage:* All Types, Normal/Dry, Oily

toiletries & cosmetics

DOLMA√ø™§πΩfcd76

Jojoba & Sandalwood; *Nettle & Pectin:* Bitter Orange & Tangerine, Cedarwood & Cypress, Lavender, Rosemary, Tea Tree & Thyme

ESCENTIAL BOTANICALS√ø™πΩΔfcd76

Everyday Fruit; *Classic:* Balancing, Moisturising

ESSENTIAL OIL CO√øπΩfcd93

Base

ESSENTIALLY OILSøπ

Base

FSCπ

Head High: Aloe Vera Shampoo & Revitaliser, Rosemary Frequent Use, Tea Tree Oil Dandruff

FAITH IN NATUREø

Aloe Vera & Ylang Ylang, Lavender & Geranium, Tea Tree

FAITH PRODUCTSøπΩΔ88

Aloe Vera, Essential Duo, Jojoba, Lavender & Geranium, Rosemary, Seaweed, Tea Tree

FANTÔME√§πΩfcd78

Tea Tree

FARROW & HUMPHRIES√øΩfcd80

Mini

GR LANEøπΩΔfcd87

Tea Tree; *Tiki:* Camomile, Marigold, Nettle, Rosemary

GREEN PEOPLEø™πΩ

Hair & Body Bar; *Herbal:* Aloe Vera, Rosemary

HEALTH IMPORTSπΩfcd95

Thursday Plantation Tea Tree: Anti-Dandruff, Deep Cleansing

HEMP UNIONø™§πΩfcd93

Hemp Oil

HONESTY√ø§πΩΔ76

Essential Nettle & Lavender, Unscented Hair & Body; *Fruit:* Apple & Rosemary Conditioning, Chamomile & Orange, Lemon & Vanilla, Peach & Coconut

HUMANE RESEARCH TRUST√ø§πΩfcd

Berwitz Natural Cosmetics Coconut

KOBASHI√ø™πΩΔ76

All

LOGONA

Surfactant Free: Powder, Ready To Use w Patchouli

LUSHøπΩ

Antiphilitron, Grass Roots, Ibiza Party, Plantational, Washday Greens; *Bar:* Dr Peppermint, Featherweight Fruit, Irresistible Bliss, Jumping Juniper, Soak & Float, Ultimate Shine; *Solid:* Chamomile, Gentil Lentil, Trichomania

MARTHA HILLøπΩ

Coconut Conditioning, Seaweed & Nettle, Seaweed & Rosemary

MEADOW SWEET OILS√øπΩfcd92

Base

MEADOWSWEETø™§πΩ△86

Aloe Vera, Banana & Vanilla Cream, Camomile, Coconut Frequency, Comfrey & Nettle All Purpose, Fragrance Free, Kiwi & Lemon Balm, Mandarin & Papaya, Mango & Apricot, Nettle Herbal Care, Thyme & Mint, Ultra Mild Formula; *Conditioning:* **Herb/Protein, Seaweed;** *Hair & Body:* **Men's Cologne, Men's Jaztec, Men's Sandalwood, White Musk, Wild Dewberry;** *Men's:* **Aroman, Boston,**

MILL CREEKπΩ

Aloe Vera, Biotin, Henna, Jojoba, Protein

NATRACAREø

Perfume-free Vegan

NEAL'S YARD REMEDIESø

Calendula, Chamomile & Orange Flower, Coconut & Jojoba, Nettle & Sage, Rosemary & Thyme, Seaweed

NEW SEASONS√øπΩfcd76

Neutral Base Conditioning

NIRVANA NATURAL√ø™§πΩfcd85

Nettle & Jasmine, Orange & Barley, Rosemary, Wheatgerm & Honey (contains honeysuckle not honey), Wild Mint

NORFOLK LAVENDERΩfcd84

All

POTTER'S

Rosemary

POWER HEALTHøπΩ

Nature Knows Best Apricot; *Banfi Naturelle Salon:* Cucumber, Ginseng, Nettle & Weatgerm, Rosemary, Scarborough Fair, Seaweed; *Dannex:* Anti-Dandruff Treatment, Medicated Plus Conditioner, Vitamin & Orange; *Nature Knows Best Natural:* Cucumber, Ginseng, Rosemary, Scarborough Fair, Seaweed, Wheatgerm & Nettle; *Vita Youth:* Aloe Vera, Vitamin E

PURE PLANT√Ωfcd76

Comfrey & Sage, Grapefruit & Almond, Lime & Hops, Marshmallow & Rosemary, Orange Spice & Ginger, Orchid 2-in-1 Shampoo & Conditioner

QUINESSENCE√øπΩ△fcd84

All

ROMANDA HEALTHCAREø§πΩ

Scalp Serum

SABEL™

Acid Balance, Moisturising, Tea Tree Hair & Scalp, Volumising

SAINSBURY'SΩfcd88

Almond & Mallow, Wash & Shine Chlorine Neutralising for Swimmers; *Anti-Dandruff:* Frequent Use, Normal/Dry; *Michaeljohn:* Colour & Curl Saver, Hair Thickening, No More Frizz!, Tea Tree

SHANTI√øπΩ

Herbal

toiletries & cosmetics

SUPERDRUGΩfcd87

Hair Sensations Volumizing Thickening, Peach & Wheat, Wild Cherry; *3 in 1 Shampoo & Conditioner:* Dry/Damaged, Fine Hair, Normal Hair; *All-in-One:* Dry/Perm, Fine, Normal; *Fragrance Free:* Aloe Vera, Apple & Mint; *Hair Art Ultimate:* Clarifying, Shine On; *Hair Solutions:* Anti Dandruff, Dry Scalp, Thicker Hair; *Head Gear:* 2 in 1, Dandruff Control, Rebalancing, Thickening; *Naturals:* Coconut Oil, Camomile, Dewberry & Rosehip, Henna, Hops & Barley, Tea Tree Oil; *pH Balance:* 2 in 1, Dry Scalp, Normal; *Vitamin Active:* 2 in 1 for Dry/Damaged Hair, 2 in 1 for Fine Lifeless Hair, 2 in 1 for Frequent Use, 2 in 1 for Permed/Coloured Hair, Dry Damaged Use, Permed/Coloured Hair

TIGI∮øΩ

Deep Cleanse, Essensual Thickening, Gentle Cleanse, Moisture & Shine, Treatment

VINDOTCO√ø™§$\pi\Omega$fcd75

Hair

WELEDAø$\pi\Omega$fcd85

Calendula, Rosemary Gel, Rosemary Liquid; *Concentrated [tube]:* Chestnut, Rosemary

XVø§$\pi\Omega$

Hemp; *Citrus:* Grapefruit & Ylang Ylang, Lemon & Peppermint, Lime & Evening Primrose, Orange Aloe Vera; *Hemp Bar:* Juniper & Thyme, Lavender & Nettle, Rosemary & Lime, Sandalwood & Wheatgerm

YIN YANG BEAUTY CARE√ø$\pi\Omega$fcd72/81

Moisturising Hair Wash

YOUR BODY√ø™$\pi\Omega\Delta$

Aloe Vera, Anti-Dandruff, Vitamin E

SHAVING PRODUCTS

AMBER ESSENCE√ø$\pi\Omega$fcd84

Aftershave Lotion

AUSTRIAN MOOR√ø§$\pi\Omega\Delta$

Moor Life Aftershave

BODY REFORM√ø§$\pi\Omega$fcd85

Reform for Men: Aftershave Balm, Body Splash, Shaving Cream; *Reform for Men Aftershave Toners:* all; *Reform for Men Colognes:* all

BODYLINEø§$\pi\Omega$fcd84

Men's Hydro-Gel Aftershave Balm

CAMILLA HEPPERøπ

Skin Demands for Men: Aftershave Balm, Birch Shaving Cream, Panther Aftershave

CARIADø$\pi\Omega$

Shaving Oil: Alternative, Original

CO-OP$\pi\Omega\Delta$fcd85

Mankind Shaving: Foam, Moisturising Gel, Sensitive Gel

DESERT ESSENCEøΩfcd

Aroma Essence Shaving Oil

DOLMA√ø™§πΩfcd76

Unisex Wet Shaving Fluid; *For Men:* De-Luxe Aftershave Balm, Sandalwood & Orange Skin Protector, Sirius Aftershave/Cologne

DROYT√øπΩfcd84

Glycerine Shaving Soap

HEMP UNIONø™§πΩfcd93

Hemp Oil Shaving Oil

MARTHA HILLøπΩ

David Hill Skin Care for Men: Aftershave Gel, Daytime Moisturiser & Skin Shield, Shaving & Cleansing Gel, Shaving Cream

MEADOWSWEETø™§πΩΔ86

Aloe Vera Aftershave Skin Gel, Pre Wet Shave Moisturising Cream; *Aftershave Balm:* Aroman, Boston, Cologne, Evening Primrose, Jaztec, Sandalwood

MICHELINE ARCIERøΩfcd

Sirius Face Oil for Gentlemen

NEAL'S YARD REMEDIESø

Aromatic Aftershave; *Shaving:* Lavender & Vitamin E Soap, Oil

NEW SEASONS√øπΩfcd76

Neutral Aftershave Gel Base

NOIRøΩΔfcd87

Aftershave: Soothing Balm, Splash, Spray

NORFOLK LAVENDERΩfcd84

Shaving Products: all

SAINSBURY'SΩfcd88

Regular Shaving Gel; *Reflex Shaving:* Foam, Foam for Sensitive Skin, Gel for Sensitive Skin, Regular Gel; *Shave Foam:* Lemon & Lime, Regular Economy

SUPERDRUGΩfcd87

Men's: Aromatherapy Cooling Aftershave 'BRRR!', Aromatherapy Soothing Shaving Oil 'OOH!', Clear Water Aftershave, Clear Water Pre-Shave Cologne, Fragrance Free Aftershave, Fragrance Free Basic Pre-Shave Cologne; *Skin Fitness:* Aftershave, Pre-Shave Facial Wash, PST Shaving Balm

WAITROSE

Sensitive Skin: Shave Foam, Shave Gel

WELEDAøπΩfcd85

Men's Range: Eau de Cologne, Shaving Lotion

YIN YANG BEAUTY CARE√øπΩfcd72/81

Shaving Cream

SKIN CARE

ABSOLUTE AROMAS√øπΩ

Thermal: Body Pack, Facial Mask

ALADDIN AROMASøπΩfcd87

Cocoa Butter, Emulsifying Wax, Glycerin, Shea Butter, Skin Toner, Witch Hazel; *Cream:* Aqueous, Carrot, Comfrey, Jojoba, Moisturising, Nourishing, Vitamin E; *Face:* Mask, Seaweed Mask, Scrub; *Gel:* Aloe Vera, Body; *Green Clay:* Cotton Plasters for Body Wraps,

toiletries & cosmetics

Fine Powder, Rough Broken; *Lotion:* Cleansing, White; *Natural Floral Water:* Chamomile, Elder Flower, Jasmine, Lavender, Orange Flower, Peppermint, Rose, Rosemary, Tea Tree, Verbena; *Oil:* Anti-Wrinkle Face & Body, Dry Face, Emulsifying, Normal Face, Oily Face

AMBER ESSENCE√ø𝜋Ω𝑓cd84

Stimulating Massage Lotion; *Cream:* Cleansing Face, Moisturising

ANIMAL AID√ø§𝜋Ω∆𝑓cd76

Apricot & Jojoba Moisturising Cream, Exotic Body Lotion

AUSTRIAN MOOR√ø§𝜋Ω∆

Moor Life: Body Cream, Body Lotion, Body Oil, Body Pack, Cleansing/Toning Lotion, Day Cream/Moisturiser, Face Mask, Skin/Face Cream

BEAUTY THROUGH HERBS√ø𝜋Ω∆87

Cream: Galeno Integra Plus Moisture Infusion, Moisturising Massage Base; *Galeno Marine:* Cleanser, Intensive Nourishing Cream, Nourishing Cream, Sea Freshener

BIO-D√ø™𝜋Ω∆83

Comfrey Cream; *Borage Oil:* Cleanser, Cream; *Hemp Oil:* Body Lotion, Cleanser

---

DOLMA

Vegan Perfumes, Toiletries, Skin Care & Aqueous Aromatics

Dolma offer an exclusive range of high quality original vegan perfumes, skin care & toiletries based on pure essential oils, herbal extracts, floral waters and vegetable oils. All products are carefully blended from safe, long established vegan ingredients and a fixed cut-off date of 1976 applies.

The range includes perfumes, aromatic shampoos for the body, hair, face and feet, lip salves, cleansers, toners, moisturisers, facial scrubs and masks, aromatherapy facial and massage oils, eye make-up removers, eye cream and gel, body lotions, talc, antiseptic cream, hair conditioners, deodorants, shaving fluid, aftershave balm and cologne, hand creams, pure essential oils and soaps etc.

Send S.A.E. for free mail order catalogue or £14.95 for a boxed set of ten trial size perfumes. Cheques/postal orders to be made payable to DOLMA.
DOLMA, 19 ROYCE AVENUE, HUCKNALL, NOTTINGHAM. NG15 6FU
WEBSITE: www.veganvillage.co.uk/dolma

All perfumes include a large proportion of natural essential oils with quality perfumery synthetics and ethyl alcohol.

A member of The Cosmetics Industry Coalition For Animal Welfare

BODY REFORM√ø§πΩfcd85

Pure Herbal Roll-On Wrinkle Care, Rosemary Cleanser, Tea Tree Facial Freshener, Unfragranced Massage Lotion, White Musk Body Scrub; *Body Contouring:* Gel, Treatment Pack; *Cream:* Aloe Vera Day, Anti-Wrinkle, Avocado Night Nourishing, Body Sculpture Thigh, Neck Smoothing Complex, Peppermint Day, Relaxing Moisture, St John's Wort Day, Tea Tree Treatment, Wheatgerm Night, White Musk Body; *Face Mask:* Arnica, Peppermint; *Facial Scrub:* Apricot, Reform for Men Walnut; *Moisturiser:* Reform for Men Facial, White Musk; *Skin Care Packs:* Anti-Ageing Treatment, Contouring Treatment, Dry/Sensitive Skin, Normal/Combination Skin, Oily Skin; *Skin Friendly:* Body Lotion, Cleanser, Facial Moisturising Cream, Toner; *Toning Lotion:* Chamomile, Orange Blossom, Peppermint

BODYLINEø§πΩfcd84

Aqua Cleanser Make-Up Remover, Elizabethan Skin Tonic, Foaming Face Scrub, Fragrance Free Toner, Million Year Old Mud Body Mask, Nutritional Neck Cream, Soap Free Facial Wash, Tea Tree Cleansing Gel, Ultra Dry Skin Wash, Vitamin Skin Replenisher, Watermelon Facial Spray, White Grape & Pumpkin Body Soufflé; *Aloe Vera:* Moisture Lotion, Moisturising Gel; *Body Lotion:* Dewberry, Freesia, Fresh As A Daisy, Grapefruit & Lemon, Lilac, Magnolia, Musk, Peach & Apricot, Rose, Sheer Water, Vanilla; *Body Scrub:* Chocolate, Orange; *Cleanser:* Camomile, Carrot Oil, Cucumber, Fragrance Free, Glorious Melting; *Face Pack:* Cucumber Cleansing, Mango & Honeydew Melon, Moisturising, Strawberry Cleansing; *Flower Water:* Elderflower, Orange; *Hooked On Classics:* Great Expectations, Midsummer Night Cream, Sense & Sensitivity 2 Phase Cream; *Moisture Cream:* Glycerine & Rosewater Rehydrating, Jojoba & Camomile Hydrating, Simply Pure; *Moisturiser:* Avocado & Bergamot, Butternut, Shampagne & Strawberries 2 Phase; *Vitamin E Cream:* Day, Night

CACHETøΩΔ87

Moisturising Body Lotion

CAMILLA HEPPERøπΩfcd86

Cleanser: Azufre, T-Zone Foaming; *Cleansing:* Camilla's Cream, Lemon Balm Milk, Marsa-Med Bar, Meadowsweet Milk; *Cream:* Avocado Moisture, Azufre, Evening Primrose Night, Facial Wash, Herbal, Regenerative, T-Zone Moisturising Control, Wheatgerm & Marigold Moisture; *Facial Toner:* Azufre Lotion, Orange Flower Water, Rose Flower Water, T-Zone Balancing Freshener; *Facial Treatment:* Exfoliating Tropical Skin Polisher, Herbal Clay Mask, Mint & Olive Stone Scrub, Oatmeal & Almond Oil Mask; *Skin Demands for Men:* Face Protection, Face Wash, Mint & Olive Stone Scrub; *Skin Toner:* Elderflower, Yarrow

CARABAY√øπΩ

Seaweed Face Mask

CARE FOR LIFE√ø™πΩfcd76

Facial Moisture Lotion, Gentle Cleanser, Gentle Toner

CARIADøπΩ

Body Lotion; *Cream:* Chamomile, Rose, Sandalwood; *Gel:* Lavender, Muscle Rub, Rose Face, Tea Tree, Vitamin E Body; *Flower Water:* Lavender, Orange, Rose

CHRISTYøΩΔ87

Facemask Sachet: Cucumber, Galia Melon & Poppy, Jasmine & Evening Primrose, Lime & Coriander, Sea Clay, Tea Tree, Ylang Ylang & Orange Blossom; *Facemask Tube:* Cucumber, Lime & Coriander, Sea Clay, Tea Tree; *Facial Express 4 in 1 Mousse:* Jojoba & Waterlily, Mimosa & Rosehip, Starfruit & Honeysuckle, Tea Tree & Lemongrass

CONSCIENCE COSMETICS√ø§πΩΔ86

Cleanser: Cucumber & Fennel Foaming, Elderflower Soapless; *Cleansing Milk:* Creamy Apricot, Pure & Light; *Mask:* Apple Blossom Refreshing, Cool Avocado & Cucumber, Fruity Tropical; *Moisturiser:* All Over, Caring Nighttime, Carrot Oil Cream, Evening Primrose Rich Cream, Gentle Daily, Melon & Carrot Special Day Cream, Melon & Jojoba Cream; *Scrub:* Creamy Exfoliating Wash, Creamy Passionfruit Scrub, Cucumber Toning Cream, Oatmeal; *Skin Freshener:* Avocado & Cucumber, Elderflower, Orange Flower, Rosemary Tonic, Tonic

CO-OPπΩΔfcd85

Excellence Skin Cleansing Lotion; *Facial Wash:* Excellence Skin, Exfoliating, Skin, Pineapple & Oatmeal; *Peach & Apricot:* Cleanser, Facial Scrub, Facial Wash

DE VEREø

Aloe Vera: Gel, Rich Skin Cream

DEB§πΩfcd90

Industrial Protective Cream: Protect, Proteks After Work, Proteks Dry, Proteks Wet, Restore, Swarfega Protect, Swarfega Restore

DESERT ESSENCEøΩfcd

Daily Essential Moisturiser, **Moist Towelettes, Natural Cleansing Pads & Tea Tree Oil, Thoroughly Clean Face Wash;** *Body Wash:* **Body Rain, Moisture Management**

DOLMA√ø™§πΩfcd76

Aloe Vera Hand & Body Lotion, Ho-Leaf & Orange Moisturising Body Wash; *Body Lotion:* Aloe Vera, Niamh Deluxe; *Cleanser:* Carrot Oil Cream, Fragrance Free Lotion, Lavender & Camomile, Oil Free; *Facial Wash:* Almond & Orange Scrub, Aromatic Shampoo, Camomile & Mint Wash, Rosemary & Seaweed Mask; *Moisturising Cream:* Avocado & Ylang Ylang, Carotene, Carotene Fragrance Free, Evening Primrose & Marigold, Geranium & Evening Primrose Night, Ho-Leaf & Orange, Wheatgerm & Lavender; *Toner:* Astringent, Gentle, Freshening, Purifying

ESCENTIAL BOTANICALS√ø™πΩΔfcd76

Fruit Foaming Facial Cleanser; *Classic:* Body Lotion, Day Moisturiser, Gentle Facial Toner for Dry Skin, Gentle Facial Toner for Normal to Oily Skin, Night Replenishing Cream for Dry Skin, Night Replenishing Cream for Normal to Oily

Skin, Sensitive Skin Cleanser for Dry Skin, Sensitive Skin Cleanser for Normal to Oily Skin; *Exotic:* Body Lotion, Day Moisturiser for Dry Skin, Day Moisturiser for Normal to Oily Skin, Deep Cleansing Lotion for Dry Skin, Deep Cleansing Lotion for Normal to Oily Skin, Invigorating Body Tonic

ESSENTIAL OIL CO√øπΩfcd93

Base: Aloe & Seaweed Gel, Light Cream, Moisturising Lotion, Orange Blossom Flower Water, Rosewater, Tea Tree Gel, Vitamin E Cream, Witch Hazel

ESSENTIALLY OILSøπ

Cocoa Butter, Green Clay [powder], Lecithin [liquid], Pure Monoi, Shea Butter; *Gel Base:* Aloe Vera, Aqueous, Ormagel Seaweed; *Cream/Lotion Base:* Cleansing Lotion, Cream, Lotion, Moisturising Cream, Moisturising Lotion, Protein Cream; *Floral Water:* Chamomile, Cornflower, Eucalyptus, Fir Silver, Juniper, Lavender, Linden Blossom, Marigold, Melissa, Orange Blossom, Peppermint, Pine, Rose Otto, Sage, Thyme, Verbena, Witch Hazel

FAITH IN NATUREø

Skincare Travel Pack

FAITH PRODUCTSøπΩΔ88

Almond Scrub, Aloe Vera Moisturising Cream, Essential Facial Wash, Skin Care Travel Pack; *Lotion:* Jojoba Moisturising, Rosewater Toning, Seaweed Cleansing

FANTÔME√§πΩfcd78

Austrian Blue Glass: Anti-wrinkle Fragrance Free, Avocado & Vanilla Moisturiser, Calendula Fragrance Free Moisturiser, F14 Night Treatment Cream, Marigold & Lemon Verbena Face Cleanse, Orange & Hamamelis Face Tone; *Floral Water:* Hamamelis, Orange Flower, Rose Tripled Distilled; *Tea Tree:* Cream, Facial Wash

FARROW & HUMPHRIES√øΩfcd80

After Bath Body Creamer, Mini Body Cream

FELICIø

Exfoliating Gel; *Cream:* Cellulite, Facial Therapy

FLEUR AROMATHERAPYø™

Floral Waters: all

GR LANEøπΩΔfcd87

Tiki Marigold Cream; *Tiki Camomile:* Cleanser, Moisturiser, Toner; *Tiki Cucumber & Lime:* Cleanser, Moisturiser, Toner; *Tiki Witch Hazel:* Cleanser, Moisturiser, Toner

GREEN PEOPLEø™πΩ

Cleansing Milk, Facial Gel, Skin Tonic; *AHA Fruit Complex:* Cream, Lotion; *Body:* Lotion, Toning Lotion; *Cream:* Exfoliating Scrubbing, Mask, Multi Vitamin Day & Night; *Day Cream:* Dry, Normal/Sensitive, Oily

HAMBLEDEN HERBSøπΩfcd82

Vegetable Glycerine; *Flower Water:* Chamomile, Lavender, Rose

HEALTH IMPORTSsøπΩfcd95

Thursday Plantation Macadamia Face & Body Oil; *Thursday Plantation Tea Tree:* **Hand & Body Lotion, Herbal Skin Wash, Lotion, Skin Cleanse Blemish Gel, Skin Cleanse Daily Face Wash, Walkabout Lotion & Roll-On**

HEALTHY HERBSsøπΩfcd96

Creams: all; *Gels:* all; *Lotions:* all

HEMP UNIONø™§πΩfcd93

Hemp Oil: Body Lotion, Cleanser, Tea Tree Cream

HONESTY√ø§πΩΔ76

Essential: **Geranium & Ylang Ylang Moisturising Lotion, Lavender & Geranium Cleanser, Lavender & Geranium Toner, Lavender & Sandalwood Moisturising Cream;** *Fruit:* **Papaya Facial Wash, Peach & Vanilla Moisturising Lotion;** *Unscented:* **Cleansing Lotion** w **Chamomile, Cocoa Butter Moisturising Lotion, Moisturising Cream** w **Vitamin E, Rich Moisture Cream** w **Carrot & Jojoba, Toner** w **Chamomile**

HUMANE RESEARCH TRUST√ø§πΩfcd

Berwitz Natural Cosmetics Moisturiser

INNOXAøΩΔ87

Neck & Bust Firming Cream; *Definitive:* Moisturising Toning Lotion, Revitalising Cleansing Oil, Revitalising Moisture Fluid; *Sensitivity:* Creme Moisturiser, Gentle Cleansing Milk, Gentle Toner, Nourishing Creme

KOBASHI√ø™πΩΔ76

Floral Water: **Lavender, Neroli, Rose**

Otto; *Moisturisers:* all

LOGONA

Aloe & Green Tea Cleansing Milk; *Scrub:* Body, Facial

LOTHIAN HERBSøΔ91

Rose Floral Water, Unfragranced Moisturising Cream

LUSHøπΩ

Fresh Plant Life Body & Hand Dream Cream; *Ultra Fresh Fridge:* Athelbrose Mask for Dry Sensitive Skin, Enzynamite Face Cleanser, More Than Mortal Body Scrub, Staff of Life Facial Exfoliator & Mask, Strawberry & Ginger Posset, Wow Wow Face Mask; *Fresh Plant Life Cleanser:* Angels on Bare Skin, Draught of Immortality, Fresh Farmacy, Spring Cleanser, Queen of Hearts Complexion Soap; *Fresh Plant Life Moisturiser:* Imperialis, Skin Drink; *Fresh Plant Life Toner Water:* Angel, Eau Roma, Tea Tree

MARTHA HILLøπΩ

Enriched Moisture Cream, Mint Mud Mask; *Body:* Citrus Moisturising Wash, Enriched Moisturiser; *Body Oil:* Evening Primrose & Lavender, Orange; *Camomile:* Cleansing Gel, Moisture Milk; *Evening Primrose:* Body Lotion, Cleansing Lotion, Moisturiser, Toning Gel; *Herbal:* No 1 Cleansing & Conditioning Milk, No 2 Toning Gel, No 3 Day Cream; *Seaweed:* Body Toning Gel, Pack, Peeling Mask; *Skin Tonic:* Cucumber Camomile & Elderflower, Rosewater

MEADOW SWEET OILS√øπΩfcd92

Base: Body Lotion, Cleanser, Cream,

Face Mask, Toner, Moisturiser

MEADOWSWEETøᵀᴹ§πΩΔ86

Aloe Vera Skin Repair Gel, Wild Dewberry After Bath Moisturiser; *Cleansing Gel:* Cucumber & Fennel, Lime Blossom & Orange Flower; *Cleansing Milk:* Apricot, Orchid; *Cream:* Aloe Vera Day, Aloe Vera Night, Carrot Oil, Comfrey & Carrot Night, Comfrey & Jojoba Complex Repair, Comfrey & Vitamin E Moisturising, Cucumber Astringent, Elderflower Wash, Evening Primrose, Facial Blemish, Fragrance Free Day, Fragrance Free Night, Herbal Skin Soothing, Melon & Carrot Day, Melon & Jojoba Night, Oatmeal Scrub, Pineapple & Peach Wash, Vitamin E; *Face Mask:* Apple Blossom, Avocado & Cucumber, Comfrey & Marshmallow, Tropical; *Facial:* Comfrey & Oatmeal Wash, Freshening Spray; *Facial Scrub:* Comfrey & Clivers, Passion Fruit; *Lotion:* Aloe Vera Moisturising, Avocado & Cucumber Moisturising, Avocado & Cucumber Toning, Comfrey & Cocoa Butter, Comfrey & Yarrow Cleansing, Elderflower Toning, Evening Primrose Body, Fragrance Free Cleansing, Fragrance Free Moisturising, Fragrance Free Toning, Herbal Aromatic Soothing Body, Orange Flower Toning, Problem Skin, Rosemary Herbal Face

MICHELINE ARCIERøΩfcd

Eau de Rose Face Tonic

MILL CREEKπΩ

72% Aloe Vera Creme *w* Vitamin E, Aloe

Vera & PABA Moisturising Lotion

MONTAGNE JEUNESSEøπΩfcd78

Cleansing Milk, Dead Sea Mud Pac, Peach Body Moisturising Soufflé, Skin Toner, Vitamins A & E & C Cleansing Milk, Vitamins E & A Skin Toner; *Body Moisturiser:* Evening Primrose Oil Body, Pink Musk Cream, Vitamin, Vitamin Repairing; *Masque:* Apricot & Almond Oil Hot, Red Hot Earth Sauna, Strawberry Gel; *Skin Soothing Bar:* Lavender Oil, Vitamin E

NATRACAREø

Perfume-free Vegan Body Lotion

NEAL'S YARD REMEDIESø

Calendula Cleanser, Chamomile & Aloe Vera Body Lotion, Cocoa Butter; *Clay:* Green, Bentonite, Kaolin; *Cream:* Frankincense Nourishing, Jasmine Enriching, Vitamin E & Avocado Night; *Facial Oil:* Citrus Tonic, Rose; *Floral Water:* Lavender, Orange, Rose; *Skin Oil:* Exotic, Jasmine Nourishing, Soothing, Stimulating; *Water:* Chamomile Flower, Lavender, Rose

NELSONøπΩ

Rosewater Facial Spritz

NEW SEASONS√øπΩfcd76

Solubiliser, Vegetable Glycerine, Witch Hazel; *Flower Water:* Chamomile, Lavender, Orange Flower, Rosewater; *Neutral Base:* Cleanser, Facial & Body Scrub, Moisturising Cream, Moisturising Face & Body Gel, Moisturising Lotion

NORFOLK LAVENDERΩfcd84

Skin Care Products: all

PHYTO PRODUCTS√ø§πΩ

Water: Hamamelis, Triple Elderflower, Triple Orange Flower, Triple Rose

POTTER'S

Distilled Witch Hazel, Skin Clear Lotion

POWER HEALTHøπΩ

Arthur's Oil, Comfrey Arnica & Witch Hazel Lotion, **Pure Vegetable Glycerine**, Romany Rosewater Cooler Spray, **Rosewater**, Soothing Witch Hazel Cream; *Balm:* Arthur's w Boswellin Extract, Comfrey & Vitamin E, Comfrey Arnica & Witch Hazel, Double Comfrey, Evening Primrose, Extra Strong Garlic, Garlic w Lemon Oil, Marshmallow & Slippery Elm, Tea Tree; *Biocosmetics Gel:* Aloe Vera, Aloe Vera Galvanic, Aroma Contour Wrap, Rosewater, Soothing Witch Hazel; *Biocosmetics Starflower:* Body Lotion, Cream, Oil Blend, Scalp & Hair Oil; *Nature Knows Best:* Pure Vegetable Glycerine, Rosewater, Witch Hazel; *Nature Knows Best Apricot:* Body Lotion, Moisture Cream, Skin Cleanser, Toner; *Nature Knows Best Vitamin A:* Cleanser, Cream, Foaming Facial Wash; *Romany Cream:* Anti-Wrinkle, Lavender Essential Oil; *Vita Youth Aloe Vera:* Cleanser, Moisturiser, Skin Gel, Toner; *Vita Youth Tea Tree Oil:* Antiseptic Wipes, Foaming Skin Cleanser, Moisturiser; *Vita Youth Vitamin E:* Cleanser, Moisturiser w Rosewater, Moisturising Oil, Skin Conditioner

PURE PLANT√Ωfcd76

Aloe Vera: Deep Cleansing Lotion, Deep Moisture Lotion, Facial Scrub, Nourishing Cream, Toner; *Peaches & Cream:* Cleanser, Facial Scrub, Moisture Cream (Day), Nourishing Cream w Vitamin E, Toner

PURPLE FLAME AROMA.øπΩfcd80

Base: Aloe Vera Gel, Solubiliser

QUINESSENCE√øπΩ∆fcd84

Creams: all; *Massage Lotions:* all

SAINSBURY'SΩfcd88

Oil of Evening Primrose Rich Moisturising Cream; *Fragrance Free:* Cleansing Lotion, Facial Wash, Moisturising Lotion, Toner; *Moisturising Body:* Wash, Wash Starter Pack w Puff; *Skin Deep:* Cleansing & Toning Lotion, Cleansing Pads, Face Wash, Face Wash for Sensitive Skin

SCOTTISH HERB. SUPPLIES√ø™§πΩfcd89

Creams: all

SHIRLEY PRICE AROMA. øπΩfcd84

Rejuvenating Facial Treat, Starter Kit, White Carrier Lotion; *Essentia Skin Care 7 Day Action Pack:* Normal/Dry, Normal/Oily; *Young Essentials:* Cleansing Milk, Moisture Lotion, Nourishing Mask; *Young Essentials 7 Day Action Pack:* Normal/Dry, Normal/Oily; *Young Essentials Cream:* Cleansing, Moisture, Moisture Base, Skin Clarifying, Skin Balancing, Velvety Night; *Young Essentials Freshener:* Melissa, Rosemary

SUPERDRUGΩfcd87

Active Botanical Extracts Moisturising Complex Cream, Mud Mask, Purite Gentle Exfoliating Body Scrub, Rich Creme Cream Wash; *Active Botanics:* Cleansing Milk, Freshener, Light Moisture Lotion, Protecting Day Cream; *Aloe Vera:* Body Cream, Body Gel, Body Lotion, Cream, Enriched w Active Moisturisers, Moisturising; *Camomile:* 2 in 1 Cleanse & Tone, Cleanser, Face Mask, Freshener, Moisturising Cream, Moisturing Lotion, Three Min Facial Mask; *Cocoa Butter:* Body Cream, Cream, Enriched w Active Moisturisers; *Coconut:* Body Cream, Body Lotion, Oil Enriched w Active Moisturisers, Nut Oil Cream; *Evening Primrose Oil:* Body Scrub, Cleansing Lotion, Day Cream, Facial Skin Care Oil, Facial Wash, Moisturising Cream, Moisturising Lotion; *Face Mask:* Evening Primrose Oil, Secret Weapon Intensive Moisture, Secret Weapon Moisturising; *Facial Wash:* pH for Dry Skin, pH for Sensitive Skin; *Fragrance Free:* 2 in 1 Cleanse & Tone, Facial Mask, Cleansing Lotion, Face Mask, Freshener, Moisturing Cream, Moisturising Lotion; *Life Sense Body Lotion:* Go Wild, Passion, Spirit; *Natural Vitamin E:* Gentle Cleansing Lotion, Gentle Refreshing Toner, Moisture Cream, Moisturising Facial Wash; *Oil of Evening Primrose:* Cleansing Lotion, Moisturising Cream; *Optimum:* Cleansing Lotion, Foaming Facial Wash, Hydrating Toner, Moisturising Complex, Moisturising Lotion, Protective Daily Moisturising Cream, Skin Refining Treatment, Wrinkle Control Cream; *Secret Weapon Body Lotion:* Energy, Purity, Temptation; *Secret Weapon Body Scrub:* Desire, Energy,

Purity, Temptation; *Secret Weapon Cream Swirl Skin Quencher:* Desire, Energy, Purity, Temptation; *Sensitive:* Dry Skin Cream, Dry Skin Lotion; *Skin Complex:* Smoothing, Softening, Soothing; *Skin Fitness:* Exfoliating Facial Wash, Facial Protein; *Tropical Body Scrub:* Blueberry, Dewberry; *Tropical Pick & Mix Body Lotion:* Blueberry, Cool Coconut, Dewberry, Melon, Passion Fruit, Vanilla; *Tropicals:* Blueberry Body Lotion, Blueberry Body Scrub; *Vitamin E:* Body Gel, Body Scrub, Cleansing Lotion, Day Cream, Facial Mask, Moisturising Lotion, Soothing Freshener

VINDOTCO√ø™§πΩfcd75

Skin Reconditioning Cream

WELEDAøπΩfcd85

Specialist Skin Care Akneadoron Lotion, Wild Rose Body Oil; *Almond Skin Care:* Cleansing Lotion, Facial Masque, Facial Oil; *Iris Skin Care:* Facial Masque, Facial Toner, Intensive Treatment Masque

WORLDS END TRADING√ø§πΩfcd

Vicco Turmeric Skin Cream

XVø§πΩ

Hemp: Body Lotion, Cleanser

XYNERGYøπΩ

Aloe Vera: Facial Cleanser, Gel *w* Vitamin E, Lotion

YIN YANG BEAUTY CARE√øπΩfcd72/81

Cleansing Wash, Precious Earth Face Mask; *Cream:* **Organic Aloe, Wild Yam;** *Four Herb:* **Cream, Lotion;** *Moisturiser:* **Natural, pH Amino Gold Body;** *pH Amino Protein Treatment Cream:* **1 (puberty), 2 (pregnancy), 3 (menopause), 4 (after menopause);** *Skin:* **Cleanser, Orange Water Tonic;** *Skin Conditioner Cream:* **Botanical Protein, Provit-En, Rich Protein, Yin Yang;** *Skin Power Cream:* **CHL, MSM, SBG, ZSB6**

YOUR BODY√ø™πΩΔ

Aloe Vera: **Body Lotion, Cleansing Milk, Facial Scrub, Facial Wash, Moisture Cream, Night Cream, Toner;** *Tea Tree:* **Antibacterial Lotion, Skin Wash;** *Vitamin E:* **Body Lotion, Cleansing Milk, Facial Scrub, Facial Wash, Moisture Cream, Night Cream, Toner**

SKIN MAKE UP

BEAUTY THROUGH HERBS√øπΩΔ87

Galeno Foundation

BEAUTY WITHOUT CRUELTY√øπΩfcd76

Blusher: Cranberry, Hot Chestnut, Rosetta, Sugar Almond, Sun Gold, Tawny Whisper; *Bronzing Powder:* Copper, Gold; *Concealer:* Fair, Medium; *Cream Make-Up:* Ash, Coffee, Cool, Honey, Sun; *Liquid Make-Up:* Almond, Damask, Golden, Ivory, Tawny; *Loose Face Powder:* Fair, Medium; *Pressed Face Powder:* Fair, Medium; *Tinted Moisturiser:* Fair, Medium

DESERT ESSENCEøΩfcd

Tea Tree Blemish Touch Stick

toiletries & cosmetics

INNOXAøΩΔ87

Complexion Mousse Untinted Foundation

MARTHA HILLøπΩ

Cream Rouge; *Cream Blusher:* Natural Blush, Natural Glow

MEADOW SWEET OILS√øπΩfcd92

Vegetable Based Cosmetics: all

POWER HEALTHøπΩ

Biocosmetics Soothing Concealer

SUPERDRUGΩfcd87

Secret Weapon Body Glitter Roll-On: Blue Green, Clear, Orange/Yellow, Pink/Lilac; *Secret Weapon Body Paint:* Aqua, Cloud 9, Envy, Henna Hue, Lady Marmalade, Perky, Pinky, Silver Lining; *Secret Weapon Glitter Pot:* Baby Belle, Electro Babe, Space Babe, Star Struck

SOAPS

21st CENTURY HEALTH√ø§πΩfcd

Dr Bronner's Peppermint Pure Castile

ASTONISH√øπΩfcd95

Hand

AUSTRIAN MOOR√ø§πΩΔ

Moor Life Soap/Cleansing Bar

BEAUTY THROUGH HERBS√øπΩΔ87

Vegetable: all

BIO-D√ø™πΩΔ83

Hemp Bran, Hemp Oil; *Aromatherapy Hand Made:* Cinnamon Scrub, Citrus Burst, Good Morning, Good Night, Shower Splash, Special Occasion; *Complexion:* Aloe Vera, Avocado & Cucumber, Coconut Palm, Oatmeal Scrub, Tea Tree; *Floaty Balls:* Amorous Apple, Cheeky Chocolate, Gorgeous Grapefruit, Luscious Lime, Luxurious Lavender, Marvellous Marzipan, Racy Raspberry, Sexy Sandalwood; *Fragranced Hemp Oil:* Avocado & Cucumber, Lemongrass, Sandalwood, Sweet Orange, Tea Tree, Wild Raspberry; *Fragrant:* Anise, Golden Grapefruit, Saffron & Almond, Violet; *Just for Fun:* Dandelion & Blackcurrant, Sea Kelp, Vanilla & Ginger, Wild Raspberry; *Traditional Hand Made:* Camomile Lime, Elderflower & Apple, English Lavender, Rose Petal, Sandalwood, Victoria Macassar

BODYLINEø§πΩfcd84

Slice: Citrus Sensation, Musk, Red Hot Poker, Tutti Frutti

CALDER VALLEY√ø™πΩΔ96

Almond Blossom, Aloe Vera, Anise, Avocado & Cucumber, Camomile & Lime, Coco Palm, Dewberry, Eastern Orange, Elderflower & Apple, English Lavender, Grapefruit, Lavender, Lemongrass, Lime, Oatmeal Scrub, Orchard Apple, Peppermint & Poppyseed, Rose Petal, Saffron & Almond, Sandalwood, Sea Kelp, Tea Tree, Toasted Oatbran, Vanilla, Vanilla & Ginger, Violet, Wild Raspberry

toiletries & cosmetics

CAMILLA HEPPERøπΩ**fcd86**

Avocado Oil, Coconut Oil, Grapefruit, Orange Blossom, Vitamin E

CO-OPπΩ∆**fcd85**

Oatmeal

DE VEREø

Aloe Vera Luxury

DEB§πΩ**fcd90**

Industrial Soaps & Washing Lotions: Cradle Skin Sanitiser, Florafree, Green, Heiress, Peach, Pure, Salute, Sceptre, Swarfega Pure, Verve

DESERT ESSENCEøΩ**fcd**

Tea Tree Oil Liquid Castile; *Bar:* **Lavender, Tea Tree Therapy**

DOLMA√ø™§πΩ**fcd76**

Caurie: **Geranium Essential Oil, Original & Mandarin Wholesoaps, Tea Tree Essential, Vitamin E;** *Faith:* **Lavender, Rosemary**

DROYT√øπΩ**fcd84**

Glycerine: **Craft Collection, Cube, Gift Basket Assorted, Lavender, Raffia Tie, Ribbon Tie, Rose, Special, Three Pack, Unperfumed, Vegetas;** *Glycerine Bath:* **Avocado Green, Blue Citrus Woods, Blue Mint, Fresh Green, Fudge, Green Grass, Herb Green, Lavender, Lemon Yellow, Mandarin Orange, Peach, Red Rose, Unperfumed, Yellow Eau de Cologne;** *Glycerine Fruit:* **Apple, Lemon, Peach, Strawberry**

ESSENTIAL OIL CO√øπΩ**fcd93**

Liquid Base

ESSENTIALLY OILSøπ

Flakes, Kanuka & Manuka, Liquid Base, Monoi, Monoi Noodles, Surfactant

FAITH IN NATUREø

Aloe Vera & Ylang Ylang, Essential Gift Set, Hemp & Lemongrass, Lavender & Geranium, Tea Tree

FAITH PRODUCTSøπΩ∆**88**

Pure Vegetable: Aloe Vera & Ylang Ylang, Essential Gift, Hemp *w* Lemongrass & Green Tea, Lavender, Orange, Pine, Rosemary, Seaweed, Tea Tree

FANTÔME√§πΩ**fcd78**

Tea Tree

FARROW & HUMPHRIES√øΩ**fcd80**

Liquid Elderflower & Primrose, Mini Gift/Accessory; *Bath [individual, boxed]:* Chamomile & Clover, Elderflower & Primrose, Fresh Lavender, Rose & Cornflower; *Celtic:* Frieze Yellow, Ingot Pink, Oval Blue, Square Green; *Chunky:* Fruit Juice, Grapefruit, Lavender, Lime, Ocean Wave, Rosie, Spice, Spring Blossom; *Chunky Whole Leaves:* Fruit Juice, Grapefruit, Lavender, Lime, Ocean Wave, Rosie, Spice, Spring Blossom; *Essential Oil:* Bergamot, Lavender, Mandarin, Tea Tree; *Friend:* Fame at Last, Green Tree, Heart to Heart, Movie Star; *God/desses [clear]:* Easter Islander, Sun Gold, Venus of Willendorf; *Kaleido Individual Slice:* Forest Tree, Kaleido, Love Heart, Midnight Blue, Minty Chocolate, Ocean Wave, Pineapple & Coconut, Plum & Spice; *Kaleido Wedge:* Grapefruit & Lime, Lavender, Rhubarb & Custard; *Kaleido Whole Flans:* Grapefruit &

Lime, Lavender, Rhubarb & Custard; *Kaleido Whole Leaves:* Forest Tree, Kaleido, Love Heart, Midnight Blue, Minty Chocolate, Ocean Wave, Pineapple & Coconut, Plum & Spice; *Petroglyph:* Eagle, Elk, Lizard, Monkey; *Waterworld:* Finny Fish Blue, Finny Fish Orange, Purple Turtle, Ribbit Frog

FLEUR AROMATHERAPYø™

Soap

GEORGE SKOULIAKSπΩ**fcd**

Oliva Olive Oil

HEALTH IMPORTSøπΩ**fcd95**

Thursday Plantation Tea Tree Vegetable

HEMP UNIONø™§πΩ**fcd93**

Hemp Oil: Exfoliating, Original

HONESTY√ø§πΩ△**76**

Caurnie: Cucumber, Lavender, Mandarine, Original Unscented, Rose, Vitamin E

HUMANE RESEARCH TRUST√ø§πΩ**fcd**

Treatment Bar: Calendula, Tea Tree

J&E IMPORTS√øπΩ**fcd**

The Touch Collection Olive Oil: Aloe Vera, Chamomile, Herbs, Lavender, Pure

KOBASHI√ø™πΩ△**76**

Liquid: Fragrance Free Base, Tea Tree & Lemon

LOTHIAN HERBSø△**91**

Aromatherapy: Cypress & Cedarwood, Grapefruit & Palmarosa, Lavender,

Patchouli, Rosemary, Tea Tree

LUSHøπΩ

Alkmaar, Beautiful P Green, Bohemian, Figs & Leaves, Flotsam, No 1 Seed, Pineapple Grunt, Quinquireme of Ninevah, Red Rice, Red Rooster, Sea Vegetable, Truly Madly Veggie; *Fragrance:* Flower Market, Icon, Karma

MARTHA HILLøπΩ

Lavender Bath & Shower Liquid; *Hand Made:* Essence of Rose, Evening Primrose, Lavender, Mountain Herb, Rosemary

MAXIM MARKETING√ø™§πΩ△**95**

Amber Beauty

MEADOW SWEET OILS√øπΩ**fcd92**

Liquid Base

MEADOWSWEETø™§πΩ△**86**

Assorted Fruit Shaped, Fragrance Free Liquid; *Aromatherapy:* Bergamot & Orange, English Lavender, Grapefruit & Juniper, Neroli & Lemon Grass, Tea Tree *w* Eucalyptus, Ylang Ylang; *Complexion:* Dry Skin, Mature Skin, Normal Skin, Oily Skin, Rejuvenaid Scrub Bar; *Fragrance:* Banana & Vanilla, Coconut Ice, Mango & Apricot, Pine Forest Vapours, Rose & Cinnamon, Wild Dewberry

MONTAGNE JEUNESSEøπΩ**fcd78**

Evening Primrose Oil Nourishing, Peach Oil Nourishing, Seaweed & Mineral Moisturising, Strawberries & Cream Conditioning, Tuscany Apple Moisturising

toiletries & cosmetics

NEAL'S YARD REMEDIESø

3 In A Box, Aloe Vera & Oatmeal, Calendula & Evening Primrose, Geranium & Orange, Geranium & Sweet Almond Oil, Lavender, Lavender & Olive Oil, Lavender & Tea Tree, Lemon & Coriander, Lime & Green Clay, Marseille Block, Rose, Rosemary, Sandalwood & Coriander, Seaweed

NORFOLK LAVENDERΩfcd84

All

SAVONNERIE MARIUS FABRE√Ω

Le Coq Hardi: **Bitter Almond, Lavender, Marseille Copfra/Palm Oil, Marseille Olive Oil, Peach, Sandalwood, Vanilla, Verbena, Wild Rose**

SOAP TUBøπΩ

Alpine Breeze, Best Of The Zest, Breath Of Fresh Air, Chamomile Lawn, Cool As A Cucumber, Dash Of Pash, Frankincense, Green Apple Tub, In Ya Face, Lavender Fields, Lemongrass, Strawberry, Summer Bouquet, Tea Tree, The Dizzyac, Turkish Delight, Zing

SODASAN

Chamomile, Meadow Blossom, Nordic Grass

SUMA™§πΩ

Citrus: all; *Complexion:* all; *Old English:* all; *New World:* all — **except** Australian honey; *Spice:* all

VEGAN SOCIETY√ø§Ω

Fragrant Soap: **Aloe Vera, Apple Blossom, Avocado & Cucumber, Camomile** & Lime, Cocopalm, English Lavender, Golden Grapefruit, Oatmeal Scrub, Rose Petal, Sea Kelp, Tea Tree, Vanilla & Ginger

WELEDAøπΩfcd85

Rosemary

WORLDS END TRADING√ø§πΩfcd

Chandrika Ayurvedic, Mysore Sandalwood

XVø§πΩ

Connemara; *Aromatherapy:* **Cinnamon Scrub, Citrus Burst, Good Morning, Goodnight, Shower Splash, Special Occasion;** *French:* **Lavender & Olive Oil, Lemon & Almond, Olive Oil Block;** *Hemp:* **Avocado, Lemon Grass, Sandalwood, Sweet Orange, Tea Tree, Wild Raspberry**

YOUR BODY√ø™πΩ∆

Aloe Vera, Chamomile, Cinnamon, Mint, Vitamin E, Watermelon, White Jasmine

SUN CARE

AMBER ESSENCE√øπΩfcd84

After Sun Lotion

ANIMAL AID√ø§πΩ∆fcd76

Honesty Sun-tan Lotion High Protection SP15

BODY REFORM√ø§πΩfcd85

Reform Sun Protection: After Sun Moisturising, SPF2 Burns Minimally, SPF2

Tans Easily, SPF6 Burns Moderately, SPF25 Total Protection

CAMILLA HEPPERøπΩfcd86

Tropical: After Sun Soother, Coconut Sun-tan Oil, Sun-tan Lotion Factor 10, Sun-tan Oil Factor 8, Tanning Butter Factor 6

CO-OPπΩΔfcd85

After Sun Lotion; *Suncare Lotion Factor:* 4, 8, 15, 35

CULPEPERøπΩ

Sun Oils (after sun): all

DE VEREø

Aloe Vera Moisturiser & After Sun

DESERT ESSENCEøΩfcd

Desert Sun Tanning Lotion

GREEN PEOPLEø™πΩ

Water Lily After Sun; *Edelweiss Sun Lotion SPF: 8, 15, 22*

HONESTY√ø§πΩΔ76

Sun Preparation: **Aftersun, Holiday Pack, Moisturising Lotion** *w* **UVB Filter SPF 4, Sun & Sport Shower Gel, Sun Lotion High Protection SPF 15, Sun Lotion Medium Protection SPF8**

MARTHA HILLøπΩ

Sun Protection Lotion Medium Protection

MEADOWSWEETø™§πΩΔ86

Totally Tropical Sun Screen Lip Balm

MICHELINE ARCIERøΩfcd

Helios Sun Oil

NEAL'S YARD REMEDIESø

Chamomile & Aloe Vera After Sun Lotion, Lavender Sun Block, Lemongrass Sun Lotion

NEW SEASONS√øπΩfcd7

Neutral After Sun Gel Base

POWER HEALTHøπΩ

Romany: After Sun Lotion, Coconut Suntan Oil

TALCUM POWDERS

ANIMAL AID√ø§πΩΔfcd76

Fragrant

BODYLINEø§πΩfcd84

Dewberry, Men's

CACHETøΩΔ87

Talc

CAMILLA HEPPERøπΩfcd86

Avocado, Orange Blossom, White Musk

CO-OPπΩΔfcd85

Wild Herb

CULPEPERøπΩ

All

DESERT ESSENCEøΩfcd

Talc Free Body Powder

DOLMA√ø™§πΩfcd76

Orange Blossom

FARROW & HUMPHRIES LTD√øΩfcd80

Chamomile & Clover, Elderflower & Primrose, Fresh Lavender, Rose & Cornflower

HUMANE RESEARCH TRUST√ø§πΩfcd

Berwitz Calendula

LUSHøπΩ

Dusting Powder: Allelujah!, Dust to Dust, Silky Underwear, T for Toes, The Ologist; *Fragrance Powder:* Flower Market, Icon, Karma

MARTHA HILLøπΩ

Body, Lavender

NEAL'S YARD REMEDIESø

Calendula, Geranium & Orange

NOIRøΩΔ87

Les Essentiels

NORFOLK LAVENDERΩfcd84

All

PURE PLANT PRODUCTS√Ωfcd76

Peaches & Cream

SUPERDRUGΩfcd87

Benefit: Family, Medicated, Sports

TOOTHPASTES & ORAL HYGIENE

AUSTRIAN MOOR√ø§πΩΔ

Moor Life: Mouthwash, Toothpaste

BIOFORCE

Echinacea Toothpaste; *Dentaforce:* Mouthspray, Mouthwash, Toothpaste

CAMILLA HEPPERøπΩfcd86

Natural Spearmint Mouthwash

CO-OPπΩΔfcd85

Denture Powder, Mildmint Mouthwash, Pearlette Denture Powder; *Extra Strong Mouthwash:* Coolmint, Original; *Toothpaste:* Fluoride Free, Freshmint, Freshmint Pump, Mildmint, Mildmint Pump, Sensitive, Ultra Care

DESERT ESSENCEøΩfcd

Tea Tree Dental Pics, Tea Tree Oil Mouthwash; *Tea Tree Toothpaste:* **Fennel, Ginger, Mint, Neem**

FSCπ

Herbcraft Fresh Breath Cinnamint Spray

GREEN PEOPLEø™πΩ

Mouthwash: **Citrus, Fennel, Mandarin, Mint;** *Toothpaste:* **Citrus, Mint**

HEALTH IMPORTSπΩfcd95

Thursday Plantation Tea Tree: **Mouthwash, Toothpaste**

HOLLYTREESø

Mouthwash: Fennel, Sage & Calendula; *Toothpaste:* Fennel, Lemon, Orange

HONESTY√ø§πΩΔ76

Vicco Herbal Toothpaste

KINGFISHER NATURAL√√πΩfcd88

Toothpaste: Baking Soda, Fennel, Fennel Fluoride Free, Mint *w* Lemon, Mint *w* Lemon Fluoride Free

MAXIM MARKETING√ø™§πΩΔ95

Amber Toothpaste

MITOKUø

Dentie: Toothpaste, Toothpowder

NEAL'S YARD REMEDIESø

Lemon & Mint Mouth Freshener; *Toothpastes:* all

NELSONøπΩ

Unflavoured Toothpaste

SAINSBURY'SΩfcd88

Breath Fresheners, Dental Tape, Denture Cleansing Tablets, Fresh Breath Spray

TOM'S OF MAINE

Silly Strawberry Toothpaste For Children

WAITROSE

Toothpaste: Freshmint, Total

WELEDAøπΩfcd85

Children's Tooth Gel; *Toothpaste:* Calendula, Plant Gel, Ratannia, Salt

WORLDS END TRADING√ø§πΩfcd

Vicco Ayurvedic: Toothpaste, Toothpowder

notes

- **Body Shop** Some products contain beeswax, honey, lanolin, milk, whey protein, gelatine, fish derivatives or the following animal-derived ingredients: PEG 120 Methyl Glucose Dioleate, PPG 20 Methyl Glucose Ether, PEG Oleyl Alcohol. Brushes may be made of hog, pony or goat hair *(see also **MULTIPLE OUTLET QUICK REFERENCE GUIDE**, page ii)*.

- **Care for Life** MD states that they have evidence from suppliers that all stocks are GM free, but believe that no company can honestly claim this if their supplies come from an international source (as hers do) unless they have visited the original sources. **Ecover** states the same.

- **contact lenses** Classed as a medicine under the Medicines Act, all contact lens solutions and associated products have been safety-tested (which invariably entails animal testing at some point). Such products are listed in the *Vegan Shopper only* if the company under whose name they are sold meets the Shopper's 'animal testing' criterion *(see **ANIMAL-FREE CRITERIA**, page 226)*.

- **dental products** Little research has been conducted in this area, however, it is known that glycerin *(possibly animal-derived)* is used extensively — especially in the manufacture of mouthwashes and toothpastes. Floss may contain beeswax or propolis.

- **Safeway** The only animal derived products in their personal care section are beeswax (cera alba) and milk derivatives (casein or caseinates). If these are in a product they will be listed on the packaging.

health care

contraceptives & lubricants   170
food supplements   170
insect repellents   172
remedies   172
vitamins & minerals   177

notes   *181*

CONTRACEPTIVES & LUBRICANTS

CONDOMIø™

Condomis Condoms: Extra Large, Family Planning Clinic Packs, Fruit, Mix, Nature, Noppy, Red Ribbon, Strong, Supersafe; *Mondos Condoms:* all

HARLOW LUBRICANTS√ø§πΩfcd94

Astroglide (personal lubricant & vaginal moisturiser)

VEGAN SOCIETY√ø§Ω

Animal-Free Condoms: Fruit (Chocolate, Banana, Strawberry), Nature (Silicone-lubricated), Supersafe (Spermicide-lubricated)

FOOD SUPPLEMENTS

AQUA SOURCEø™πΩ

Acidophilus & Algae [Vegicaps], Bifidus & Klamath Lake Algae [Vegicaps], Digestive Enzymes & Klamath Lake Algae [Vegicaps], Green Energy [Vegicaps], Klamath Lake Algae [liquid, powder, Vegicaps], Spirulina Pacifica, Start Easy Programme, Vanilla Lighten Up Meal Replacement; *Protein Shake:* Banana, Vanilla

AROVITEø§π

All One Powder Base: **Green Phyto, Rice**

AUSTRIAN MOOR√ø§πΩ∆

Moor Life Herbal Drink

BEST FOODS

Orange Dextro Energy Glucose Tablets Doubles; *Dextro Energy Glucose Tablets Singles:* Blackcurrant, Lemon, Orange, Original, Tropical

BIOCAREø

Banana Acidophilus, Bio-acidophilus, Boswellic Acid, EFAs, Lecithin Emulsion, Linseed Oil, Milk Thistle, Mycopryl 400, Phosphatidyl Serine, Phytosterol, Procydin, Resveratrol, Spectrumzyme; *Complex:* Artemisia, Butyric Acid, Isoflavone, Oregano; *Forte:* Eradicin, Ginkgo, Polyzyme; *Mega:* Dricelle GLA, EPA, GLA; *Plus:* CoQ10, Ginkgo, Quercetin

BLUE GREEN PLANETøπΩfcd95

Green Supermix, Hawaiian Spirulina, Japanese Chlorella, Upper Klamath Algae [tab, powder]

CARABAY√øπΩfcd

Kelp Powder, Dillisk

EVERETT HEALTHCAREø™

The Ultimate: Blue-Green, Defense, Florazyme, Meal

FSCπ

Icelandic Kelp Herbal Formula, Vegetarian Digestive Enzymes

FELICIø

Meno-Active, Phyto-Esterol

FOUR SEASONSøπΩ

Fibre Clean [tab], Pure Gar [tab], Quiet Time [tab], Uptime [tab] (new vegan version only), Wheat Grass [tab], Wheat Grass Juice [powder], Whole

Leaf Dissolving Wheat Grass Powder; *E-mer'gen-C Vitamin C Drink Mix:* Cranberry, Kola, MSM Lite, Original, Tangerine, Tropical

FRESENIUS KABI

Calsip; *Thick & Easy Instant Food:* Thickened Juices, Thickener

GR LANEøπΩΔfcd87

Brewer's Yeast Tablets, Inulin, Lecigran, Spirulina, Thompsons Slippery Elm Unmalted

GRANOVITAπ

Leci PLUS, Organic Golden Linseed; *Vitaslim (dairy free meal substitute):* Banana, Chocolate, Peach, Strawberry, Vanilla

GREEN PEOPLEø™πΩ

Herbal Elixir, X-tra Herbal Energy Drink

HERBALTRIM

Herbaltrim

NATURAL WOMANø

Quick Fibre Plus *w* Carob, Udo's Choice Oil

NATURE'S GOLDøπfcd95

Digestive Enzymes Plus Six [powder, Vegicaps], Klamath Lake Blue Green Algae [powder, tab, Vegicaps], Klamath Lake Blue Green Algae *w* EDS [Vegicaps], Klamath Lake Blue Green Algae *w* Organic Apple Juice, Lactobacillus Acidophilus Plus Seven [powder, Vegicaps], Premium Anti-Ox *w* EDS [powder, Vegicaps]

NATURE'S OWNø§π

Acidophilus Plus Powder, Brewer's Yeast, Kelp Plus, Linseed Oil, Linseeds, Psyllium Husks Powder, Rutin, Spirulina

NEAL'S YARD REMEDIESø

Spirulina; *Tablets:* Anti-Oxidant, Kelp

PHILLIPS NUTRITIONALSø

Joint Support

POWER HEALTHøπΩ

Alfalfa, Alfalfa Kelp & Yeast, **Davina Sports Nutrition Soya Protein Powder (Natural)**, Kelp; *GLA Supplements Liquid Cold Pressed Oil:* **Borage (Starflower) Oil**, **Evening Primrose**; *Herbal Supplement:* Bilberry, Cat's Claw, Echinacea, Kava Kava Root Powder, Olive Leaf, Valerian & Hop; *Lifestyle Supplement:* Bromelain & Papain, Power ACE Super Antioxidant, Pro-Amino Yeast; *Reevecrest Healthcare:* **Ginseng Red Roots**, Nutrimental Plus, Super Nutrimental Plus; *Supplement For Slimmers:* Citrin, Spirulina, Superlec Liquid (Soya Lecithin)

QUEST™π

Enzyme Digest, Glucosamine Sulphate, Lactase, Non Dairy Acidophilus Plus

ROMANDA HEALTHCAREø§πΩ

Food Supplement Formula: B-Calm, Hair, Powerhouse

SALUSø§πΩ

Siberian Ginseng Elixir

SEAGREENS™

Wild Seaweed Food Capsules

VEGA NUTRITIONALS™§πΩfcd96

Soya Lecithin Plus Starflower Oil (dry); *Probiotics & Digestive Aid:* **Acidophilus Plus Bifidus, Digestive Enzymes Formula, Psyllium Fibre;** *Special Care Formula:* **Brain Fuel, Cellulite, Energiser, PMS, Prostate (Saw Palmetto Complex), Slimming, Vegatonic Herbal;** *Specialised Supplement:* **Co-Enzyme Q10, Cran-Biotic Formula, Garlic (Deodorised High Potency), Multigluco-Tolerance Factors (Karella Complex)**

XYNERGYøπΩ

Spirolight Energy Bars, Spirulina [powder, tab, Vegicaps], Sweet Wheat Powder, Vita Synergy Tablets

INSECT REPELLENTS

ALADDIN AROMASøπΩfcd87

Aromas Blends Bug Off! Natural Midge Repellent

AMBER ESSENCE√øπΩfcd84

Insect Repellent

ESSENTIALLY OILSøπ

Buzz-Off Candle

KOBASHI√ø™πΩ∆76

Insect Repellent Moisturising Lotion

LOTHIAN HERBSø∆91

Aromatherapy Push Up Sticks Insect Repellent

MAROMA√πΩfcd85

Colibri Anti Moth: Candle, Essential Oils, Hanging Sachets for Wardrobes, Incense Sticks Indoors, Incense Sticks Outdoors, Sachets for Drawers, Terracotta Circles; *Colibri Natural Insect Repellent:* Body Lotion, Candle, Cone, Essential Oils, Incense Sticks

MEADOWSWEETø™§πΩ∆86

Pebble Pot Pourri Kitchen Cooks

NEW SEASONS√øπΩfcd76

Buzz Off Insect Repellent

REMEDIES

ALADDIN AROMASøπΩfcd87

Arnica Aqueous Extract, Tea Tree Pessaries; *Bath Oil:* **Aches & Pain, Colds & Flu**

AMBER ESSENCE√øπΩfcd84

Lotion: **for Muscle Pain, for Women**

BEAUTY THROUGH HERBS√øπΩ∆87

Galeno Classique: Aloe Vera, Avocado Oil, Echinacea Extract, Ginkgo Extract, Hawthorn Extract, Olive Oil, Shea Butter, Wheat Germ Oil

BIO-D√ø™πΩ∆83

Mycological Supplement: **Condyceps, Ganoderma**

BIOFORCE

Complex: Hypericum, Saw Palmetto, Valerian Hops; *Cream:* Comfrey, Echinacea; *Organic Fresh Herbal Tincture:*

Aesculus, Agnus Castus, Avena Sativa, Bilberry, Centaurium, Crataegus, Echinaforce, Eleutherococcus, Euphrasia, Ginkgo Biloba, Harpagophytum, Hypericum, Menosan, Milk Thistle, Urtica Dioica, Valerian

BIOPROGRESS TECHNOLOGY

Xgel Capsule Shell

BIZ NIZø

Head Lice Treatment: Conditioner, Shampoo Block

BODY REFORM√ø§πΩfcd85

Reform Sport Muscle: Balm, Soothing Lotion

CAMILLA HEPPERøπΩfcd86

Oil: Hair Loss Treatment, Muscular Massage, Tension; *Ointment:* Comfrey, Garlic, Leg & Vein, Marigold

CHIRALI OLD REMEDIES√ø§πΩ

Remedy Cream: 1 Muscle & Joint Soothing, 2 Dry Skin

DANIEL FIELD√øΩfcd76

Natural Head Lice Treatment & Prevention: 10 Day Super Louse Treatment Oil, Leave In Prevention Treatment Conditioner Spray, Weekly Lice Treatment Conditioner

DE VEREø

Aloe Vera: Juice w Red Grape, Natural Juice, Tablets

DESERT ESSENCEøΩ

Tea Tree: Anti-Microbial Cream, Athlete's Ointment, Relief Spray

DOLMA√ø™§πΩfcd76

Avasab Antiseptic Cream

EPHYTEM√π

10 day Organic De-Tox Programme, Frutex Laxative Bar; *Combination Herb Supplement [Microsphere]:* Age 50+, Bowel Care, Circulatory Care, Hair Skin and Nail Care, Healthy Heart, Joint Care, Men, Pre-Menstrual, Restful, Revitalising, Soothing, Summer Months, Uplifting, Winter Months, Women; *Single Herb Supplement [Microsphere]:* Agnus Castus, Devil's Claw, Echinacea, Feverfew, Ginkgo Biloba, Ginseng, Guarana, Kava Kava

ERNEST JACKSON

Imps, Mac Sugar Free Lozenges, Nigroids; *Mac Dual Action Lozenges:* Blackcurrant, Honey Lemon (honey *flavour*); *Potter's Pastilles:* Pholcodine, Strong Bronchial Catarrh

ESSENTIALLY OILSøπ

Citricidal

FSCπ

Aloe Vera Juice: 4X Strength, Full Strength; *Herbal Tinctures:* all; *Herbcraft Formula:* Agnus Castus Premenstrual, Black Cohosh & Crampbark, Black Cohosh & Wild Yam Menopause, Black Walnut & Calendula, Burdock & Nettle, Dandelion, Dandelion & Burdock Cleansing, Echinacea, Echinacea Eyebright & Bilberry, Feverfew, Garlic & Horseradish Winter, Ginseng & Saw Palmetto for Men, Hawthorn, Liquorice, Mullein, Passiflora & Valerian, Peppermint, Reishi Shiitake Mushrooms; *Her-*

bcraft Spray: Aloe Lavender, Calendula & Goldseal; *Topical Cream:* Evening Primrose Oil, Vitamin E

FANTÔME√§πΩ**fcd78**

Herbal Cream: Arnica, Borage, Comfrey, Marigold, St John's Wort, Tea Tree, Wild Yam Root; *Herbal Tinctures:* all; *Tea Tree Head Care Set for Head Lice (Normal):* 100% Essential Oil, Headcare Spray, Shampoo; *Tea Tree Head Care Set for Head Lice (Sensitive Skin):* 100% Essential Oil, Headcare Oil, Shampoo

GR LANEøπΩ∆**fcd87**

Charcoal Tablets, Heemex Pile Ointment, Herbalene Laxative, Herbelix Mucous Decongestant, Naturest, Pileabs Herbal Pile Tablets, Quiet Life Herbal Tranquillisers; *Dual-Lax:* Extra Strong, Normal; *Olbas:* Bath, Inhaler, Oil, Pastilles

GRANDMA VINE'Sø

Traditional Antiseptic Gel

HAMBLEDEN HERBSøπΩ**fcd82**

Aloe Juice; *Organic Herbal Tinctures:* all — except Propolis

HEALTH AID

Alfalfa, Astragalus, Bilberry, Cat's Claw, Dong Quai, Echinacea, Feverfew, Fibre Aid, Golden Seal, Kava Kava, Milk Thistle, Pycnogenol, Saw Palmetto, Spirulina, St John's Wort, Valerian Root, Chlorella; *Fibre Plus:* Orange, Lime

HEALTH IMPORTS LTDøπΩ**fcd95**

Thursday Plantation Tea Tree: Antiseptic Cream, Antiseptic Ointment, Eucalyptus Inhalant, Lavender Solution, Lotion, Pure Oil

HUMANE RESEARCH TRUST√ø§πΩ**fcd**

Berwitz Homoeopathic: Calendula Tincture, Cough Linctus, Ear Drops, Eye Drops, First Aid Kit, Healing Ointment, Rescue Remedy; *Berwitz Homoeopathic Cream:* Acne, Anal Itching, Arnica, Athlete's Foot, Burns, Chillblains, Comfrey, Dry Skin, First Aid (Bach), Fractures, Haemorrhoids, Healing, Hypercal, Itching Eczema, Rashes, Rheumatism, Strains & Sprains, Tennis Elbow, Varicose Veins, Warts, Weeping Eczema

JL BRAGG√πΩ**fcd**

Braggs Medicinal Charcoal: Biscuits, Tablets

KOBASHI√ø™πΩ∆76

Aloe Vera: Gel, Juice

LE MYOSOTISø

Ear Candle: Eucalyptus, Lavender

LIFESTREAM

Biogenic Aloe Juice; *Biogenic Aloe Vera:* Capsules [Vegicaps], Gel, Gel *w* Vit E, Juice, Mist

LINPHARMAø

Herbal Refresh Tincture; *Herbal Complex Tincture:* 1, 2, 3, 4, 5, 6, 7

LOTHIAN HERBSø∆91

Tea Tree Antiseptic Cream

MASON'S√ø$\pi\Omega$fcd76

Dog Oil For Massaging (for dogs, horses, humans)

MEADOWSWEETø™§$\pi\Omega\triangle$86

Comfrey & Vitamin E Ointment; *Nature Power:* **Arthritis & Muscular Pain Lotion, Athlete's Foot Oil, Cellulite & Thigh Intensive Massage Oil, PMT Relief Foam Bath**

MONTAGNE JEUNESSEø$\pi\Omega$fcd78

Bath: Dead Sea Mud Aches-Away, Eucalyptus & Camphor Anti-Cold

NATURAL WOMANø

Flor Essence

NATURE'S AID

Dong Quai Extract, Ginkgo Biloba, St John's Wort

NATURE'S GOLDø$\pi\Omega$fcd95

Peyava For Coughs Colds & Flu [powder]

NATURE'S OWN§π

Aloe Vera Concentrate, Siberian Ginseng

NATURE'S SOURCEø

Aid: Arthritis, Digestion, Stress

NEAL'S YARD REMEDIESø

Aloe Vera Juice, Borax BP, Cellulose Herb Bags, Homeopathic First Aid Kit, Swedish Bitters, Travel Roll, Vegicaps, Witch Hazel; *Bach Flower Remedies:* all; *Capsule:* Chamomile, Cranberry Extract, Dandelion Root, Don Quai, Echinacea, Feverfew, Ginger Root, Ginkgo, Korean Ginseng, Milk Thistle, Valerian; *Homoeopathic Tinctures:* all; *Macerated Oil:* Arnica, Calendula, Carrot, Comfrey, Mullein, St John's Wort; *Medicinal Herbs & Powders:* all; *Mixture:* Balm Of Gilead, Elderflower Peppermint & Composition Essence, Horehound & Aniseed Linctus; *North American Flower Essences:* all; *Oil:* Detox Toning, Evening Primrose, Ginger & Juniper Warming, Grapeseed, Inhalation, Wheatgerm; *Ointment:* Arnica, Base, Calendula, Comfrey, Hypericum & Calendula, Hypericum & Urtica, Rhus Tox & Ruta, Stellaria; *Remedies to Roll for:* Energy, Jetlag, Passion, Sleep; *Tablets:* Passiflora Herbal, Rutin, Slippery Elm; *Tincture:* Benzoin, Burdock, Chaste Berry, Chinese Herbal, Cleavers, Comfrey Leaf, Damiana, Dandelion Root, Echinacea, Ginkgo, Hawthorn, Lemon Balm, Marigold, Marshmallow Leaf, Milk Thistle, Oak, Raspberry Leaf, St John's Wort, Sage, Saw Palmetto, Skullcap, Valerian

NELSONø$\pi\Omega$

Aura Tinctures: all; *Bach Remedies [liquid only]:* **Agrimony, Aspen, Beech, Centaury, Cerato, Cherry Plum, Chestnut Bud, Chicory, Clematis, Crab Apple, Elm, Gentian, Gorse, Heather, Holly, Honeysuckle, Hornbeam Impatiens, Larch, Mimulus, Mustard, Oak, Olive, Pine, Red Chestnut, Rock Rose, Rock Water, Seleranthus, Star of Bethlehem, Sweet Chestnut, Vervain, Vine, Walnut, Water Violet, White Chestnut, Wild Oat, Wild Rose, Willow, Rescue Remedy;** *Cream:* **Arnica, Calendula Skin Salve, EPO Skin, Graphites, Hypercal, Haemorrhoid, Rhus Tox, Tea Tree;**

health care

Spray: Hypercal, Pyrethrum

NUTRICIA

Cantassium: Agnus Castus Extract, Bio Echinacea Forte, Concentrated Cranberry Juice *w* Vitamin C, Ginkgo Biloba Extract, St John's Wort

PHILLIPS NUTRITIONALSø

Estrofemme: Cream, Tablets; *Perfect Woman Herbal Yam Cream:* 8.5%,10%; *Perfect Woman Premenopausal & Menopausal Formulae:* all; *Perfect Woman Sublingual:* Drops, Tablets

PHYTO PRODUCTS√ø§πΩ

Garlic Juice, Vegetable Glycerine; *Herbal Fluid Extracts:* all; *Herbal Organic Tinctures:* all; *Herbal Tinctures:* all; *Pure Organic Skin Cream:* Arnica, Chamomile, Chickweed, Comfrey, Echinacea, Garlic, Marigold, Tea Tree, Witch Hazel; *Oil:* Comfrey, Marigold, St John's Wort, Sweet Almond; *Syrup:* Marshmallow, Thyme *w* Liquorice, Wild Cherry; *Tablets:* Agnus Castus, Buchu & Dandelion Complex, Celery Complex, Cramp Bark, Damiana, Devil's Claw, Echinacea, Garlic, Ginger, Ginkgo, Ginseng, Golden Seal, Hawthorn, Helonias Complex, Kelp, Papaya & Charcoal Complex, Passiflora, Prickly Ash, Rutin & Vitamin C, St John's Wort, Slippery Elm, Valerian Complex, White Willow Complex, Wild Yam

POTTER'S

9 Rubbing Oils, Indian Brandee, Life Drops, Medicated Extract Of Rosemary, St John's Wort Compound, Skin Clear Ointment, Vegetable Cough Remover, Winged Lion Cleansing Herbs; *Elixir Of:* Black Haw & Golden Seal, Echinacea; *Mixture:* Acidosis, Adiantine, Appetiser, Catarrh, Chest, Horehound & Aniseed Cough, Indigestion, Nodoff, Pegina, Protat, Skin Eruptions, Spanish Tummy, Stomach, Watershed; *Remedy:* Kas-Bah Herb, Lightning Cough; *Tablets:* Acidosis, Buckwheat, Chlorophyll, Echinacea, Feverfew, GB, Out Of Sorts, Rheumatic Pain, Skin Clear, Slippery Elm, Tabritis, Well Woman, Winged Lion Cleansing Herb

POWER HEALTHøπΩ

Cranberry & Aloe Vera, Pilewort Ointment, Vita Youth Tea Tree Oil Antiseptic Spot Oil; *Aloe Vera Supplement:* Double Strength, **Juice Drink Liquid**, Standard Strength, Ultra Strength One A Day Chewable; *Cranberry Juice:* Concentrate Drink Mix, Concentrate Drink Mix *w* Vitamin C, Double Strength; *Jan de Vries Botanical Formula:* Blood, Digestive, Head Clear, Nerve; *Rub:* Chest, Chilli Muscle

PROBIOTICSø™π

Protexin Natural Care

PURPLE FLAME AROMA.øπΩfcd80

Pessaries: Tea Tree, *w* Neem Oil

QUEST™π

Agnus Castus, Bilberry, Devil's Claw, Echinacea, Feverfew, Ginger, Ginkgo Biloba, Green Tea, Kyolic [100, 350, 600, liquid], Milk Thistle, St John's Wort [extract, powder], Saw Palmetto, Siberian Ginseng, Uva Ursi, Valerian

SAINSBURY'SΩfcd88

Lemon Cold Powder, Washproof Dressing Strip; *Plasters:* Washproof, Waterproof Family Pack; *Throat Lozenges:* Antiseptic Menthol & Eucalyptus, Cubes Blackcurrant Menthol, Cubes Cherry Menthol, Cubes Extra Strong Menthol, Cubes Menthol Plus Eucalyptus, Dual Action Blackcurrant

SCOTTISH HERB. SUPPLIES√ø™§πΩfcd89

Thigh Cream (anti cellulite); *Herbal Tinctures:* all; *Ointments:* all

SHANTI√øπΩ

Lotion: **Antiseptic/Acne, Burn, Hair Lice;** *Oil:* **Anti-Cellulite, Arthritis & Rheumatic, Backache Relief, Body Rub, Cold Sore, Eczema/Psoriasis, Facial Massage, Sciatica Relief, Sinus/Head & Nose Pain Relief, Skin Nourishment, Tinnitus Control, Varicose Vein Pain Relief**

SHIRLEY PRICE AROMA. øπΩfcd84

Care For Ready Mixed Lotion: Cellulite, Circulation, Head Tension, Joints, Muscles, Problem Skin, Sinuses, Stresses, Visible Veins, Women

VEGA NUTRITIONALS™§πΩfcd96

Vega Herbals: **Agnus Castus, Aloe Vera, Cat's Claw, Champignon Mushroom Formula, Devil's Claw, Dong-Quai, Echinacea, Feverfew, Ginkgo Biloba, Ginseng (Korean), Ginseng (Siberian), Kava Kava, Milk Thistle, St John's Wort Formula, Valerian**

WELEDAøπΩfcd85

Homeopathic Remedies (request vegan versions); *Cough & Tonic Elixir:* Birch, Blackthorn, Cough, Sandthorn; *Over the Counter Anthroposophic Medicine:* Arnica 6x [tab], Arnica Lotion, Arnica Massage Balm, Avena Sativa Comp, Bidor 1% [tab], Bidor 5% [tab], Calendula Lotion, Calendula Massage Balm, Carbo Betula 3x [tab], Carvon [tab], Cinnabar 20x [tab], Combudoron Lotion, Combudoron Spray, Erysidoron 2 [tab], Feverfew 6x [drops], Fragador [tab], Fragaria/Vitis [tab], Lapis Cancri/Silic [tab], Laxadoron [tab], Medicinal Gargle, Melissa Comp; *Pharmacy Only Anthroposophic Medicine:* Aconitum/Bryonia [drops], Apatite 6x Comp [tab], Bolus Eucalypti Comp [powder], Choleodoron [drops], Cinnabar 20x/Pyrites [tab], Cough Drops, Crataegus Comp [drops], Digestodoron [drops, tab], Dulcamara/Lysimachia [drops], Erysidoron 1 [drops], Ferrum Sidereum 6x [tab], Fragaria/Urtica [drops], Mandragora Comp [drops], Menodoron [drops], Oleum Rhinale [drops], Onopordon Comp A [drops], Onopordon Comp B [drops], Pertudoron 2 [drops], Pyrites 3x [tab], Rheumadoron 1 [drops], Rheumadoron 2 [drops], Rheumadoron 102A [drops], Scleron [tab], Vitis Comp [tab], WCS Dusting Powder

XYNERGYøπΩ

Aloe Vera [juice, Vegicaps], Aloe Vera Mist, Aloe99 Gel

VITAMINS & MINERALS

AQUA SOURCEø™πΩ

[Vegicaps]: **CoQ10 Complex w Chromi-**

um Polynicotinate, **Super Anti-Ox** *w*
Pycnogenol

AQUARIUS HEALTHCAREø

Zodiac Birth Sign: Aries, Aquarius, Cancer, Capricorn, Gemini, Leo, Libra, Pisces, Sagittarius, Scorpio, Taurus, Virgo; *Zodiac Element:* Air, Earth, Water

BIOCAREø

Adult Multivitamin & Minerals, Beta Carotene, Bio Magnesium, Calcium EAP2, Cervagyn, EyeCare, Femforte I, Femforte II, Folguard Folic Acid & B12, HepaGuard, Magnesium EAP2, Magnesium Pantothenate, MaleForte, Mixed Ascorbates, One a day Vitamins Minerals & Bilberry/Lutein, Optizinc, OralTect, Organic Selenium, Osteoplex, ProsTect, ReCall, SucroGuard, VitasorbB6; *Complex:* Ante-natal, B, Iron, Vitamin E; *Support:* Adrenal AD206, Hair & Nail , Pituitary PT208, Thyroid TH207; *Vitamin:* Active B6, B12, C

BIO-D√ø™πΩΔ83

Borage Ointment, Chromium Picolinate, Co-Enzyme Q10, Colloidal Silver, Magnesium, Selenium, Vegebalanz, Zinc

BOOTS

Vegetarian Multi Vitamins and Minerals

EARTH FORCEøπΩ

Source Naturals: Cat's Claw [tab], Co-Enzymate & B Complex [lozenge], Co-Enzymate Q10 Sublingual [lozenge], Colloidal Silver [liquid], Ginko [tab], Kava Kava Root [tab], Mental Eye [tab], Urban Air Defence [tab], Vitamin C *w* Rosehips [tab], Wellness Formula [tab], Wellness Zinc [lozenge]

FSCπ

Biotin, Calcium Magnesium & D, Calcium Magnesium & Zinc, Folic Acid, L-Lysine, Magnesium & B6, Niacinamide, Pantothenic Acid, Sea Kelp & Potassium, Zinc, Zinc Lozenges; *Super:* Cal/Mag, Multi-Minerals; *Vitamin B:* 6, Complex, Supreme (Hi Potency); *Vitamin C:* Complex, Low Acid, Powder, Sustained Release Sugar Free & Low Acid; *Vitamin C Sugar Free/Chewable:* Lemon/Lime, Orange

GR LANEøπΩΔfcd87

B12 Vegevit, Preconceive Folic Acid Tablets, Wheatgerm Oil (Vit E); *Top C:* Buffered, Chewable, High Potency Volcanic Rock Dust

HEALTH AID

Biotin, Calcium, Calcium Pantothenate, Citrus Bioflavonoid, Co-Enzyme Q10, DLPA, Dolomite, Folic Acid, L-Lysine HCl, Magnesium *w* Calcium, Mega B99, Multi Vitamin & Minerals A-Z; *Strong:* B50, Full B & C, Iron, Mega Multi Mineral; *Vitamin:* B6, B12, C Chewable, C Powder, C PR

LIFEPLAN

Organic Yeast Free Selenium Bonus

LIFESPRINGø

Colloidal Mineral Solution

NATURAL WOMANø

Missing Link Human Nutrient Formula

NATURE'S AID

Beta Carotene, Kelp *w* Calcium, Magnesium, Multivits & Multimineral, Vitamin B Complex *w* Vitamin C & Magnesium, Vitamin B6, Vitamin C, Vitamin E150 (D Alpha Tocopherol), Zinc & Copper; *Vitamin C:* Chewable Orange, Chewable Sugar Free, Low Acid Formula, Time Release Chewable Orange

NATURE'S OWN§π

Bromelain, Calcium & Magnesium Carbonates, Dolomite, Evening Primrose Oil, Multimineral, Pangamic Acid (B15); *Food State Mineral:* Calcium, GTF Chromium, Iron & Molybdenum, Magnesium, Manganese, Potassium, Selenium, Zinc/Copper; *Food State Nutritional Supplement:* Biotin, Choline, Inostil, PABA; *Food State Vitamin Supplement:* Beta Carotene, Vit B Complex Plus Vit C & Magnesium, Vit B1 (Thiamin), Vit B2 (Riboflavin), Vit B3 (Niacin), Vit B5 (Pantothenic Acid), Vit B6 (Pyridoxine), Vit C, Vit E (D Alpha Tocopherol); *Orotate:* Calcium, Chromium, Copper, Magnesium, Manganese, Potassium, Zinc; *Vitamin:* B3 (Niacin), B5 (Pantothenic Acid), B6 (Pyridoxine), B Complex Plus, C, C Plus Bioflavonoids, C Powder

NEAL'S YARD REMEDIESø

Folic Acid, Multi-Vitamin & Mineral Capsules, Vitamin C Powder; *Chelated Tablets:* Iron, Magnesium, Zinc; *Tablets:* Calcium *w* Vitamin D, Multi-Mineral, Selenium, Vitamin B Complex, Vitamin C

NUTRICIA

Cantassium: Folic Acid, Magnesium, Pycnogenol *w* Alpha Lipoic Acid, Vitamin C *w* Extracts of Rosehip & Acerola, Zinc

PHILLIPS NUTRITIONALSø

Vitamin E Capsules

POWER HEALTHøπΩ

Calcium, Calcium Pantothenate (Vitamin B5), Chromium Picolinate, Dolomite, Ester C, Folic Acid, Iron Amino Acid Chelate, Magnesium, MSM, Multimineral & Zinc, Potassium & Vitamin C; *Selenium:* Organic Gold Seal, *w* Zinc; *Tri:* Calc, Iron, Mag, Zinc; *Vitamin:* B1, B6, **B12, B12 Yeast Free**, C, C *w* Citrus Bioflavonoids, C Powder (Drink Mix), Children's C Chewable, **Super B Complex**; *Vitamin C Fruiti:* Blackcurrant, Orange Sugar Free, Orange *w* Sugar; *Zinc:* Hi, **Oral Lozenges**, Reevecrest Healthcare Ultra, Xtra

QUEST™π

Co-Enzyme Q10, Folic Acid *w* B Vitamins, L-Lysine, Mega B-50, Mega B-100 Timed Release, Multi B Complex, Multiminerals, Pre-Natal Folic Acid, Super Mega B & C, Super Once A Day Vegan Multi-Vitamin & Mineral Supplement, Molybdenum B Complex & Vit C; *Synergistic:* Boron, Iron, Iron *w* Copper, Magnesium, Selenium Plus Vitamins C & E, Zinc *w* Copper; *Vitamin:* B6, B12, Buffered C, C, C Plus Bioflavonoids, C Timed Release, Chewable C

RENAHALLø

Evening Primrose Oil [bottle]; *Powder:*

Calcium Ascorbate, Vitamin C, Vitamin E

SAINSBURY'SΩfcd88

Folic Acid [tab]; *Vitamin:* B Complex [tab], B6 [tab], Chewable C [blister pk, tab], High Strength C [blister pk, tab]

SALUSø§πΩ

Epresat Multi-Vitamin; *Liquid Supplement:* Calcium, Floravital Yeast Free, Magnesium, Saludynam

SEVEN SEAS™

One-A-Day Multivitamin Plus Minerals for Vegetarians & Vegans

TREFRIW WELLS SPA√øπΩ

Spatone Iron +

VEGA NUTRITIONALS™§πΩfcd96

Amino Complex Freeform Plus B6, Anti-Oxidant Formula, Beta-Carotene Dunaliella Salina Source, Biotin, Calcium Citrate (Elemental), Calcium Magnesium Zinc Plus Boron, Chelated Calcium, Choline Plus Inositol, Chromium Polynicotinate Yeast Free (Elemental), Colloidal Minerals Formula Plus Kelp, Evening Primrose Oil Plus B6 & Mexican Yam (Dry), Folic Acid, Iron Bisglycinate (Non Constipating Elemental), Kelp & Greens Formula, Magnesium Citrate (Elemental), Nicotinamide B3 (No Flush), PABA, Pyridoxal 5-Phosphate, Selenium Yeast Free (Elemental), Zinc Citrate (Elemental), ZMM Multi-Mineral Complex; *Vitamin:* B Complex, B Complex Plus C, B1, B2, B5 (Calcium Pantothenate), B6 Plus P-5-P, B12, C, C Plus Rose Hips, E Plus Selenium Yeast Free, E (Natural Dry Source)

WAITROSE

60 Chewable Calcium & Vitamin D Tablets

WASSENøπ

Chromium GTF, Co-Enzyme Q10 & Magnesium, Co-Enzyme Q10 & Vitamin E, Confiance, Vitamin C

notes

- **alternatives** Herbalists, homoeopaths *(but see **homoeopathy**, below)*, acupuncturists etc; self-health books; and remedies available from health/wholefood shops and chemists, may provide an alternative to animal-tested synthetic drugs.

- **beta-carotene and D$_2$** (*See **gelatine carrier**, page 85*)

- **capsules** Most are still made of gelatine. Vegicaps are an increasingly popular animal-free alternative.

- **contraceptives** May have been tested on animals or contain animal-derived ingredients.
  Condoms Usually made from latex — in which case casein (a milk protein) will have been used as a processing aid. Those available from The Vegan Society and Condomi are the only known animal-free brands in the UK.
  Femidom (female condom) Made by Chartex, it is free of animal substances but has been tested on animals outside the UK.
  Oral Lactose (milk sugar) and magnesium stearate (possibly animal-derived) are found in virtually every contraceptive pill. The only product free of animal ingredients (but not animal testing) is Femulen — a progestrogen-only pill made by PD Searle & Co (a branch of Monsanto).
  PERSONA Launched in 1996, Unipath's PERSONA monitors hormone levels through urine testing. The urine Test Sticks contain minute quantities of a bovine protein. It has not been tested on animals, however, the urine test technology is based on a standard immunoassay technique which utilises monoclonal antibodies from cell lines originally derived from mice. These cell lines are now cultured *in vitro* (test tube).

- **drugs** May or may not contain animal-derived ingredients but all will have been tested on animals at some stage of production.

- **homoeopathy** Homoeopathic remedies are derived from plant, mineral or animal substances. Tablets usually contain lactose, and remedies may also include animal-derived minerals. *Common: Apis* — honey bee, *Cantharis* — Spanish fly, *Lachesis* — snake poison; *Uncommon: Ambra grasea* — secretion from the sperm whale, *Astacus fluviatilis* — crawfish, *Asterias rubens* — Red Starfish, *Badiaga* — freshwater sponge, *Blatta americana* — cockroach, *Blatta orientalis* — Indian cockroach, *Bufo* — poison of toad, *Castor equi* — rudimentary thumbnail of horse, *Castoreum* — beaver, *Cenchris-contortrix (Ancistrodon)* — Copperhead snake, *Chenopodi glauci aphis* — plant lice from *Chenopodium*, *Cimex-acanthia* — bed bug, *Coccinella septempunctata* — ladybird, *Crotalus horridus* — rattlesnake, *Doryphor* — Colorado potato bug, *Elaps corallinus* — Coral snake, *Fel tauri* — ox gall, *Formica rufa (Myrmexine)* — crushed live ants, *Hydrophobinum* — saliva of rabid dog, *Latrodectus mactans* — spider, *Medusa* — jelly fish, *Murex* — Purple fish, *Mygale lasiodora* — Black Cuba spider, *Naja tripudians* — cobra venom, *Oleum animale* — Dippel's animal oil, *Oleum jecoris aselli* — cod liver oil, *Oniscus asellus-millipedes* — wood louse, *Pulex irritans* — common flea, *Robinia* — Yellow Locust, *Sepia* — inky juice of cuttlefish, *Tarantula cubensis* — Cuban spider, *Tarantula hispania* — Spanish spider, *Theridion* — Orange spider, *Thyroidinum* — live wasp, *Vespa vulgaris* — live wasp, *Vipera* — German viper.

- **prescriptions** The Department of Health's Medicines Control Agency (MCA) states it is lawful for a doctor to prescribe *any* medicinal product (whether or not it has marketing authorisation from the MCA) to a named patient. Theoretically this means that providing an animal-free product is available, a GP can prescribe it. If a GP is unwilling to ascertain the animal-free status of a product, the patient may have to undertake his/her own research. Chemists are useful sources of information and libraries may be able to help with manufacturers' addresses.

- **prevention** Regular exercise; rest and relaxation; avoidance of caffeine, tobacco, alcohol etc; bodily awareness; and a predominantly wholefood animal-free diet, may help prevent the onset of many minor complaints and reduce the risk of developing certain long-term illnesses. A list of vegan healthcare practitioners is available in exchange for an SAE from the Vegan Society *(see **CONTACT NETWORKS**, page 242).*

baby, infant & child care

food & drink   186
footwear & clothing   187
health care   187
nappies   187
toiletries etc   187

notes   *189*

FOOD & DRINK

BABY ORGANIXøπ

Stage I (from 4 months): **Apple & Apricot [jar], Apple & Blueberry [jar], Apple & Raspberry [dry], Apple First Food [jar], Apricot Cereal [jar], Baby Rice [dry], Baby Rice & Garden Vegetables [dry], Banana Porridge [cereal], Fruit Compote [cereal, jar], Fruity Rice Pudding [cereal], Garden Vegetables [jar], Oat Apple & Pear [cereal], Pea First Food [jar], Pear First Food [jar], Potato Courgette & Pea [jar], Prunes & Oatmeal [jar], Squash & Apple [jar];** *Stage II (from 7 months):* **ABC's Pasta, Apple & Banana Muesli [cereal, dry], Ducks Pasta, Mushroom Pasta Sauce [jar], Pea & Carrot Risotto [dry], Pear & Apple Oats [jar], Potato & Baked Beans [jar], Spaghetti Neopolitan [jar], Stars Pasta, Sweetcorn & Potato [jar], Vegetable & Coconut Korma [jar]**

BICKIEPEGS√øπ

Babies Teething Biscuits

FARLEY'S™

Soya Infant Formula

HEINZ

Baby (from 4 months): Apple & Apricot [jar], Apple & Banana [jar], Apple & Banana Drink, Apple & Cherry Drink, Apple & Mango Drink, Banana Delight [jar], Concentrated Apple & Apricot Juice, Concentrated Apple & Blackcurrant Juice, Concentrated Apple Juice, Concentrated Pear & Cherry Juice, Country Vegetables & Rice [jar], Farmhouse Vegetable Special [can], Just Apple [jar], Mixed Fruit [jar], Mixed Fruit Drink, Porridge Oats w Prunes [can], Purified Water w a Hint of Strawberry, Ready to Serve Apple & Blackcurrant Juice, Ready to Serve Apple & Cherry Juice, Ready to Serve Apple Juice, Ready to Serve Pear Juice, Summer Fruit [jar]; *Junior Cuisine (from 1 year):* Creamed Rice Pudding w Tropical Fruits, Vegetables & Rice in a Mild Sweet & Sour Sauce

HIPP

Jar: Apple & Blueberry Dessert, Apple & Pear Pudding, Apple Breakfast Cereal, Banana & Peach Dessert, Carrot & Potatoes, Creamed Porridge Breakfast, Mixed Vegetables, Wholemeal Rice & Banana; *Juice:* Apple & Grape, Redberry

KALLO

Organic: Junior Rice Cakes, Rusks

ORIGINAL FRESH BABY FOOD COπ

Fresh Organic Baby Food (4 months): **Carrot w Apple & Mint, Cauliflower & Carrot, Courgette Risotto w Banana, Creamy Parsnip & Potato, Minted Pea & Potato, Sweet Potato & Carrot, Sweetcorn & Potato;** *Fresh Organic Baby Food (7 months):* **Caribbean Beans w Banana, Lentil Casserole, Ratatouille, Tomato Pasta**

SAINSBURY'SΩfcd88

From 7 Months Vegetable Pasta Bake; *From 4 Months:* Apple & Peach Fruit Purée, Apple & Summerberry Fruits, Apple Pudding, Autumn Fruits Compote, Orange & Banana Fruit Purée

WOOD'S

Mom's Organic Choice Baby Food — Fruits (from about 3 months): Apples & Blueberries, Apples & Mangoes, Apples & Plums, Applesauce, Peaches, Pears, Pears & Strawberries, Plums Bananas & Oatmeal, Rice & Bananas; *Mom's Organic Choice Baby Food — Vegetables (from about 3 months):* Green Beans & Brown Rice, Green Beans & Rice, Peas, Spinach & Carrots, Summer Vegetables, Sweet Potatoes, Winter Squash

FOOTWEAR & CLOTHING

ANIMAL AID√ø§πΩΔfcd76

Animal Pride T-Shirt (age 12-13 years)

GREEN SHOESø™

Children's: Bar Sandal, Bridge Sandal, Buckle Boot, Dart Shoe, Ivy Boot, Lace Up Boot, T-Bar Sandal

VEGETARIAN SHOES√øπ

Kids' Boot, New Balance Trainers

VIVA!√ø§π

T-Shirt (ages 5-6, 7-8, 9-10): Fish, If It's Got a Face I Don't Eat it!, No Animals In My Tummy

HEALTH CARE

BUTTERFLY EFFECT√ø™

Camomile Organic Hemp & Flower Body Spray Mists (for baby)

CO-OPπΩΔfcd85

Sterilising Tablets

FSCπ

Herbcraft Formula Chamomile for Children

MICHELINE ARCIERøΩfcd

Pregnancy Oils: Bath, Kit, Lavender, New Breath, New Life Body Oil

SAINSBURY'SΩfcd88

Feeding Bottle Sterilising Tablets, Mr Bump Children's Plasters

SALUSø§πΩ

Kindervital For Children Liquid Supplement

WELEDAøπΩfcd85

Over the Counter Anthroposophic Medicine Chamomilla 3x (colicky pain, teething troubles) [drops, pillules]

NAPPIES

BIO-D√ø™πΩΔfcd83

Nappy Fresh

NATRABABYø

Form-Fitting Cotton Nappy: Size One (5-16lbs), Size Two (17-30lbs)

TOILETRIES ETC

ALADDIN AROMAS√øπΩfcd87

Baby Bath, Kids Fun Time

baby, infant & child care

BODYLINEø§πΩfcd84

Mother & Baby: Barrier Cream, Bubble Bath, Dusting Powder, Lotion, Nipple Gel, Shampoo, Stretch Mark Cream

CARIADøπΩ

Mother & Baby Pack: **Baby Massage Oil, Calm Bath Milk, Chamomile Body Lotion;** *Pregnancy:* **Bath & Massage Oil, Bath Milk**

CO-OPπΩ△fcd85

Babywise Powder, Children's Toothpaste, Children's Treasure Island Foam Bath, Petroleum Jelly; *Sponge:* Baby, Children's Dinosaur Bath

DROYT√øπΩfcd84

Glycerine Baby Soap

GREEN PEOPLEø™πΩ

Happy Kids Organic Range: **Aloe Vera Shower Gel, Body Lotion, Camomile Body Lotion, Lavender Body Lotion, Lavender Shampoo, Lavender Shower Gel, Mandarin Shampoo, Mandarin Toothpaste, Tea Tree Shampoo, Sun Lotion (SPF 15), Sun Lotion (SPF 22)**

KOBASHI√ø™πΩ△76

Baby Moisturising Lotion

MEADOWSWEETø™§πΩ△86

Baby Cream, Baby Soft Bubble Bath, Gentle Baby Lotion

MICHELINE ARCIERøΩfcd

Children's: Face & Body Oil, Sila Jiva Bath Oil, Svetlina

NATRACAREø

Perfume-Free Vegan: Baby Bath, Barrier Cream

NEAL'S YARD REMEDIESø

Baby Massage Oil

POWER HEALTHøπΩ

Baby Naturals: Bubble Bath, Cream, Lotion, Oil, Powder (Talc Free), Scalp Oil, Shampoo, Wipes; *Nature's Mother Stretch Mark:* Cream, Oil

SAINSBURY'SΩfcd88

White Petroleum Jelly; *Baby:* Economy Wipes, Soap, Sponge, Wipes; *Essentially You:* Breast Pads, Maternity Towel Wings

SHANTI√øπΩ

Baby Massage Oil

SUPERDRUGΩfcd87

Baby: Bath, Lotion, Oil, Powder, Shampoo

VINDOTKO√ø™§πΩfcd75

Barrier Creams: all

WELEDAøπΩfcd85

Children's Tooth Gel; *Calendula:* Baby Oil, Baby Powder

XVø§πΩ

Petroleum Jelly

notes

- **infant formula** Farley's Soya Infant Formula is the only known animal-free complete infant formula

- **nappies** At present we have no information on disposable nappies. For information on reusable cloth nappies, send two 1st class stamps on an A4-size SAE to: Real Nappy Association, PO Box 3704, London SE26 4RX or 'phone 020 8299 4519 or visit www.realnappy.com

footwear & clothing

belts, wallets & bags etc   192
clothing   192
footwear — general   193
footwear — sports   197
waterproofers, polishes & cleaners   197

notes   *198*

BELTS, WALLETS, BAGS ETC

ALADDIN AROMASøπΩfcd87

Aromas Carry Case for essential oils

ANIMAL AID√ø§πΩ∆fcd76

Belt: Black, Brown

DR HADWEN TRUST√ø§

Trust Purse

ESSENTIALLY OILSøπ

Aromatherapist's Briefcases

ETHICAL WARES√ø™§

Fun Fleece Rucksack: Blue, Red; *Unisex Belt:* Black, Brown

GREEN SHOESø™

Bags, Belts, Purses (made to order)

HEARTLAND PRODUCTS√ø§πΩ

Belts & Wallets: all

HEMP UNIONø™§πΩfcd93

Bags & Accessories: all

KOBASHI√ø™πΩ∆76

Kobashi Bag

SUPERDRUGΩfcd87

Tropical PVC Purse: Purple Hearts, *w* Stars

VEGAN SOCIETY√ø§Ω

Black Wallet-Purse

VEGANLINE√øπ

Belt: Chunky Buckle, Cloth, Cowboy, Fancy; *Wallet:* Bouncing Wrist, Card Holder, Hemp, Hemp Portfolios, Purse-Come-Wallet

VEGETARIAN SHOES√øπ

Record Bag, Wallet; *Belt:* Black, Brown

VIVA!√ø§π

Pencil Case, Purse/Wallet

CLOTHING

ANIMAL AID√ø§πΩ∆fcd76

Pique Polo Shirt, Polar Fleece, Sports Vest; *Sweatshirt:* Living Without Cruelty, Zip-Up Hooded; *T-shirt:* Animal Pride, Badger Sunset, Bite Back at Animal Experiments, Bite Back at Fur, Eat Beef?!, Living Without Cruelty

ARCULUS√§

Knitwear: all

DR HADWEN TRUST√ø§

T-shirt: 'Grey Ghost' Wolf, 'Mother's Love'

ETHICAL WARES√ø™§

Dales Jacket, Polar Fleece Hat; *Fleece:* Arctic, Blue Dolphin, Oatmeal; *T-shirt:* Cat, Hell for Leather, Moon; *Walking Sock:* Euro, Forester

HEARTLAND PRODUCTS√ø§πΩ

Ball Gloves & Jackets: all

HEMP FOOD INDUSTRIES ASSOC.ø§πΩ

Clothing: all

HEMP UNIONø™§πΩfcd93

Clothing: all

PLANET V√ø§π

Full Length Double Breasted Coat; *Gent's:* Caban Jacket, Leather-Look Blouson, Suedette Blouson, Three Quarter Length Coat, Three Quarter Length Zip Fastening Suedette Coat; *Ladies' Coat:* Double Breasted, Single Breasted; *Ladies' Jacket:* Button Fastening Suedette Safari, Caban, Waterproof; *Unisex Jacket:* Aviator, Button Fastening Three Quarter Length, Pilot

VEGAN SOCIETY√ø§Ω

Polar Fleece Jacket; *T-shirt:* Animals, Environment, People

VEGANLINE√ø§π

Hemp T-shirt, James Dean PVC Jacket

VEGETARIAN SHOES√øπ

Cow T-shirt; *Leather-Free Jacket:* 70s Button Blazer, Angel Jacket, Biker Style, Box Jacket, James Dean, Ladies' Reefer, Ladies' Swingcoat, Men's Skipper Coat, Phoenix Jacket; *Polyurethane Gloves:* Ladies', Men's

VIVA!√ø§π

Hooded Sweatshirts: all; *Long Sleeved T-shirts:* all; *Short Sleeved T-shirts:* all

XYNERGYøπΩ

Organic T-shirt

FOOTWEAR — GENERAL

ANIMAL AID√ø§πΩΔfcd76

Everyday Wear: Black Oxford, Buggles Shoe, Jungle Shoe, Women's Ebony Sandal, Women's Loafer Shoe, Women's Twin Zip Boot; *Leisure Boots:* Studland, Town & Country, Trekking

BIRKENSTOCKø

Denim Boston Vegan Sandals, Navy Florida Vegan Sandals; *Arizona Vegan Sandals:* Black, Brown; *Milano Vegan Sandals:* Black, Brown

ETHICAL WARES√ø™§

Safety Boot *w* steel toe-cap, Trainer (casual use); *Fabric leisure boots:* Studland, Town & Country, Trekking; *Brown 'suede' finish:* Buggles Shoe, Desert Boot, Rempstone Boot, 'Suede' Gibson; *Classic styles:* Derby, Gibson, Oxford, Semi-Brogue; *Gem Ladies':* Amethyst Sanda, Amethyst Wedge, Ebony Sandal, Onyx Mule, Onyx Wedge, Sapphire Mule; *Slip-ons:* Billie, Durlstone Boot, Monk; *Summer Sandals:* Birkenstock Arizona, Birkenstock Milano, Closed-Toe; *Street Life:* Buckle Boot, Chukka Boot, Creeper, Jungle Shoe; *Women's Wear:* Biker Boot, Court Shoe, Jodhpur Boot, Laced Ankle Boot, Loafer, Susie Boot, Twin Zip Suedette Boot, Zip Suedette Boot

FREERANGERSø™

Shoes for Men: Cedar, Maple, Oak, Pine; *Shoes for Women:* Ash, Beech, Birch, Holly, Laurel

GATESπ

Hunter Rubber Boots: Classic, Galloway, Hunter, Huntress, Huntsman, Royal, Stablemate, Young Hunter

GREEN SHOESø™

Boots: Beltstone, Brutus Calf, Brutus Knee High, Buckle, Dartmoor, Field, Piecrust; *Open Sandals:* Bridge, Clasp, Open-Toed Denbury; *Sandals:* Bridge T Bar, Eclipse Mule, Hope, New Bar, Open-Toed Mule, Wide Bar; *Shoes:* Dartmoor, Eclipse Lace, Eclipse Strap, Pump

HEARTLAND PRODUCTS√ø§πΩ

Shoes & Boots: all

HEMP UNIONø™§πΩfcd93

Slippers

MADE TO LAST§πΩ

Vegan: Ankle Shoe, Bar Shoe, Chelsea Boot, Oxford Shoe, Peep Toe *w* Trim, Short Derby Boot, T-Bar Shoe

PLANET V√ø§π

Comfort Fit Court Shoe; *Boot:* Grainy Tie, Knee Length *w* Stretch Leg; *Gent's:* Classic Gibson Brogue, Metal Trim Slip-on Loafer; *Gent's Boot:* Biker Style Velcro Strap, Highland, Impact, In Weathertex, Italian Ankle, Padded Walking, Redwing Chunky, Terrain; *Gent's Shoe:* Redwing Tie, Square Toe Italian; *Ladies' Ankle Boot:* Italian, Italian *w* Gold Buckle Trim, Padded Collar, Platform; *Ladies' Bar Shoe:* Satin, Velcro Fastening; *Ladies' Boot:* Chunky Buckle, Fleece-Lined Winter, Panel Front; *Ladies' Casual Shoe:* Comfort Fit , Italian Pronto Ballet, Italian Toggle Trim; *Ladies' Loafer:* Chunky Heeled, Classic, Metal Trim, Wedge; *Ladies' Slip-on:* Asymmetric, Square Toe Chunky, Trainers; *Ladies' Tie Shoe:* Asymmetric, Asymmetric in Water Resistant Flannel

RTR SAFETYøπ

All PVC Safety Boot

VEGANLINE√ø§π

Boots: Biker, Bouncing, Brown Strap, Moon, Mrs Merton, OHO! Mid Brown, Palladium Style Canvas, Rempstone, Small Chelsea, Tartan Safety, Tracker; *Sandals:* Buckle, Cross Strap, Strap; *Shoes:* Bouncing, Buckle, Court, Leicester Loafers, Plimsolls, Sensible

VEGETARIAN SHOES√øπ

150cm Laces, Moisture Absorbing Insoles; *Airseal boots & shoes:* 3 Eyelet Gibson, 14 Eye Boot *w* Steel Toe, 20 Eye Boot *w* Steel Toe, Boulder Boot, Bump Shoe, Chelsea Boot, Nevis Boot, Para Boot *w* Steel Toe, Ranger Boot, Redstone Boot, Trail Boot, Troopa Boot, Veggie Trekker, Walker Shoe; *Birkenstock:* Arizona, Boston, Milano; *Classic casual comfort:* Bridgeport Shoe, Hampton Loafer, Havana Boot; *Dr Marten's:* 4 Eye Coppa Shoe, Black Boot, Cherry Boot, Mary Jane SM Sandal, Purple Boot; *Everyday footwear:* Approach Shoe, Decker Shoe, Explorer Shoe, Hobart Boot, Mariner Shoe, Side Walk Sneaker; *For men & women:* Active Sandal, Canyon Sandal, Chunky Gibson, Chunky Monk Shoe, Classic 8 Eye Derby Boot, Classic Gibson Town Sole, Creeper, Dune Boot, Engineers

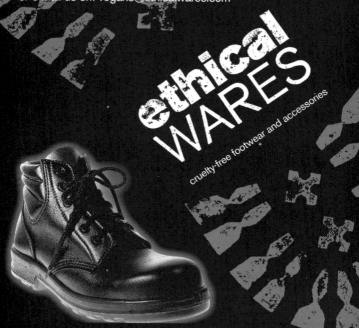

Boot, Jodhpur Boot, Tank Boot, Three Strap Footbed Sandal, Timbercat Boot, Town Boot, Two Strap Footbed Sandal; *Men's shoes & boots:* Broker Shoe, Casino Shoe, City Oxford, Dr Marten's Shoes, Dr Marten's SM Hiker, Men's Brogues, Men's Office Shoe, Men's Oxfords, Plain Loafer, Site Boot *w* Steel Toe, Square Toe Lace Upshoe, Square Toe Loafer; *Women's shoes & boots:* Becky Boot, Capital Court, Comfort Sandal, Daisy Sandal, Dinky Zip-Up, Dolly Sandal, Don't Wanna B, Katy Sandal, Ladies Slip-on, Lisa Loafer, Molly Mule, Oasis Boot, Sally Sandal, Shari Shoe, Strappy Boot, Vimmi Boot

FOOTWEAR — SPORTS

ANIMAL AID√ø§πΩΔfcd76

Walking Boots: Ranger, Woodland

ETHICAL WARES√ø™§

Walking Boots: Ranger, Weald, Woodland

PLANET V√ø§π

Unisex Sports Trainers; *Boots:* Gents Padded Walking, Unisex Mountain For Serious Walkers, Unisex Walking/Training

VEGAN SOCIETY√ø§Ω

Boots: Ranger, Studland

VEGETARIAN SHOES√øπ

New Balance Trainers: all

WATERPROOFERS, POLISHES & CLEANERS

ETHICAL WARES√ø™§

Nikwax: Fabric & Leather (clean & reproof fabric footwear), Waterproofing Wax

VEGETARIAN SHOES√øπ

Black Polish, Clear Dubbin

VINDOTCO√ø™§πΩfcd75

Saddle & Bridle Conditioner

notes

• **footwear** Quality animal-free footwear is generally available only by mail order from specialist companies. Cheap, non-leather styles are stocked by many high street shoe retailers. It has become common practice to use synthetic adhesives, but it is difficult to obtain guarantees.

• **jeans** May have decorative leather patches.
  Falmer Uses only non-leather patches.
  Levi Some of its fabric suppliers occasionally use animal fat as a lubricant during one stage of the weaving process. The 'Two Horse' patches on jeans are non-animal.

• **motorcyclist clothing** For details of gloves, boots and suits contact the Vegan Bikers Association (see **CONTACT NETWORKS**, page 242).

• **running and training shoes** Models change frequently and are invariably manufactured in the Far East. Many sports footwear companies stock models made entirely of non-animal materials but commonly are unable to guarantee, or are unwilling to ascertain, that the adhesives used are non-animal.
  Be wary of the term 'synthetic leather'; it may well describe a non-leather material but it *may* also indicate leather which has been treated differently to 'normal' leather! 'Nubuck' is leather; 'Durabuck' is non-leather, animal-free and tends to be more expensive.
  Nike Cannot guarantee shoes or clothing to be free from animal products.

• **textiles** Under The Textile Products (Indications of Fibre Content) Regulations 1986, the term 'textile fibres' may include wool from sheep or lamb; wool or hair from alpaca, llama, camel, cashmere goat, angora goat, angora rabbit, vicuna, yak, guaco, beaver or otter; horse, goat or other animal hair — with or without an indication of the kind of animal; silk from the silkworm; protein obtained from natural protein substances regenerated and stabilised through the action of chemical agents.

PEOPLE
ANIMALS
ENVIRONMENT

PAE T-Shirts
M, XL
£11.99 (+ p&p) each
or buy all 3 for
£32.97 (+ p&p)
and save £3!

**PAE Computer
Mousemat**
£4.99 (+ p&p)

Wallet-Purse
£4.99 (+ p&p)

PAE Window/Car Sticker
£1.49 (+ p&p)

PAE Mug
£4.45 (+ p&p)

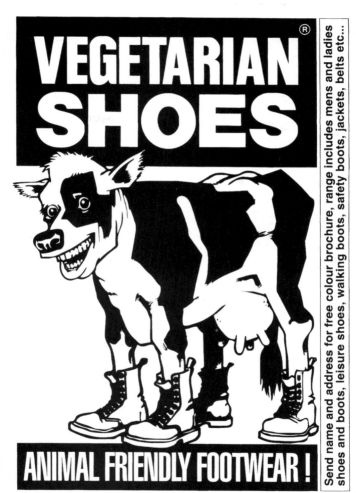

VEGETARIAN SHOES ®

ANIMAL FRIENDLY FOOTWEAR !

Send name and address for free colour brochure, range includes mens and ladies shoes and boots, leisure shoes, walking boots, safety boots, jackets, belts etc...

12 Gardner Street, Brighton, East Sussex BN1 1UP. Tel/Fax: 01273 691913
E-mail: information@vegetarian-shoes.co.uk Web: http://www.vegetarian-shoes.co.uk

home & office

air fresheners	204	fire-lighters	209
bleaches	206	floor products	209
brushes	206	furniture & other polishes	209
candles	206	home furnishings	209
carpet products	207	paint brushes — DIY	209
cleaners — general	207	toilet products	209
cleaners — industrial	208	washing powders, starch etc	210
dishwasher products	208	washing-up products	210
disinfectants	209		
fabric conditioners	209	*notes*	*211*

AIR FRESHENERS

ALADDIN AROMASøπΩfcd87

Pot Pourri/Perfume Oil: Amber, Blue Violet, Briar Rose, Country Garden, Dew Berry, Eastern Temple, Egyptian, Gardenia, Indian Summer, Jasmine, Kyphi, Light Musk, Lily of the Valley, Orchard, Oriental, Peach Melba, Persian Garden, Sandalwood, Spring Flowers, Summer Bouquet, Victorian Posy

BIO-D√ø™πΩ△83

Air Therapy: Lime, Orange

BODY REFORM√ø§πΩfcd85

Room Fragrance Mood Spray: Relaxation, Romance, Vitality

CO-OPπΩ△fcd85

Air Freshener Twin Pad: Alpine Breeze, Citrus Zest; *Dry Aerosol:* Alpine Breeze, Anti-Tobacco, Citrus Zest, Woodland Fruits; *Gel w Odour Neutraliser:* Alpine Breeze, Anti-Tobacco, Citrus Zest, Woodland Fruits

ESSENTIALLY OILSøπ

Floral Water Spray Mist: Chamomile, Cornflower, Eucalyptus, Fir Silver, Juniper, Lavender, Linden Blossom, Marigold, Melissa, Orange Blossom, Peppermint, Pine, Rose, Sage, Thyme Linalol, Verbena Lemon, Witch Hazel

FANTÔME√§πΩfcd78

Strong Perfume Burning Oil: Amble, Apple, Blackberry, Bluebell, Camellia, Carnation, Cedarwood, Chamomile, Cinnamon & Orange, Coconut, Dewberry, Frangipani, Frankincense & Myrrh, Freesia, French Vanilla, Gardenia, Honeysuckle, Hyacinth, Japanese Musk, Jasmine, Lavender, Lemon Verbena, Lilac, Lily of the Valley, Magnolia, Mango, Meadowsweet, Night Scented Stock, Orange Spice, Patchouli, Peach, Pine Forest, Pink Orchid, Primrose, Raspberry, Rose Musk, Sandalwood, Sea Breeze, Stephonotis, Strawberry, Sweet Pea, Tea Rose, Tranquillity, Vanilla, Violet, White Musk, Ylang Ylang

FARROW & HUMPHRIES√øΩfcd80

Drawer Liner: Chamomile & Clover, Elderflower & Primrose, Rose & Cornflower; *Drawer Sachet:* Chamomile & Clover, Elderflower & Primrose, Rose & Cornflower; *Wardrobe Freshener:* Chamomile & Clover, Elderflower & Primrose, Rose & Cornflower

HONESTY√ø§πΩ△76

Pot Pourri: Country Garden, Red Rose

LOTHIAN HERBSøΩ△fcd91

Fragrant Oil (for pot pourri): Camellia, Cedarwood, Cottage Garden, Dewberry, Jasmine, Lavender, Mediterranean, Mexican Vanilla, Opium, Red Rose, Sicilian Lemon, Spiced Orange, White Musk, Wild Rose, Yuletide; *Pot Pourri & Pot Pourri Gift Packed Bag:* Camellia, Cedarwood, Cottage Garden, Dewberry, Jasmine, Lavender, Mediterranean, Mexican Vanilla, Opium, Red Rose, Sicilian Lemon, Spiced Orange, White Musk, Wild Rose, Yuletide; *Room Fragrancer [pump spray]:* Apple Orchard, Chinese Magnolia, Passion Flower, Peach Tree, Wild Rose

MAROMA√πΩfcd85

Encens d'Auroville Incense Cones, Goa Mini Incense; *Ambient Perfume (for pot pourri or house):* Jasmine, Lavender, Lily of the Valley, Musk, Opium Flowers, Orange Blossom, Patchouli, Rose, Rosewood, Sandalwood, Vanilla, Vetyver; *Encens d'Auroville Aromatherpy Wand:* Clear Thoughts, Happy Heart, Joy, Meditation, New Energy, Pure Air, Quiet Mind, Sweet Dreams, Tranquility; *Encens d'Auroville Incense Stick:* Almond Flowers, Amber, Cedarwood, Cinnamon, Coconut, Fern & Moss, Flowers, Frankincense, Gardenia, Geranium, Honeysuckle, Jasmine, Lavender, Lemongrass, Lilac, Lily of the Valley, Lotus, Mimosa, Musk, Myrrh, Opium, Orange Blossom, Orchid, Patchouli, Pine, Rose, Rosewood, Sandalwood, Tuberose, Vanilla, Vetyver, Ylang Ylang; *Encens d'Auroville Mini Incense Stick:* Amber, Fern & Moss, Frankincense, Honeysuckle, Lavender, Lemongrass, Mimosa, Musk, Opium, Rosewood, Sandalwood, Vanilla, Ylang Ylang; *Encens d'Auroville Perfume Sachet (for drawers, wardrobes, cars):* Fern & Moss, Honeysuckle, Jasmine, Opium, Rosewood, Sandalwood; *New Encens d'Auroville Incense Stick:* Dawn, Desert Dunes, Into the Night, Mountains, Oceans, Rain Forest, Rajasthan, Red Spices, Spiritual Perfume, Sweet Sandal, White Musk, Wild Roses; *The Five Elements Incense Stick:* Air, Earth, Ether, Fire, Water

MEADOWSWEETø™§πΩ∆86

Fantasy Fragrant Oil: **Antique Delight, Atlantic Breeze, Fantasy Fruit, Forest Walk, Meadow Fresh;** *Flowers Fragrant Oil:* **Carnation, Freesia, Honeysuckle, Hyacinth, Jasmine, Lilac, Lotus, Rose, Sweet Pea, Violet;** *Fruit Fragrant Oil:* **Apple, Blackberry, Coconut, Dewberry, Grape, Lemon, Mango, Orange, Passion Fruit, Peach, Pineapple, Pomegranate, Strawberry;** *Fragrant Oil:* **Camomile, Eucalyptus, Frankincense, Lavender, Musk, Myrrh, Oriental Pastel Musk, Patchouli, Peppermint, Pine, Rosemary, Sandalwood, Verbena, Vetivert, Ylang Ylang;** *Pebble Pot Pourri:* **Relaxing, Sensual, Tobacco Masking;** *Pot Pourri:* **Arabian Nights, Bouquet of Roses, Caribbean Calypso, Exotica, Floral Garden, Forest Trek, Fresh & Fruity, Honeysuckle, Midnight Passion, Musk Rose, Pacific Cascade, Peach Paradise, Promise of the Orient, Rhapsody, Strawberry Sundae, Wild Dewberry, Wildwood;** *Pot Pourri Reviver Oil:* **Arabian Nights, Bouquet of Roses, Caribbean Calypso, Exotica, Floral Garden, Forest Trek, Fresh & Fruity, Honeysuckle, Midnight Passion, Musk Rose, Pacific Cascade, Peach Paradise, Promise of the Orient, Rhapsody, Strawberry Sundae, Wild Dewberry, Wildwood**

MICHELINE ARCIERøΩfcd

Burning Essence: Ambiance d'Or, Bouquet de Printemps, Crystal Clear, Joie de Vivre, Les 4 Fleurs, Serenity

NEAL'S YARD REMEDIESø

Flower Freshener, Tibetan Incense

NEW SEASONS√øπΩfcd76

Smelling Strips

NORFOLK LAVENDERΩfcd84

Pot Pourri: all; *Room Sprays:* all

PERFUMERS GUILDø§πΩ∆81

Country House Collection of Home Fragrances: Cinnamon & Orange, English Rose, Flower Shop, Lemon Verbena, Lily of the Valley, Provence Lavender, White Musk

WORLDS END TRADING√ø§πΩfcd

Incense Cone: Himalayan Breeze, Mysore; *Incense Stick:* Lakshmi, Siro

BLEACHES

ASTONISH√øπΩfcd95

Thick Bleach

CO-OPπΩ∆fcd85

Thick: Alpine Fresh, Citrus, Thick; *Thin:* Every Day, Thin

BRUSHES

CLEARSPRING√ø§π

Vegetable Washing Brush

CANDLES

ABSOLUTE AROMAS√øπΩ

Tea-lights

ALADDIN AROMASøπΩfcd87

Nightlights; *Scented Hand Dipped Taper:* Geranium & Orange, Lavender,

Lemon & Citronella, Pine & Rosemary; *Vegetable Oil Candle:* Green (Cedarwood), Orange (Petitgrain), Pink (Rosewood), White (Spicy), Yellow (Verbena)

CARIADøπΩ

Night-lights

DR HADWEN TRUST√ø§

Candles: all

ESSENTIAL OIL CO√øπΩfcd93

Night-lights

ESSENTIALLY OILSøπ

Essential Oil Candle (coloured conical w crystals): Cinnamon, Citronella, Clove, Eucalyptus, Fruit & Spice, Geranium, Lavender, Patchouli, Petitgrain, Rosemary, Vetiver, Ylang Ylang

FANTÔME√§πΩfcd78

Night-lights

HEMP UNIONø™§πΩfcd93

Large Square, Small [tin]

LOTHIAN HERBSøΩ∆fcd91

Aromatherapy Candle in Tin: Citronella & Lemongrass, Cypress & Cedarwood, Lavender & Geranium, Orange & Bergamot, Ylang Ylang & Patchouli; *Fragranced Candle:* Apple Orchard, Dewberry, Jasmine, Lavender, Mexican Vanilla, Opium, Red Rose, White Musk

MAROMA√πΩfcd85

Candles: all

NEAL'S YARD REMEDIESø

White Night-lights

NEW SEASONS√øπΩ**fcd76**

Night-lights

NORFOLK LAVENDERΩ**fcd84**

Candles: all

PERFUMERS GUILDø§πΩ∆**81**

Scented Candle: Amber & Mure, Café Creme, Cedar & Sandalwood, Christmas, Fig Tree, Mandarin, Rose & Geranium, Scent of India, Tuberose & Gardenia, Warm Apple Tart

PRICE'S

Candles: all — **except** Church Candles

PURPLE FLAME AROMA. øπΩ**fcd80**

Cinnamon, Citronella, Clove, Eucalyptus, Geranium, Lavender, Night-lights, Patchouli, Petitgrain, Rosemary, Vetiver, Ylang Ylang

SHEARER CANDLES

Advent, Angelchimes, Arctic Lites, Aromatherapy, Classic Dining, Floating, Glitter, Lighting Tapers, Metallic Pillars, Millennium Tins, Nite Lites, Obelisks, Outdoor, Rustic, Scented, Silk Pillars, Spiral, Volcanic Pillars, Wirebrushed Pillars

VEGAN SOCIETY√ø§Ω

Ivy Pillar

CARPET PRODUCTS

ASTONISH√øπΩ**fcd95**

Carpet Shampoo: Automatic, Instant Use, Manual

CO-OPπΩ∆**fcd85**

Carpet Freshener: Alpine Breeze, Citrus Zest

VINDOTKO√ø™§πΩ**fcd75**

Super Concentrated Cleaner

CLEANERS — GENERAL

21st CENTURY HEALTH√ø§πΩ**fcd**

Citra Solv Cleaner & Degreaser, Clean House Clean Planet Kit (recipes & empty dispensers to make household cleaners & furniture polish)

ASTONISH√øπΩ**fcd95**

Anti-Bacterial Cleanser; *Cleaner:* All Purpose, Bathroom, Cream *w* Bleach, Cream *w* Lemon, Glass & Tile, Kitchen, Multi-Purpose, Oven & Hob [paste], Wood; *Remover:* Mould & Mildew, Stain, Tea & Coffee Stain

BIO-D√ø™πΩ∆**83**

Citri-Glow Stain Remover, Glass & Mirror Cleaner, Multi-Surface Cleanser

CO-OPπΩ∆**fcd85**

Cleaner: Bathroom Gel, Pine Multi Surface; *Bathroom Mousse:* Citrus, Pine; *Cream Cleaner:* Aqua, Pine; *Trigger:* Bathroom, Kitchen

ECOVER™πΩ

Cleaner: Cream, Multi-Surface

FOOD SAFE√ø§πΩ**fcd76**

Bathroom Safe, Kitchen Safe, Nurs; *Veggi-Wash:* Concentrate, Ready to

home & office

Use Spray, Wipes

HOMECARE√ø§πΩfcd82

Bar Keeper's Friend All Purpose Powder Cleaner, Bath Brite, Copper Clo, Hob Brite Ceramic Top Cleaner, Homecare Stainless Steel Cleaner & Polish, Shiny Sinks Cream Cleaner

HONESTY√ø§πΩ△76

Little Green Shop: All Purpose Cleaning Concentrate, Cream Cleaner

PURPLE FLAME AROMA. øπΩfcd80

Sweet Feet Pre-Reflexology Wipes: Handy Size, Salon Size; *Tea Tree Moist Wipes:* Bathroom Dispenser, Pocket/Handbag Dispenser

Q2

Cleaner: Bathroom, Brass, Silver

SODASAN

All Purpose, Glass

VINDOTKO√ø™§πΩfcd75

Dirt & Stain Remover

WHOLISTIC RESEARCHøπΩ

Mildew Remover Spray X-14, Mould Stop Spray (Damp-Rid Fresh-All)

CLEANERS — INDUSTRIAL

DEB§πΩfcd90

Detergents & Disinfectants: Ambisan, Fastapine, Florafresh, Tot, Treetop;

Hand Cleaning Wipes: Printers Hand Wipes, Red Box Workshop Wipes; *Hard Surface Cleaners:* Janitol, Janitol Plus, Janitol Rapide; *Heavy Duty Hand Cleaners:* Cradle, Lime, Great White, Natural, Resinega, Swarfega, Swarfega Orange, Swarfega Paint, Swarfega Power, Tufaneg; *Speciality Products:* Altrans, Contect 'Duck Oil'

VINDOTCO√ø™§πΩfcd75

Adhesive/Urethane Remover, All-in-One, Degreaser, Graffiti Remover, One-Step Graphic Ink Remover, Paint & Varnish Stripper Gel; *Power Towels (impregnated towels for work or domestic use):* Heavy Duty (*w* slightly abrasive surface), Really Works

DISHWASHER PRODUCTS

ASTONISH√øπΩfcd95

Automatic Dishwasher Liquid, Rinse Aid

CO-OPπΩ△fcd85

Dishwasher: Rinse Aid, Salt, Ultra Liquid; *Dishwasher Powder:* Automatic, Lemon

ECOVER™πΩ

Dishwash Rinse Aid, Dishwash Tablets

FAITH PRODUCTSøπΩ△88

Dishwasher Gel, Rinse Aid

SODASAN

Clear Rinse; *Concentrated Dishwasher Powder:* Hard Water, Soft Water

DISINFECTANTS

ASTONISH√ønΩfcd95

Germ Clear

CO-OPπΩΔfcd85

Antiseptic, Each Day Pine, Thick Fresh Pine, Thick Lemon

HONESTY√ø§πΩΔ76

Little Green Shop Disinfectant

FABRIC CONDITIONERS

ASTONISH√ønΩfcd95

Fabric Conditioner

BIO-D√ø™πΩΔ83

Fabric Conditioner

ECOVER™πΩ

Concentrated Fabric Conditioner

FIRE-LIGHTERS

CO-OPπΩΔfcd85

Fire-lighters

FLOOR PRODUCTS

ASTONISH√ønΩfcd95

Floor Polish; *Floor Cleaners:* No Rinse, Wood

ECOVER™πΩ

Floor Cleaner

FURNITURE & OTHER POLISHES

21st CENTURY HEALTH√ø§πΩfcd

Clean House Clean Planet Kit (recipes & dispensers to make household cleaners & furniture polish)

BIO-D√ø™πΩΔ83

General Purpose Polish

HOME FURNISHINGS

HEMP UNIONø™§πΩfcd93

Fabric & Furnishings To Order: all

PAINT BRUSHES — DIY

GREAT MILLS

Smoothflow Brushes: all; *Smoothflow Rollers:* all

LG HARRISøπ

No Loss Paint Brush Range: all

TOILET PRODUCTS

BIO-D√ø™πΩΔfcd83

Toilet Cleaner

CO-OPπΩΔfcd85

Lavatory Cleaner: Alpine, Citrus, Pot Pourri; *Toilet Flush:* Blue, Green; *Toilet Fresh:* Alpine Fresh, Pot Pourri

home & office

ECOVER™πΩ

Concentrated Toilet Cleaner

HONESTY√ø§πΩΔ76

Little Green Shop Toilet Cleaner

SODASAN

Toilet Cleaner

WASHING POWDERS, STARCH ETC

21st CENTURY HEALTH√ø§πΩfcd

Aquaball

ASTONISH√øπΩfcd95

Spray Starch; *Laundry (bio):* 2 in 1, Liquid

BIO-D√ø™πΩΔfcd83

Laundry Liquid, Washing Powder

ECOVER™π

Concentrated Autowash Liquid, Concentrated Washing Powder, Laundry Bleach, Water Softener, Wool Wash

FAITH PRODUCTSøπΩΔ88

Laundry Liquid

SODASAN

Bleach Additive, **Compact Laundry Powder, Concentrated Liquid Laundry Detergent**, Water Softener, Wool Detergent

TASUNAMI WAVEø

Natural Papaya Bright

WHOLISTIC RESEARCHøπΩ

Eco-Ball

WASHING-UP PRODUCTS

ASTONISH√øπΩfcd95

Washing-Up Liquid

BIO-D√ø™πΩΔfcd83

Washing-Up Liquid

CO-OPπΩΔfcd85

Concentrated Washing-Up Liquid: Apple, Green, Lemon; *Washing-Up Liquid:* Antibacterial, Every Day, Green, Lemon

ECOVER™πΩ

Washing-Up Liquid, Washing-Up Liquid w Aloe Vera

FAITH PRODUCTSøπΩΔ88

Washing-Up Liquid

HONESTY√ø§πΩΔ76

Little Green Shop Washing-Up Liquid

SODASAN

Concentrated Washing-Up Liquid

notes

- **adhesives** May be processed from hide, bones, fish or dairy products — eg casein. Non-animal adhesives are based on starch, cellulose, natural rubbers, or inorganic substances based on silicone. The trend is towards using cheaper, synthetic materials.
  Humbrol Say Poly Adhesives and Enamel Thinners are vegan, but not prepared to confirm this in writing.
  Sellotape "do not feel it appropriate for Sellotape to be included in [this] publication"

- **Artex** No questionnaire returned. However, confirmed by phone that Artex Ready-To-Mix is free from animal ingredients. The powder mixes contain gelatine and the main product — Artex Textured Finish — contains an animal-based glue.

- **bank notes** Are produced without the use of gelatine.

- **beds, mattresses, pillows** Modern beds and mattresses generally contain synthetic materials — such as acrylic, viscose, polyester, polypropylene, nylon or acetate. However, wool may be used in some mattresses. Feather or down may still be used in pillows and continental quilts.

- **ceramics, glass, pottery** Bone china goods contain around 50% bone. Porcelain, *plain* sanitary items (toilets, cisterns, sinks, etc) and *plain* urbanware glazed mugs (the glazes used are inorganic pigments made from minerals) appear to be animal-free. However, if a motif is added, it may be fixed with animal-derived glues.
  Glass consists of silica (in the form of sand), sodium oxide, calcium oxide, magnesium oxide and aluminium oxide, and appears to be animal-free.

- **envelopes** Members of the Envelope Makers & Manufacturing Stationers' Association agree that the adhesives used in making envelopes, and the adhesives on gummed envelopes are animal-free. However, some of the adhesives used on self-seal envelopes contain casein.

- **fabric dyes** (home use) Usually synthetic, from chemicals, and tested on animals (under current regulations new chemicals must be animal tested). "Natural" dyes are more likely to contain animal substances.

- **floor covering** The British Resilient Flooring Manufacturers' Association say that many resilient floor covering manufacturers use stearates (principally animal-derived) as stabilisers for PVC and stearic acid (principally animal-derived) as a lubricant during certain production processes.

- **furniture** May contain synthetic/plant fibres (eg nylon, acrylic, polyester, cotton) or animal-derived materials — including leather, suede, wool felt, animal hair (especially horse) and feathers. Adhesives are commonly PVA (polyvinyl acetate).

Courts With the exception of leather upholstery and the inclusion of wool in some mattresses, no other animal products are used in the manufacture and/or development of goods sold by Courts in the UK.

• **incense sticks** May contain gelatine or other animal substance as a binder.

• **matches** The heads contain gelatine, which is used as a binder.

• **paint** May contain shellac. For further details please send stamped SAE marked 'Home Decorating' to: Vegan Society, Donald Watson Hse, 7 Battle Rd, St Leonard's-on-sea, E Sussex TN37 7AA.

• **paper** Most papers are sized (enhances the resistance of paper to liquid penetration and provides surface strength, stiffness and a glaze to the finished sheet) with starch derived from maize, wheat, potatoes or rice — but gelatine is still used for high-grade paper products. Casein is sometimes used as a binder in high quality food board and art papers. Some very specialist grades may contain chitin/chitosan.

Daler-Rowney All paper except Saunders Waterford is animal-free. Says specialised hand made papers from small traditional paper mills may be pressed between felt layers (the wool in the felt gives the paper texture and depth) and top sized using gelatine. Use of gelatine by major manufacturers is rare.

Inveresk Plc Repeat recycled copier papers are animal free.

John Dickenson (Basildon Velvet, Three Candlesticks, Basildon Bond, Challenge, Croxley Script, Lion Brand) Products are free from gelatine and all adhesives and gums used are animal-free.

WH Smith The glue in its paper products is oil-based.

• **postage stamps** The gum on British stamps is animal-free — consisting of polyvinyl alcohol (petroleum based) and dextrin (from starch).

• **rubber** Natural rubber is made from latex (sap obtained from rubber trees) combined with other materials — including the following which could be animal-derived: carbon black (E153), glycerol (E422), salts of fatty acids (E470), stearic acid (E570), calcium stearate (E572). Synthetic rubbers are made from oil and a combination of chemicals.

• **rubber gloves** All gloves made by the London Rubber Company (makers of the Marigold range) involve the use of milk casein as a processing aid in the latex. However, Safeway have one variety suitable for vegans — Mapa Hypoallergenic — and Sainsbury's own brand are also free from casein and any other milk derivatives.

• **video cassette tapes** It would appear that these are animal-free.

• **water filters** The charcoal is normally vegetable based.

animal care

food & food supplements 216
health & care products 216
humane traps & deterrents 217

notes 218

FOODS & FOOD SUPPLEMENTS

AUSTRIAN MOOR√ø§πΩΔ

Moor Bouquet for Pets

CARABAY√øπΩfcd

Seaweed Animal Meal

DENES

Wholegrain: Biscuits, Mixes, Treats

GREEN ARK√ø™§πΩfcd

Cereal Mix, Green Food Supplement, Herbal Tonic, Herbie Wellbeing, Rhino, Slippery Elm Gruel; *Powder:* **Pure Garlic, Pure Seaweed, Raspberry Leaf**

HARBINGERS√ø

Vegedog (supplements — which when added to recipes supplied provide complete meals for dogs)

SEPTICO√øπΩ

Seaweed Supplement (for cats, dogs, birds, goats & all domestic pets)

VEGAN SOCIETY√ø§Ω

Vegecat, Vegekit (supplements — which when added to recipes supplied provide complete meals for cats/kittens)

VINK SALESø§π

Yarrah Organic Petfood: Chewing Bones, Vegie Ears

HEALTH & CARE PRODUCTS

AUSTRIAN MOOR√ø§πΩΔ

Moor: Cream for Pets, Shampoo for Pets

HEALTH IMPORTSøπΩfcd95

Thursday Plantation Tea Tree Dog Shampoo

HEMP UNIONø™§πΩfcd93

Hutch Hemp (biodegradable bedding)

HUMANE RESEARCH TRUST√ø§πΩfcd

Assisi: Natural Grooming Lotion for Small Animals (guinea pigs, rabbits, rats, hamsters, gerbils, etc), Rescue Remedy (for cats, dogs, caged birds, small animals); *Assisi (for cats):* K-Purr Grooming Lotion, Shampurr Aromatic Shampoo; *Assisi (for cats & dogs):* Kennel Spray, Natural Eye Drops, Tea Tree Grooming Oil; *Assisi (for cats, dogs & small animals):* Homoeopathic Ear Drops, Homoeopathic Eye Drops, Natural Ear Drops, Sore Paws All Purpose Ointment; *Assisi (for dogs):* Aroma Tea Tree Shampoo, Aromatic Shampoo, Coat Conditioner, Original All Purpose Grooming Lotion, Tea Tree Concentrated Shampoo; *Assisi Homoeopathic Cream (for cats & dogs):* Anal Itching, Arnica, Eczema, Rheumatism, Warts

MASON'S√øπΩfcd76

Dog Oil For Massaging (for dogs, horses, humans)

NEW SEASONS√ø𝜋Ωfcd76

Bright Eye Wipes (for cats, dogs, horses, rabbits, hamsters), Pad Balm for Dogs, Travel Trauma Conditioner; *Conditioners:* Relax-a-Cat, Relax-a-Dog; *Deodorant:* Cat, Dog; *Dog Conditioner:* Fierce, Timid; *(for dogs, cats, horses, rabbits):* Battle Wounds Cream, Battle Wounds Spray, Dry Skin Cream; *Lotion for Elderly:* Cats, Dogs; *Shampoo & Conditioner for Dogs:* Dry Skin, Herbal

PINETUM PRODUCTSø𝜋Ω

Arthritis Relief, Calmer, Deodorant, Flea/Insect Control

VINDOTCO√ø™§𝜋Ωfcd75

Hoof Enhancer; *Shampoo:* Dog, Horse

HUMANE TRAPS & DETERRENTS

ALADDIN AROMAS√ø𝜋Ωfcd87

Natural Insect Repellent

FSC𝜋

Herbcraft Bug Ban Spray

JANUSø

Live Capture Trap: Corvid for Magpies & Crows, Double Entry Multi-Rat, Feral Pigeon & Moorhen, Fox, Mink & Squirrel, Mole Tunnel Trap, Monarch Multi-Rat, Mouse Multibox, Mouse Trapease, Rabbit Cage, Rabbit Multibox, Rat, Rook & Pheasant, Sparrow, Squirrel Multicatch

NEW SEASONS√ø𝜋Ωfcd76

Anti-Flea Shampoo & Conditioner for Dogs, Cat Stroke for Fleas, Flea Spray (for dogs & cats); *Anti-Mate Spray (for use on females in season to repel males):* for Cats, for Dogs; *Bedding Spray (to repel fleas):* for Cats, for Dogs

PINETUM PRODUCTSø𝜋Ω

Snail Ban

SPR𝜋

Eradicate Louse Powder (for livestock, pets, birds)

VINDOTCO√ø™§𝜋Ωfcd75

Stable Fly: Spray & Deodoriser, System

WHOLISTIC RESEARCHø𝜋Ω

Whole Live Mouse Traps: Maxi Trip-Trap, Mini Trip-Trap

notes

because tens of thousands of domestic animals are unwanted and would otherwise be destroyed.

• **Happidog** Retailers generally stock the D_3-containing cans and/or D_3-containing dry mix packs. The D_2-containing animal-free dry packs are usually available by mail order only.

• **Humane Research Trust** Stocks products from several companies, each of which has a different fixed cut off date, ranging from 1976-81. Assisi Kennel Spray can kill fleas.

• **Janus** Not a vegan-oriented company — also produces non-humane traps.

• **Larkhall Green Farm** Advises that all its supplements are suitable for animals if doses are adjusted appropriately (try herbalists for advice, and don't ever give tinctures to cats).

• **pets** The inclusion of an 'Animal Care' section should not be construed as indicating support for the pet industry or ownership of pet (companion) animals. Pets exist solely for human gain — in the case of the pet trade: financial; in the case of pet owners: pleasure — and their freedom is necessarily restricted. In the quest for the 'perfect' pet, breeds of dog, cat, bird and fish have, through genetic manipulation, been created with 'aesthetically-pleasing' deformities. Many animal-free shoppers find pet ownership incompatible with their animal rights philosophy and those who find themselves caring for animals often do so

Save animals from the carving knife

Viva! the campaigning vegetarian and vegan charity, is determined to stop the mindless slaughter of millions of farmed animals. We launch regular, hard-hitting campaigns and have a huge commitment to youth education. *Viva!* is sowing the seeds of a more compassionate tomorrow. *Viva!* also offers a wealth of information on going, being and staying vegan including:

- *Viva! Guides*, written by experts and celebrities on all aspects of a vegan diet from easy nutrition and delicious recipes to animal rights and practical tips.

- *Viva! Books for Life*, featuring 100 titles from bringing up children to bringing down the meat industry.

- *Viva! Catalogue*, with vegan wines, hand-made chocs, T-shirts, cards, pens, mugs and much more.

- *Viva!* books – *The Silent Ark*, (for adults), *The Livewire Guide to Going, Being & Staying Veggie* and *Born to be Wild* (both for teenagers). Written by *Viva!*'s director and covering all the issues – everything you need to argue your beliefs with confidence and attitude!

Add your voice to ours and join the fight for life.

Please send your name and address for a free pack to:
Viva! (Dept. AFS), 12 Queen Sq., Brighton BN1 3FD
Tel: 01273 777688
E: info@viva.org.uk
W: www.viva.org.uk

Viva!

garden & leisure

arts & crafts   222
cleaners — outdoor   222
gardening & compost products   222
smoking products   223

notes   *224*

ARTS & CRAFTS

DALER ROWNEYø

Artists' Oil Colours: all — **except** Blue Black, Ivory Black; *Artists' Brushes:* Cryla, Dalon, Series 240, Series 270, Series 280; *Cryla & Cryla Flow:* all — **except** Ivory Black; *Designer's Gouache:* all; *FW Artists' Ink:* all; *Georgian Oil Colours:* all — **except** Coeruleum (hue), Ivory Black, Prussian Green; *Luma Brilliant Water Colours:* all; *Painting Surfaces & Equipment:* all — **except** Canvas Panels, Rabbit Skin Size, Saunders Waterford Paper; *Pearlescent Liquid Acrylic Colours:* all; *Rowney Screen & Fabric Printing Colours:* all; *Rowney Water Based & Oil Based Block Printing Colours:* all; *System 3 Acrylic Colours:* all

JP TEXTILESøπΩfcd97

Knitting/Weaving Yarn: 100% Hemp, **Organic Cotton, Recycled Denim & PET**

PERFUMERS GUILDø§πΩ∆81

Scented Watercolour Cards (floral scented)

WINSOR & NEWTON

Winsor Universal & Fine Detail Canvas; *Acrylic & Oil Mediums & Varnishes:* all; *Artisan Brushes:* all; *Artisan Oil Colours:* all — **except** Ivory Black; *Artists' Oil Colours:* all — **except** Ivory Black; *Cartridge Paper:* Medium, Smooth; *Cotman Brushes:* all; *Finity Artists' Acrylic:* all — **except** Ivory Black; *Galeria Brushes:* all; *Galeria Flow Formula Acrylic:* all — **except** Ivory Black; *Griffin Alkyd Oil Colours:* all — **except** Ivory Black; *Win-* *ton Oil Colours:* all — **except** Ivory Black

CLEANERS — OUTDOOR

DEB§πΩfcd90

Ready-to-Use Traffic Film Remover (vehicle cleaner), Wash & Wax (vehicle shampoo); *Engine & Parts Degreaser:* Jizer, Jizer Bio; *Marine:* Jizer Marine (solvent cleaner), Marinol (bilge, tank, deck wash), Rustoff (rust, scale remover)

PHOSTROGENπΩ

Cleaner: Concentrated Algae, Path & Drive; *Ready-to-Use Cleaner:* Algae, Multi-Purpose

GARDENING & COMPOST PRODUCTS

AUSTRIAN MOOR√ø§πΩ

Flora Moor Multi-Purpose Plant Food

CARABAY√øπΩfcd

Seaweed Fertilizer

DANU EARTHCARE√™§πΩ

Danu Organic: Bulb Fibre, Compost, Hanging Gardens, Herb Gardens, Houseplant Compost, Lawn Fertilizer & Conditioner, Safe-Food Grow Bags, Seedling Compost

GROWGANIC√øπ

Natural Seaweed Plant Feed [tab], Pure Seaweed Extract

MAXICROP√ø

Calcified Seaweed, Organic Plant Growth Stimulant, Seaweed Meal; *Plus:* Complete Garden Feed, Flower Fertiliser, Sequestered Iron, Tomato Fertiliser

ORGANIC GARDENING CATALOGUEøπ

Calcified Seaweed, Chase Seaweed Meal, Cocoa Shell Mulch, Coir Fibre Brick, Composted Bark, Dolomitic Limestone, Epsom Salts, Gypsum, Hop Manure, Humate AG, Leafmould Compost Kit, Liquid Comfrey, Moorland Gold, Organic Garden Potash, Organic Moisture Retainer, Perlite, QR Compost Maker, Rock Phosphate, Seaweed Plus Iron, Seaweed Root Dip, SM3 Seaweed Extract, Sulphur Chips, Wood Charcoal; *Biotal:* Compost Maker, For Grass, For Leaves; *Danu:* Bulb Fibre, Houseplant Compost, Seedling Compost, Soil Conditioner

PHOSTROGENπΩ

Acid Plant Food, Basketmate Swellgel, Food Tablets, Just Pour Plant Food, Plant Food, Rose Food, Swellgel, Tomato Food; *House Plant Care:* 20 Systemic Ins Pin, Food Spikes, Food Tablets, Leaf & Feed, Liquid Food, When to Water Indoors; *Lawn Care:* Lawn Food, Moss Killer, Rootbuild LF; *Time Release:* Cluster Card, Handipak, Plant Food

PINETUM PRODUCTSøπΩ

Cumulus Compost Maker, Refresh (biological treatment for rainwater); *Compost & Mulches:* Fertile Fibre Multi Purpose, Green Grow Soil Conditioner & Mulch; *Foliar Feed:* Flora Moor, Liquid Seaweed; *Natural Fertilisers:* Calcified Seaweed, Cumulus K (potash), Dolomite Lime, Reclaym Garden Gypsum, Rock Phosphate, Seaweed Meal, Volcanic Rock Dust

TAMAR ORGANICSøπ

Compost: Fertile Fibre Vegan Mix, Nature's Own Seed Compost; *Fertiliser:* Garden Potash/Potassium, Liquid Comfrey, Pelleted Hops, Rock Phosphate, Seaweed Liquid, Seaweed Meal; *Soil Conditioner:* Cocoa Shell Mulch, West Country Compost

SMOKING PRODUCTS

NATURAL AMERICAN SPIRIT√øπ

100% Additive Free Natural Organic Rolling Tobacco; *100% Additive Free Natural Tobacco Cigarettes:* Lights, Regular

RIZLA

Cigarette Papers: all

SWEDISH MATCH

Swan Cigarette Papers: all

garden & leisure

notes

- **Humbrol** Say Airfix Plastic Construction Kits are vegan, but not prepared to confirm this in writing.

- **musical instruments** All modern guitar strings are made from metal or nylon. Guitar picks are now made of plastic. The heads of most modern percussion instruments are non-animal 'skin'. 'Ethnic' percussion instruments are still made with animal skins. All Remo heads are animal-free.

- **photographic film** All photographic film and papers (the resulting photographs) contain gelatine. However, an expanding range of (animal-free) digital systems is available. The cameras are generally more expensive than their conventional counterparts and require a computer — and, if hard copies are required, a printer.
  Olmec SECURE — the next generation digital photographic material created by ICI Imagedata — is beginning to be used in photo booths and film processing shops.

- **Plasticine** Contains tallow.

- **tennis balls** Contain wool

The Overseas Aid Charity for Vegetarians & Vegans is

VEGFAM

(Registered Charity No. 232208, Inland Revenue Ref XN8555)

FEEDS THE HUNGRY WITHOUT EXPLOITING ANIMALS

The Fragile Environment of Developing Countries cannot support TWO populations
Humans and their Food Animals.

For over 30 years VEGFAM has provided short and long-term Relief to People who have been
the victims of Drought, Flood, Cyclone or War in over 40 countries. Our Supporters control how
much of their Donation goes on Administration since VEGFAM operates three separate Funds for
the use of Donors/Testators the particulars of which are:

GENERAL DONATIONS paid into a/c No 65023307 00   The Co-operative Bank
will be apportioned (by % shown) between   plc, 242 High Street, EXETER,
PROJECTS (91%)   a/c No 65023323 00   at   EX4 3QB, Sort Code 08-92-90
Administration Expenses (7%)   a/c No 65023310 00   (Midland Bank a/cs retained
Office Building Fund (2%)   a/c No 65023336 53   for use by existing Donors)

SUPPORTERS ARE INVITED TO PAY DONATIONS DIRECT TO ANY OF THESE ACCOUNTS
Tel/Fax Lydford (01822) 820203 or (01550) 721197 for more details - Covenant Forms/Bankers Order
Forms etc (& self catering visitors accommodation) or write (SAE appreciated) to:
VEGFAM, "The Sanctuary", Nr Lydford, OKEHAMPTON, Devon, EX20 4AL
Website: http://www.veganvillage.co.uk/vegfam/   Email: vegfam@veganvillage.co.uk
THANK YOU FOR YOUR SUPPORT

ANIMAL-FREE CRITERIA

> To qualify for inclusion in the *Vegan Shopper*, products must, as far as is possible and practical, be *entirely* free of animal involvement.

NO ANIMAL INGREDIENTS

The manufacture and/or development of the product, and where applicable its ingredients, must not involve, or have involved, the use of any animal product, by-product or derivative

such as:

• **animal-derived additives** — *(see ADDITIVES, page 228)* • **animal fibres** — angora, astrakhan, cashmere, mohair, wool • **animal milk derivatives** — casein, caseinates, lactates, lactic acid, lactose • **animal milks** • **bee products** — bee pollen, bee venom, beeswax, honey, propolis, royal jelly • **dairy products and by-products** — butter, cheese, whey, yoghurt • **eggs and their derivatives** (eg albumen, lecithin, lutein • **items obtained directly from the slaughter of animals** — fish (including anchovies), game and their derivatives (eg meat/fish extracts and stocks), poultry, meat • **marine animal products** — ambergris, capiz, caviar(e), chitin, coral, fish scales, fishmeal, isinglass, marine oils and extracts (eg fish oils, shark oil (squalene or squalane), seal oil, whale oil), natural sponge, pearl, roe, seal meat, shellfish, sperm oil, spermaceti wax, whale meat • **miscellaneous** — amniotic fluids, animal and fish glues, carmine/carminic acid, catgut, chamois, cochineal, crushed snails or insects, fixatives (eg musk, civet, castoreum) hormones (eg oestrogen, progesterone, testosterone) ivory, lanolin(e), oil of mink, parchment, placenta, silk, shellac, snake venom, some vitamins (eg D3), urea, vellum, and *any carriers, processing aids or release agents containing/comprising substances of animal origin* • **slaughter by-products** — animal fats (eg dripping, lard, suet, tallow), amino acids, aspic, bone, bone charcoal, bone meal, bristles, collagen, down, dried blood, fatty acid derivatives, feathers, fur, gelatin(e), glycerin(e)/glycerol, hair, hides (leather, suede etc), hoof & horn meal, oleic acid, oleoic oil, oleostearin, pepsin, proteins (eg elastin, keratin, reticulin), rennet, skins, stearates, stearic acid, stearin(e)

Vegetable, mineral or plant/mineral-derived synthetic forms of the substances above are acceptable, as are microbiologically-fermented substances of plant origin.

NO ANIMAL TESTING

The development and/or manufacture of the product, and where applicable its ingredients, must not involve, or have involved, testing of any sort on animals conducted at the initiative of the manufacturer or on its behalf, or by parties over whom the manufacturer has effective control

ADDITIVES

A food additive alters the properties of a basic foodstuff or mixture of foodstuffs for the purpose of achieving one, or a combination of, the following: aiding the production process, preserving, modifying consumer perception. The majority of additives possess *no* nutritive value. All the countries of the European Union share a common list of additives. They are preceded with an 'E' to show they have been approved for use within the Union and must be displayed on the labels of all foods containing them. Some additives do not have 'E' numbers and therefore do not have to be declared. These include solvents, used to dilute other additives such as colourings and to extract flavours. Flavourings constitute the largest group of non-'E' additives.

The addition of substances to modify food is by no means a new phenomenon. Salt, for example, has been used as a preservative since c 3000BC. However, the routine and insidious use of animal-derived substances, the known health problems associated with some additives (including eczema, hyperactivity, nausea, allergies, asthma and migraine), and the totally unnecessary and morally objectionable requirement to *test new additives on animals*, all provide the animal-free shopper with an incentive to avoid additive-containing products where alternatives are available.

Note: All products appearing in the *Vegan Shopper* containing additives listed in the **POSSIBLY ANIMAL-DERIVED** category have been judged to be animal-free on the basis of manufacturer/distributor declarations.

ANIMAL-DERIVED ADDITIVE

• **E120** cochineal • **E542** edible bone phosphate • **E901** beeswax • **E904** shellac • **calcium mesoinositol hexaphosphate** • **lactose** • **sperm oil** • **spermaceti**

POSSIBLY ANIMAL-DERIVED

• **E101** riboflavin, lactoflavin, vitamin B12 • **E101a** riboflavin 5'-phosphate • **E153** *(believed animal-free version only may be used in food)* carbon black, vegetable carbon • **E161(b)** lutein • **E161(g)** canthaxanthin • **E236** formic acid • **E237** sodium formate • **E238** calcium formate • **E270** lactic acid • **E322** lecithin • **E325** sodium lactate • **E326** potassium lactate • **E327** calcium lactate • **E422** glycerol/glycerine • **E430** *(believed to be no longer permitted in food)* polyoxyethylene (8) stearate, polyoxyl (8) stearate • **E431** polyoxyethylene (40) stearate, polyoxyl (40) stearate • **E432** polyoxyethylene sorbitan monolaurate, polysorbate 20, tween 20 • **E433** polyoxyethylene sorbitan mono-oleate, polysorbate 80, tween 80 • **E434** polyoxyethylene sorbitan monopalmitate, polysorbate 40, tween 40 • **E435** polyoxyethylene sorbitan monostearate, polysorbate 60, tween 60 • **E436** polyoxyethylene sorbitan tristearate, polysorbate 65, tween 65 • **E470(a)** sodium, potassium and calcium salts of fatty acids • **E470(b)** magnesium salts of fatty acids • **E471** glycerides of fatty acids, glyceryl monostearate, glyceryl distearate • **E472(a)** acetic acid esters of glycerides of fatty acids, acetoglycerides, glycerol esters • **E472(b)** lactic acid esters of glycerides of fatty acids, lactylated glycerides, lactoglycerides • **E472(c)** citric acid esters of glycerides of fatty acids • **E472(d)** tartaric acid esters of glycerides of fatty acids • **E472(e)** mono and diacetyltartaric acid esters of glycerides of fatty acids • **E472(f)** mixed acetic and tartaric acid esters of mono- and di-glycerides of fatty acids • **E473** sucrose esters of fatty acids • **E474** sucroglycerides • **E475** polyglycerol esters of fatty acids • **E476** polyglycerol esters of polycondensed fatty acids of castor oil, polyglycerol polyricinoleate; polyglycerol esters of dimerised fatty acids of soya bean oil • **E477** propylene glycol esters of fatty acids; propane-1,2-diol esters of fatty acids • **E478** lactylated fatty acid esters of gylcerol and propane-1,2-diol • **E479(b)** thermally oxidised soya bean oil interacted with mono- and di-glycerides of fatty acids • **E481** sodium stearoyl-2-lactylate • **E482** calcium stearoyl-2-lactylate • **E483** stearyl tartrate • **E491** sorbitan monostearate • **E492** sorbitan tristearate, span 65 • **E493** sorbitan monolaurate, span 20 • **E494** sorbitan mono-oleate, span 80 • **E495** sorbitan monopalmitate, span 40 • **E570** fatty acids (including myristic, stearic, palmitic and oleic), butyl stearate • **E572** magnesium salts of fatty acids (including magnesium stearate); calcium stearate • **E585** ferrous lactate • **E627** guanosine 5'-disodium phosphate, sodium guanylate, disodium guanylate • **E631** sodium 5'-inosinate • **E635** sodium 5'-ribonucleotide • **E640** glycine and its sodium salt • **E920** L-cysteine hydrochloride • **E1518** glyceryl mono-, di- and tri-acetate (triacetin) • **calcium hepatonate** • **calcium phytate** • **diacetin** • **glyceryl** • **leucine** • **monoacetin** • **oxystearin** • and **any unspecified flavourings**

VEGAN SOCIETY TRADE MARK

The animal-free marketplace continues to expand as ever-increasing numbers of consumers dispense with animal products for reasons of ethics, health or ecology. Recognising that it is not always apparent whether a product is entirely animal-free, the Vegan Society promotes a trade mark for use on goods meeting its 'no animal ingredients' and 'no animal testing' criteria *(see page 226)*.

In addition, trade mark users who are unwilling to voluntarily label their GM derivative-containing registered products will be allowed until 18 July 2002 to replace the derivatives with non-GM alternatives.

There is a licensing fee for use of the Vegan Society Trade Mark which is assessed on the company's actual/estimated annual revenue. Users are entitled to a 20% discount on display advertising in *The Vegan* magazine and a 10% loyalty discount for entering into subsequent (12-month) agreements. Companies selling exclusively animal-free products receive a 25% discount.

A 'TM' after the name of a company appearing in the *Vegan Shopper* indicates that it is an authorised user of the Trade Mark on *registered* products.

Prospective applicants in the UK are invited to ring 01424 427393 for a free Trade Mark Enquiry Pack.

For a current list of authorised Trade Mark users and their registered products send an SAE marked 'Trade Mark List' to: *The Vegan Society, Donald Watson Hse, 7 Battle Rd, St Leonard's-on-Sea, E Sussex TN37 7AA.*

GLOSSARY OF ANIMAL SUBSTANCES

A 'Ω' indicates that non-animal (synthetic, vegetable or plant/mineral-derived) versions/sources by the same name are known to exist.

• **albumen/albumin** egg white *Use/s:* food binder • **alpha hydroxy acids (AHAs)** Ω naturally occurring chemicals derived from fruit or milk *Use/s:* cosmetics • **ambergris** morbid concretion obtained from the intestine of the sperm whale *Use/s:* perfumes • **amino acids**Ω 'building blocks' of proteins • **amniotic fluid** fluid surrounding the foetus within the placenta *Use/s:* cosmetics • **amylase**Ω enzyme in saliva and pancreatic juice • **anchovy** small fish of the herring family. Often an ingredient of Worcester sauce and pizza toppings *Use/s:* flavour enhancer • **angora** fibre obtained from rabbits or goats *Use/s:* clothing • **aspic** savoury jelly derived from meat and fish *Use/s:* glazing agent • **astrakhan** skin of stillborn or very young lambs from a breed originating in Astrakhan, Russia *Use/s:* clothing • **beeswax (E901)** secreted by bees to produce combs *Use/s:* furniture and floor polishes, candles, cosmetics • **bone/bonemeal** animal bone *Use/s:* horticultural fertiliser, bone china ornaments, crockery, supplements • **brawn** boiled meat, ears and tongue of pig *Use/s:* foodstuff • **bristle** stiff animal hair, usually from pigs *Use/s:* brushes • **calcium mesoinositol hexaphosphate** *Use/s:* baked goods, soft drinks, processed vegetables • **capiz** shell *Use/s:* lampshades • **carmine/carminic acid (E120)** red pigment obtained from cochineal *Use/s:* food and drink dyes • **casein** main protein of milk *Use/s:* cheese making • **cashmere** fine wool from the cashmere goat and wild goat of Tibet *Use/s:* clothing • **castoreum** obtained from the anal sex gland of the beaver *Use/s:* fixative in perfumes • **catgut** dried and twisted intestines of the sheep or horse *Use/s:* stringed musical instruments, surgical stitching • **caviar(e)** roe of the sturgeon and other fish *Use/s:* a relish • **chamois** soft leather from the skin of the chamois antelope, sheep, goats, deer etc *Use/s:* cleaning cloth • **charcoal**Ω charred bone or wood *Use/s:* clarifying agent • **chitin**Ω organic base of the hard parts of insects and crustacea eg shrimps, crabs, but also present in small amounts in mushrooms *Use/s:* conditioners and skin care products, thickener and moisturiser in shampoos • **cholecalciferol** see D3 • **civet**Ω substance scraped from glands in the anal pouch of the civet cat *Use/s:* fixative in perfumes • **cochineal (E120)** dye-stuff consisting of the dried bodies of scale insects. Used for making carmine *Use/s:* red food and drink colouring • **cod liver oil** oil extracted from the liver of cod and related fish *Use/s:* food supplement • **coral** hard calcareous substance consisting of the continuous skeleton secreted by coelenterate polyps for their support and habitation *Use/s:* ornaments • **collagen** constituent of connective tissue which yields gelatin(e) on boiling *Use/s:* cosmetics, sausage skins • **D3 (cholecalciferol)** vitamin derived from lanolin or fish oil *Use/s:* vitamin and food supplements • **deoxyribonucleic acid (DNA)**Ω controls protein synthesis/stores genetic information. Found in all animal and plant cells *Use/s:* cosmetics, genetically-modified organisms, shampoos • **down** underplummage of fowls (especially duck and goose) *Use/s:* filling quilts, pillows, sleeping bags, padded clothing • **dripping** melted animal fat *Use/s:* frying • **eider down** small, soft feathers from the breast of the eider duck *Use/s:* filling quilts • **elastin** protein uniting muscle fibres in meat *Use/s:* moisturiser in cosmetics • **fatty acids**Ω organic compounds: saturated, polyunsaturated and unsaturated • **feather**Ω epidermal appendage of a bird *Use/s:* fashion accessory, feather dusters • **felt**Ω cloth made of wool, or of wool and fur or hair *Use/s:* clothing • **gelatin(e)** jelly obtained by boiling animal tissues (skin, tendons, ligaments etc) or bones *Use/s:* confectionery, biscuits, capsules, jellies, photographic film, match heads • **glycerin(e)/glycerol (E422)**Ω clear, colourless liquid which may be derived from animal fats, synthesised from propylene or from fermentation of sugars *Use/s:* solvent for flavours, texture improver, humectant • **hide** animal skin (raw or tanned) *Use/s:* clothing and footwear, clothing accessories, upholstery • **insulin**Ω pancreas of cattle, sheep or pigs *Use/s:* managing diabetes • **isinglass** very pure form of gelatin(e) obtained from the air bladders of some freshwater fish, especially the sturgeon *Use/s:* clarifying alcoholic drinks, jellies • **keratin** protein found in hair, horns, hoofs and feathers *Use/s:* shampoos and conditioners, fertiliser • **L'cysteine hydrochloride (E920)**Ω manufactured from animal hair and chicken feathers, or synthetically from coal tar *Use/s:* shampoo, improving agent for white flour • **lactic acid (E270)**Ω acid produced by the fermentation of milk sugar but also by fermentation in pickles, cocoa and tobacco *Use/s:* acidulant in confectionery, soft drinks, pickles and sauces • **lactose** milk sugar *Use/s:* tablet filler, sweetener, 'carrier' for flavouring agents — especially in crisps • **lanolin(e)** fat extracted from sheep's wool *Use/s:* cleaning products, an emollient and emulsifier used in cosmetics — especially lipsticks • **lard** fat surrounding the stomach and kidneys of the pig, sheep and cattle *Use/s:* culinary • **leather** tanned hide (mostly from cattle but also sheep, pigs, goats etc) *Use/s:* clothing and footwear, clothing accessories, upholstery • **lecithin (E322)**Ω fatty substance found in nerve tissues, egg yolk, blood and other tissues. Mainly obtained commercially from soya bean, peanut and corn *Use/s:* emulsifier in baked goods and confectionery • **lutein(E161(b))**Ω substance of deep yellow colour found in egg yolk.

Obtained commercially from marigold *Use/s:* food colouring • **mohair** cloth or yarn made from the hair of the angora goat *Use/s:* clothing • **musk**Ω substance secreted in a gland or sac by the male musk deer *Use/s:* perfume • **oestrogen**Ω female sex hormone from cow ovaries or pregnant mares' urine *Use/s:* cosmetics, body building supplements, hormone creams • **oleic acid**Ω fatty acid occurring in animal and vegetable fats *Use/s:* soaps, cosmetics, ointments • **oleoic oil** liquid obtained from pressed tallow *Use/s:* margarines • **oleostearin** solid obtained from pressed tallow *Use/s:* soap and candle making • **parchment**Ω skin of the sheep or goat, dressed and prepared for writing etc • **pearl** ('Mother of', or 'cultured') concretion of layers of pain-dulling *nacre* formed around a foreign particle within the shell of various bivalve molluscs, principally the oyster *Use/s:* jewellery and decorative • **pepsin** enzyme found in gastric juices *Use/s:* cheese making • **placenta** organ by which the foetus is attached to the umbilical cord *Use/s:* cosmetics • **progesterone**Ω sex hormone *Use/s:* hormone creams • **propolis** bee glue. Used by bees to stop up crevices and fix combs to the hive *Use/s:* toiletries and cosmetics • **rennet**Ω extract of calf stomach. Contains the enzyme rennin which clots milk *Use/s:* cheese making, junkets • **reticulin** one of the structural elements (together with elastin and collagen) of skeletal muscle • **ribonuclic acid (RNA)** see **deoxyribonucleic acid (DNA)** • **roe** eggs obtained from the abdomen of slaughtered female fish *Use/s:* a relish • **royal jelly** food on which bee larvae are fed and which causes them to develop into queen bees *Use/s:* food supplement • **sable** fur from the sable marten, a small carnivorous mammal *Use/s:* clothing, artists' brushes • **shellac (E904)** insect secretion *Use/s:* hair spray, lip sealer, polishes, glazing agent • **silk** cloth made from the fibre produced by the larvae ('silk worm') of certain bombycine moths, the harvesting of which entails the destruction of the insect *Use/s:* clothing, cosmetics • **sodium 5'-inosinate** occurs naturally in muscle. Prepared from fish waste *Use/s:* flavour enhancer • **sperm oil** oil found in the head of various species of whales *Use/s:* candle making • **spermaceti wax** fatty substance found mainly in the head of the sperm whale, other whales and dolphins *Use/s:* medicines, candle making, cosmetics • **sponge**Ω aquatic animal or colony of animals of a 'low order', characterised by a tough elastic skeleton of interlaced fibres *Use/s:* bathing aid • **squalene/squalane**Ω found in the liver of the shark (and rats) *Use/s:* toiletries and cosmetics • **stearate**Ω salt of stearic acid *Use/s:* body building supplements • **stearic acid (E570)**Ω organic acid prepared from stearin • **stearin(e)**Ω general name for the three glycerides (monostearin, distearin, tristearin). Formed by the combination of stearic acid and glycerin; chiefly applied to tristearin, which is the main constituent of tallow or suet *Use/s:* medicines, skin softener in toiletries and cosmetics • **suede**Ω kid-, pig- or calf-skin, tanned *Use/s:* clothing and footwear • **suet**Ω solid fat prepared from the kidneys of cattle and sheep *Use/s:* cooking • **tallow** hard animal fat, especially that obtained from the parts about the kidneys of ruminating animals *Use/s:* soap and candle making • **taurine**Ω amino acid • **testosterone**Ω male hormone *Use/s:* body building supplements • **urea**Ω waste nitrogen formed in the liver and excreted by the kidneys *Use/s:* toiletries and cosmetics • **vellum**Ω fine parchment prepared from the skins of calves, lambs or kids *Use/s:* writing material • **velvet**Ω fabric made usually of silk but also rayon or nylon *Use/s:* clothing • **vitamin A**Ω (retinol) derived from fish liver oil or egg yolk *Use/s:* cosmetics, food supplement • **volaise** ostrich meat • **whey** residue from milk after the removal of the casein and most of the fat. By-product of cheese making *Use/s:* margarines, biscuits, crisps, cleaning products • **wool** hair forming the fleecy coat of the domesticated sheep (and similar animals) *Use/s:* clothing

The entirely animal-free retail outlets listed below are run by vegans and stock a wide range of products

Devon *Exeter Body Piercing* 17 Fore St Ctre, Fore St, Exeter EX4 3AN **t** 01392 494545 **e** piercing@eclipse.co.uk • **Fife** *The Hundredth Monkey* 91 South St, St Andrews KY16 9QW **t** 01334 477411 • **Gwynedd** *Vegonia Wholefoods* 49 High St, Port Madoc LL49 9LR **t** 01766 515195 • **Hampshire** *Time For Change* 167 Fawcett Rd, Southsea, Portsmouth PO4 0DH **t** 023 9281 8786 • **Hertfordshire** *Barnet Health Store* Barnet Market, St Albans Rd, High Barnet EN5 **t** 020 8441 5753 • **London** *Aluna Hairstyling* 105 Central Park Rd, East Ham, London E6 3DW **t** 020 8552 2230 • **Manchester** *Unicorn Grocery* 89 Albany Rd, Chorlton, Manchester M21 0BN **t** 0161 861 0010 **e** office@unicorn-grocery.co.uk • **Nottinghamshire** *Rainbow Centre* 188 Mansfield Rd, Nottingham NG1 3HW **t** 0115 958 5666 **e** rainbow@innotts.co.uk • **West Midlands** *One Earth Shop* 54 Allison St, Digbeth, Birmingham B5 5TH **t** 0121 632 6909

Germany *Vegan-Shop & Versand* Hohenstrasse 50, D-60385 Frankfurt am Main, Germany **t** 0049 69 440989

Internet *Animal Aid Online* **w** www.animalaid.org.uk • *Vegan Society* **w** www.vegansociety.com

SUGGESTED READING

A ' ¥' before a title indicates it is available from the Vegan Society. Ring 01424 427393 for current price details or send an SAE marked 'Catalogue'. For details of the Vegan Society's range of Information Sheets send an SAE marked 'Information Sheet Index' to: *The Vegan Society, Donald Watson Hse, 7 Battle Rd, St Leonard's-on-Sea, E Sussex TN37 7AA.*

Note: Many of the titles listed below are not written from an entirely animal-free viewpoint but are included on the basis of their informativeness or practical value. A number of the books are, or may be, no longer in print.

BOOKS

additives
Additives — Your Complete Survival Guide Felicity Lawrence, Century *(1986)* • **Food Additives — Taking The Lid Off What We Really Eat** Erik Millstone, Penguin *(1986)* • **The Additives Guide** Christopher Hughes, John Wiley & Sons *(1987)* • **The New E for Additives** Maurice Hanssen, Thorsons *(1987)* • **Understanding Additives** Consumers' Association and Hodder & Stoughton *(1988)* • **What the Label Doesn't Tell You** Sue Dibb, Thorsons *(1997)*

animal care
¥Vegetarian Cats and Dogs James Peden, Harbingers of a New Age (US) *(1999)*

animal experiments & alternatives
Animal Experimentation — The Consensus Changes Gill Langley, Macmillan Press *(1989)* • **Faith, Hope & Charity** Gill Langley, BUAV *(1990)* • **Health With Humanity** Steve McIvor, BUAV *(1990)* • **Science on Trial: The Human Cost of Animal Experiments** Dr Robert Sharpe, Awareness Books *(1994)* • **Secret Suffering** Sarah Kite, BUAV *(1990)* • **Slaughter of the Innocent** Hans Ruesch, CEFMR *(1978)* • **Vivisection Unveiled** Dr Tony Page, Jon Carpenter *(1997)* **Why Animal Experiments Must Stop** Vernon Coleman, EMJ *(1994)*

animal rights/liberation — general
¥Animal Century Mark Gold, Jon Carpenter *(1998)* • **¥Animal Liberation** Peter Singer, Pimlico *(1995)* • **¥Animal Liberation: A Graphic Guide** Lori Gruen, Peter Singer & David Hine, Camden Press *(1987)* •

Animal Rights Hilda Kean, Reaktion Books *(1998)* • **¥Animal Rights — Extending the Circle of Compassion** Mark Gold, Jon Carpenter *(1995)* • **Animal Welfare: A Cool Eye Towards Eden** John Webster, Blackwell Science *(1997)* • **Animals and their Moral Standing** Stephen Clark, Routledge *(1997)* • **¥Animals, Politics & Morality** Robert Garner, Manchester University Press *(1993)* • **Animals' Rights** Henry Salt, Centaur *(1980)* • **Caught in the Act** Melody MacDonald, Jon Carpenter *(1994)* • **Fettered Kingdoms** John Bryant, Fox Press *(1990)* • **Living Without Cruelty** Mark Gold, Merlin Press • **Political Theory & Animal Rights** Paul Clarke & Andrew Linzey, Pluto Press *(1990)* • **The Animal Welfare Handbook** Barry Kew, Fourth Estate *(1993)* • **The Case for Animal Rights** Tom Regan, Routledge *(1988)* • **¥The Dreaded Comparison: Human and Animal Slavery** Marjorie Spiegel, Heretic Books *(1988)* • **The Philosophy of Animal Rights** Tom Regan, Culture & Animals Foundation (US) • **¥The Pocketbook of Animal Facts & Figures UK** Barry Kew, Green Print *(1991)* • **The Silent Ark** Juliet Gellatley, Thorsons *(1996)* • **The Struggle for Animal Rights** Tom Regan, ISAR (US) *(1987)* • **Voiceless Victims** Rebecca Hall, Wildwood House *(1984)*

animals and law
Animals & Cruelty & Law Noël Sweeney, Alibi *(1990)*

bloodsports
Outfoxed Mike Huskisson *(1983)*

circuses and zoos
Beyond the Bars Virginia McKenna, Will Travers & Jonathan Wray, Thorsons *(1987)* • **The Rose-Tinted Menagerie** William Johnson, Heretic *(1990)*

consumerism
The Ethical Consumer Guide to Everyday Shopping ECRA *(1993)*

cookbooks
¥An Allergy Cookbook (vegetarian edition) Patricia Carter, Ian Henry Publications *(1993)* • **¥Calciyum!** David & Rachelle Bronfman Bromedia Inc (US) *(1998)* • **¥Cook Vegan** Richard Youngs, Ashgrove Press *(1993)* • **¥Cooking With PETA** Book Publishing Company (US) *(1997)* • **¥Easy Vegan Cooking** Leah Leneman, Thorsons *(1998)* • **¥Fabulous Beans** Barb Bloomfield, Book Publishing Company (US) *(1994)* • **¥Fat-Free & Easy** Jennifer Raymond, Heart & Soul Publications (US) *(1997)* • **Gourmet Vegan** Heather Lamont, Gollancz *(1988)* • **¥Green Gastronomy** Colin Spencer, Bloomsbury *(1996)* •

¥**Japanese Cooking** Mikoyo Nishimoto Schinner, Book Publishing Company (US) *(1999)* • ¥**Nonna's Italian Kitchen** Bryanna Clark Grogan, Book Publishing Company (US) *(1998)* • ¥**Rainbows and Wellies — The Taigh Na Mara Cookbook** Jackie Reading & Tony Weston, Findhorn Press *(1995)* • ¥**Simply Vegan** Debra Wasserman & Reed Mangels, Vegetarian Resource Group (US) *(1995)* • ¥**The Absolutely Animal-Free Cookbook** Wendy Turner, Book Guild *(1997)* • **The Complete Scoffer** Ronny Worsey, Miso Publications *(1998)* • ¥**The Health Promoting Cookbook** Alan Goldhammer DC, Book Publishing Company (US) *(1997)* • ¥**The New Vegan** Amanda Grant, Metro Books *(1999)* • ¥**The Single Vegan** Leah Leneman, Thorsons *(1989)* • ¥**The Vegan Cookbook** Alan Wakeman & Gordon Baskerville, Faber & Faber *(1996)* • ¥**The Vegan Cookbook** Nicola Graimes *(2000)* • ¥**The Vegan Gourmet** Susann Geiskopf-Hadler & Mindy Toomay, Prima (US) *(1995)* • **The Vegan Health Plan** Amanda Sweet, Arlington Books *(1987)* • ¥**The Vegan Kitchen Mate** David Horton, Vegan Society (NSW) *(1995)* • ¥**Vegan Barbecues & Buffets** Linda Majzlik, Jon Carpenter *(1999)* • ¥**Vegan Cooking** Eva Batt, Thorsons *(1985)* • ¥**Vegan Dinner Parties** Linda Majzlik, Jon Carpenter *(1998)* • ¥**Vegan Feasts** Rose Elliot, Thorsons *(1997)* • ¥**Vegan Vittles** Joanne Stepaniak, Book Publishing Company (US) *(1996)* • ¥**Warming Up To Living Foods** Elysa Markowitz, Book Publishing Company (US) *(1998)*

cosmetics
Cover Up — Taking The Lid Off The Cosmetics Industry Penny Chorlton, Thorsons *(1988)* • **Herbal Cosmetics** Camilla Hepper, Thorsons *(1987)*

ecology — home
Conservation At Home: A Practical Handbook Michael Allaby, Unwin *(1988)* • **Home Ecology** Karen Christensen, Arlington Books *(1989)* • **The Green Home** Karen Christensen, Judy Piatkus *(1995)*

farming
Assault & Battery Mark Gold, Pluto Press *(1983)* • **Chicken and Egg — Who Pays the Price?** Clare Druce, Green Print *(1989)* • **Lethal Legacy: BSE — the Search for the Truth** Dr Stephen Dealler, Bloomsbury *(1996)* • **The Price of Meat** Danny Penman, Gollancz *(1997)*

feminism & animal rights
Animals & Women: Feminist Theoretical Explorations CJ Adams & J Donovan, Duke University Press *(1995)* • **Feminism, Animals & Science — The Naming of the Shrew** Lynda Birke, Open University *(1994)*

food

¥**Food For Free** Richard Mabey, Harper Collins *(1996)* • ¥**Sprout Garden** Mark M Braunstein, Book Publishing Company (US) *(1999)*

gardening

¥**Forest Gardening** Robert A de J Hart, Green Books *(1991)* • ¥**Plants for a Future** Ken Fern, Permanent Publications *(1997)* • **The Natural Garden Book** Peter Harper, Jeremy Light & Chris Madsen, Gaia Books *(1994)* • **The Organic Gardener's Handbook,** Margaret Elphinstone & Julia Langley, Thorsons *(1995)* • **Veganic Gardening** Kenneth Dalziel O'Brien, Thorsons *(1986)*

land use

Beyond Beef — The Rise and Fall of the Cattle Culture Jeremy Rifkin, Thorsons *(1992)* • **Food: Need, Greed & Myopia** Geoffrey Yates, Earthright Publications *(1986)*

leather & fur

Killing for Luxury Michael Bright, Franklin Watts *(1988)*

non-violence

The Non-Violent Revolution — A Comprehensive Guide to Ahimsa Nathaniel Altman, Element *(1988)*

nutrition & health

¥**10 Days to Better Health** Kirsten Hartvig & Dr Nic Rowley, Judy Piatkus *(1998)* • **Alternatives to Drugs** Arabella Melville & Colin Johnson, Fontana *(1987)* • ¥**Foods That Cause You to Lose Weight** Neal Barnard MD, Magni Group (US) *(1996)* • ¥**Foods That Fight Pain** Neal Barnard MD, Bantam Books (US) *(1999)* • **Holistic First Aid: A Handbook for the Home** Michael Nightingale, Optima *(1988)* • **Love Yourself, So Hate the Weight!** Brother Craig, Woodbridge Press (US) *(1997)* • ¥**Pregnancy, Children & the Vegan Diet** Michael Klaper MD, Gentle World (US) *(1994)* • **The Home Herbal** Barbara Griggs, Pan *(1986)* • ¥**Vegan Nutrition** Gill Langley, Vegan Society *(1995)* • ¥**Vegan Nutrition: Pure & Simple** Michael Klaper MD, Gentle World (US) *(1997)*

products — 'traditional' alternatives

1,001 Handy Household Hints Lizzie Evans, Octopus *(1989)*

quotations

The Extended Circle: A Dictionary of Humane Thought Jon Wynne-Tyson, Cardinal *(1990)*

reference

Animals' Contacts Directory Veggies *(annual)* • **Campaign Against Cruelty — An Animal Activist's Handbook** Alex Bourke & Ronny Worsey, Miso Publications *(1998)*

religious

Animal Gospel Andrew Linzey *(1998)* • **Animals and Christianity** Andrew Linzey & Tom Regan, SPCK *(1989)* • **Christianity & the Rights of Animals** Andrew Linzey, SPCK *(1987)* • **Replenish the Earth** Lewis Regenstein, SCM *(1991)*

travel

Cruelty Free Guide to Edinburgh Edinburgh Vegans *(1998)* • **München auf Veganen Wegen** Heidrun Leisenheimer *(1994)* • **Oxford Vegetarians Restaurant & Accommodation Guide** Paul Appleby *(2000)* • **Sunflower Worldwide Vegetarian Restaurant Guide** Peter Crawshay-Williams & Marisa Pucher *(1996)* • **The Good Vegetarian Travel Guide** Catherine Mooney, Headway Books *(1995)* • **The Vegan Guide to Melbourne** Alan Glen *(1994)* • **The Vegan Guide to New York City** Max Friedman & Dan Mills *(1994)* • **The Vegetarian Guide to Australia & New Zealand** Peter Crawshay-Williams *(1997)* • **The Vegetarian Traveller** Jed & Susan Civic, Larson (US) *(1997)* • **Vegan Guide to Sweden** Henrik Shentz *(1999)* • **¥Vegan Passport** George Rodger, Vegan Society *(1996)* • **Vegan Travel Guide (UK and Southern Ireland)*** The Vegan Society *(1998)* • **Vegetarian & Vegan Guide to Ireland** *(1999)* • **Vegetarian & Vegan Guide to the Lake District & Environs** Kendal Vegetarians *(1996-97)* • **Vegetarian Britain** Alex Bourke & Alan Todd *(1998)* • **Vegetarian Europe** Alex Bourke *(2000)* • **Vegetarian France** Alex Bourke *(1998)* • **Vegetarian Israel** Mark Weintraub *(1996)* • **Vegetarian Journal's Guide to Natural Food Restaurants in the USA & Canada** Vegetarian Resource Group *(1998)* • **¥Vegetarian London** Alex Bourke & Paul Gaynor *(1998)* • **Vegetarian Visitor 2000** Annemarie Weitzel, John Carpenter • **Vegetarians Guide to Nottinghamshire** Nottingham Vegetarian & Vegan Society *(1999)* • **Viva! Guide to Vegetarian Brighton** Jo Lacey *(1998)*

veganism & vegetarianism

¥Abundant Living in the Coming Age of the Tree Kathleen Jannaway, MCL *(1991)* • **¥Compassion: The Ultimate Ethic** Victoria Moran, American Vegan Society *(1991)* • **Food for a Future** Jon Wynne-Tyson, Thorsons *(1988)* • **Living Without Cruelty** Mark Gold, Green Print *(1988)* • **McLibel — Burger Culture on Trial** John Vidal, Macmillan *(1997)* • **The New Why You Don't Need Meat** Peter Cox,

Bloomsbury *(1992)* • **The Realeat Encyclopedia of Vegetarian Living** Peter Cox, Bloomsbury *(1994)* • **The Sexual Politics of Meat** Carol Adams, Polity Press *(1990)* • **Vegan — The New Ethics of Eating** Erik Marcus, McBooks Press *(1998)* • **¥Why Vegan** Kath Clements, Heretic *(1995)*

verse

¥21st Century Toys BJ Laprade, InfoDirect Ltd *(1999)* • **¥Talking Turkeys** Benjamin Zephaniah, Penguin *(1994)*

wool

Pulling the Wool Christine Townend, Hale & Iremonger (Aus) *(1985)*

MAGAZINES

Animal Times PETA, PO Box 3169, London SW15 3ZG • **Animals Defenders** National Anti-Vivisection Society, 261 Goldhawk Rd, London W12 9PE • **Arkangel** BCM 9240, London WC1N 3XX • **Campaign Report** National Anti-Vivisection Society — see above • **Eco-Vegan** BM HEAL, London WC1N 3XX • **Ethical Consumer** ECRA Publishing, Unit 21, 41 Old Birley St, Manchester M15 5RF • **GenEthics News** PO Box 6313, London N16 ODY • **HOWL** HSA, PO Box 2786, Brighton BN2 2AX • **Outrage** Animal Aid, The Old Chapel, Bradford St, Tonbridge, Kent TN9 1AW • **Pisces** BM Fish, London WC1N 3XX • **¥The Vegan** The Vegan Society, Donald Watson Hse, 7 Battle Rd, St Leonard's-on-Sea, E Sussex TN37 7AA • **The Vegetarian** The Vegetarian Society, Parkdale, Dunham Rd, Altrincham, Cheshire WA14 4QG • **Vegan Views** 6 Hayes Ave, Bournemouth BH7 7AD • **Viva Active!** *(under 18's)* Viva!, 12 Queen Sq, Brighton, East Sussex BN1 3FD • **Viva Life** Viva! — see above • **Wales Vegan** Montpelier, Llandrindod, Powys, Wales • **Wildlife Guardian** LACS, Sparling Hse, 83-87 Union St, London SE1 1SG

'TALKING' MAGAZINES

The Vegan is available for the visually impaired on cassette from: *Talking Newspaper Association National Recording Centre, Heathfield, E Sussex TN21 8DB* **t** 01435 866102

CONTACT NETWORKS

Many of the groups listed below have limited funds and therefore would probably appreciate receiving a SAE with your enquiry.

BUSINESS

Vegan Business Connection Veggies Catering Campaign, 180 Mansfield Rd, Nottingham NG1 3HW **t** 0115 958 5666 **e** veggies@innotts.co.uk **w** www.innotts.co.uk/~rainbow/veggies • **Vegan Village** Libby, Imaner Hse, 14 Wynford Grove, Leeds LS16 6JL **t** 0113 293 9385 **e** postie@veganvillage.co.uk **w** www.veganvillage.co.uk

COMMUNITIES/PROJECTS

Creating Welhealth Frank Bowman, Ty'n Y Nant, Llanfihangel Glyn Myfyr, Corwen LL21 9UW **t** 07980 158661 *or* 01244 819088. *Planning a self-reliant, vegan community, free from domination by money* • **Living Land Housing Co-op** 25a Stanley Rd, Whalley Range, Manchester M16 8HS. *Veganic growing project* • **New Shoots** PO Box 1229, Clwyd LL16 5ZA. *Small group aiming to establish a Welsh land-based community based on vegan-permaculture* • **Organic Growers of Durham** Low Walworth Market Garden, Walworth, Darlington, Co Durham DL2 2NA **t** 01325 362466. *Experimental vegan growing project* • **Plants for a Future** 'The Field', Higher Penpoll, nr Lostwithiel, Cornwall PL22 ONG **t** 01208 873554 or 87362. *Project aiming to demonstrate the wide variety of commodities such as fuel, food, fibres, medicines etc that can be obtained from plants grown in England. Specialises in growing unusual and useful plants* • **Sunseed Dessert Technology** Shirley Savage, Apdo 9, Sorbas 04270, Almeria, Spain **t** 0034 950 525770 **e** sunseed@clara.net **w** www.sunseed.clara.net. *Holiday centre and research project run under the auspices of the Henry Doubleday Research Association. Vegetarian — caters for vegans* • **The Extended Ethic Vegan Village Project** PO Box 237, Armidale, New South Wales 2350, Australia • **Vegan Community Project** 31 Caerau Rd, Caerau, Maesteg, Bridgend, Mid Glamorgan CF34 OPB. *Aims to form a contact network between people who are interested in living in a vegan community and to establish one or more such communities* • **Vegan Views** 6 Hayes Ave, Bournemouth BH7 7AD. *Contact and news network for people interested in vegan communities as well as other aspects of veganism*

FAMILIES

Vegan Families Contact List see The Vegan Society 's web site (www.vegansociety.com) or send SAE marked 'Families List' to: The Vegan Society, Donald Watson Hse, 7 Battle Rd, St Leonard's-on-Sea, E Sussex TN37 7AA • **Vegan Families Group** Lesley & Paul Dove, 4 Wooster Mews, Harrow HA2 6QS **t** 020 8861 1233 **e** 100706.3632@compuserve.com. *Vegan children's parties & picnics in the London area*

LOCAL

Animal Concern Today Chris Deacon, PO Box 67, Plymouth PL1 1TH **t** 01752 228098 **e** deaconeig@aol.com • **Bedfordshire Vegetarians** Marina Torselli, Sunrise, Flitwick Rd, Westoning, Beds MK45 5AB **t** 01525 720629 • **Birmingham Vegetarians & Vegan Information Centre** Debbie Williams, 5 Shakespeare Rd, Erdington, Birmingham B23 7SN **t** 0121 241 0728 • **Bognor Regis & Chichester Vegans & Vegetarians** Victoria Rickeard, 220 Aldwick Rd, Bognor Regis, W Sussex PO21 3QH **t** 01243 863871 • **Bradford Vegetarian Information Centre** Cynthia & Atma Trasi, 66 Kirkgate, Shipley, W Yorks BD18 3EL **t** 01274 598455 • **Bristol Vegetarian & Vegan Society** 6 Oakridge Cl, Sidcot, Winscombe, N Somerset BS25 1LY **t** 01934 843853 • **Bromley & Environs Vegetarian Group** Kathy Silk, PO Box 317, Beckenham, Kent BR3 1WP • **Chester & Clwyd Vegetarian & Vegan Group** Brian Burnett, Nant Yr Hafod Cottage, Llandegla, Wrexham, Denbighshire LL11 3BG **t** 01978 790442 **e** brianthesquirrel@compuserve.com • **Colchester Vegetarian & Vegan Society** Annette White, 21 Laburnum Way, Nayland, Colchester, Essex CO6 4LG **t** 01206 263545 **e** vegcol@aol.com • **Croydon Vegans** 12 Firze Ct, Ashburton Rd, Croydon, Surrey CR0 6PA **t** 020 8654 3740 *or* PO Box 30516, London SW16 4FG **t** 020 8409 0679 **e** croydon-vegans@yahoo.co.uk **w** www.geocities.com/HotSprings/Villa/7000/Croydon_Vegans/Croydon_Vegans.html • **East Berks Animal Aid** Penny Noakes, 19a St Mary's Rd, Langley, Berks SL3 7EN **t** 01753 543466 • **East Sussex Vegetarians & Vegans** Rachel Crouch, 3 Cuckmere Ct, Alfriston, E Sussex BN26 5XU **t** 01323 870771 **e** rkcrouch@mistral.co.uk • **Exeter Information Centre** Phil Sleigh **t** 01647 253072 **e** psleigh@tesco.net • **Forest Vegetarian & Vegan Society** Hartley Jackson, 9 Russell Rd, Buckhurst Hill, Essex IG9 5QJ **e** forestvvs@altavista.net • **Friends Vegetarian Society** (of the Society of Friends) Charles Ryder, 9 Astons Cl, Woods La, Amblecote, nr Stourbridge, W Midlands DY5 2QT **t** 01384 423899 • **Glasgow Vegan Net-**

work Jo Crozier, 26 Elm St, Glasgow G14 9PX **t** 0141 954 6519 **e** rollocroz@aol.com or Marion Hersh, Dept of Electrical Engineering, 80 Oakfield Ave, Glasgow G12 8LT **t** 0141 330 4906 **e** m.hersh@elec.gla.ac.uk **w** www.gvn@egroups.com • **Gwent Vegetarian & Vegan Group** Carol Handcock, 3 Millbrook Ct, Undy Caldicot, Gwent NP26 3JN **t** 01633 881741 • **Highland Veggies & Vegans** c/o Maralyn Shine, Voluntary Action, 8 Castle St, Inverness IV2 3DX **t** 01456 450496 **e** veggies@loch-ness-project.co.uk • **Hull Veggies** Michele Jacques, 29 Heslerton Ave, Cottingham, E Yorks HU16 5HW **t** 01482 844165 • **Kingston & Richmond Vegetarians** Martin Lake, 87 Porchester Rd, Kingston-Upon-Thames, Surrey KT1 3PW **t** 020 8541 3437 **e** martin.lake@lineone.net or John, 49 Harrowdene Gdns, Teddington, Middx TW11 0DJ **t** 020 8977 9648 • **Leeds Vegetarian & Vegan Society** Ian Davison, 41 Hillcourt Dr, Leeds LS13 2AN **t** 0113 257 2760 • **London Vegans** 7 Deansbrook Rd, Edgware, Middx HA8 9BE **t** 020 8931 1904 **e** londonvegans@onet.co.uk **w** www.londonvegans.freeserve.co.uk • **Manchester Animal Protection** PO Box 155, Manchester M60 1FT • **Merseyside Vegans** John Robinson **t** 0151 475 6472 **e** vegan@tellurian.fsnet.co.uk **w** www.tellurian.fsnet.co.uk • **Merseyside Vegetarian Information & Helplink Group** Marguerita Johnson, 38 Hyacinth Cl, Haycock, St Helens, Merseyside WA11 0NZ **t** 01942 271761 • **Milton Keynes Vegetarians & Vegans** Peter Simpson, 13 Peers La, Shenley Church End, Milton Keynes MK5 6BG **t** 01908 503919 • **Newcastle Vegetarian Group** Jane Darling, 40 Melrose Ave, Backworth, Newcastle-Upon-Tyne NE27 0JD **t** 0191 268 0904 • **Norfolk & Norwich Vegetarian Society** Jane Johnsons, 17 St Austins Gro, Sheringham, Norfolk NR26 8DF **t** 01263 821609 **e** treep@cwcom.net • **North East Vegans** Gordon & Janet Forrest, 9 Seymour St, N Shields, Tyne & Wear NE29 6SN **t** 0191 258 6704 • **North Kesteven Vegetarian & Vegan Information Centre** Michelle Wilson, Myrtle Cottage, Main St, N Kyme, Lincoln LN4 4DF **t** 01526 861426 • **North Riding Vegans & Vegetarians** Patricia Tricker, Cottage No 3, Arrathorne, Bedale, N Yorks DL8 1NA **t** 01677 450176 **e** patricia@p-m-t.freeserve.co.uk • **Northampton Veggies** Katie Wise **t** 01604 603543 **e** veggie@wiggy23.freeserve.co.uk **w** www.wiggy23.freeserve.co.uk • **Oxford Vegetarians** Paul Appleby, 57 Sharland Cl, Grove, Wantage, Oxon OX12 0AF **t** 01235 769425 **e** oxveg@ivu.org **w** www.ivu.org/oxveg/ • **Right Life (Veg Info)** Eve Bolton, 49 Upper Chapel, Launceston, Cornwall PL15 7DW **t** 01566 776256 • **Rochester Area Vegetarian Society** **w** www.enviroweb.org/ravs • **Sheffield & District Group Vegetarian Society** Paul Pearson, 41 Old Hay Cl, Dore, Sheffield S17 3GP

t 0114 235 0511/0114 290 0718 (w) • **Sheffield Vegan Society** c/o RECYC 54 Upperthorpe Rd, Sheffield S6 3EB **t** 0114 258 8869 **e** sheffvegsoc@hotmail.com **w** www.shef.ac.uk/misc/personal/md1akj/veg/akj-svs.htm • **Solent Vegetarians & Vegans** John Curtis, 31 Cranbury Rd, Eastleigh, Hants SO50 5HB **t** 023 8064 3813 **e** jcurtis@ndsuk.com **w** www.ivu.org/solentveg • **Southend Area Veggies** Sue Coleman, 59 Stambridge Rd, Rochford, Essex SS4 1DY **t** 01702 540903 • **Taunton Animals First** 27 North St, Wellington, Somerset TA4 1HW **t** 01823 461754 • **VEGA** c/o 56 Aintree Dr, Lower Darwen, Blackburn, Lancs **t** 01254 671629. **VEGA Youth Contact** Rachel Dugdale **t** 01254 852070 • **Vegan Lifestyle Information** Mrs Beth Gourley, 66 Ravenhill Gdns, Belfast BT6 8GQ, Northern Ireland **t** 028 9045 7888 • **Vegetarian Information Centre** Derek Morrison-Brown, 114 Conway Rd, Colwyn Bay, Conwy LL29 7LL **t** 01492 532024 • **Vegetarian Society of London** Eileen Ramchandran, Top Flat, 62 Redcliffe Sq, London SW10 9BN **t** 020 7370 4276 **e** eileen.ramchandran@which.net • **V~Link** Nina Entwisle-Meeson, Foxwood Hse, 15 Dorset Cl, Buxton, Derbys SK17 9PJ **t** 01298 72772 **e** peakveg@ivu.org **w** www.ivu.org/peakveg • **Wirral Animal Concern** Jenny Jones, 13 Grove St, New Ferry, Wirral CH62 5AX **t** 0151 645 1336

INTERNATIONAL

AUSTRALIA Vegans International (Australia) PO Box 1215, Lismore, 2480 NSW, Australia **t** 0061 2 66897498 **e** veganvoice@lis.net.au **w** www.dkd.net/vegan • **AUSTRIA Vegane Gesellschaft Österreich** Postfach 27, A-1238, Wien, Austria • **BELGIUM Vegan Info** Jaak de Cock, Kapellestraat 66, 9220 Hamme, Belgium **t** 0032 52 478899 **e** jaakdc@village.uunet.be • **BRAZIL Group for Animal Liberation** Maira Moraes Mesquita, Rua Alves Guimaraes No 1211, Ap 61, CEP 05410-002, Sao Paulo SP, Brazil **t** 0055 11 8522639 **e** fepaixao@internetcom.com.br *or* Marcel Gallo, R: Argentina No. 237 - Vila Prudente, CEP - 13420 - 516, Piracicaba - SP - Brazil • **DENMARK Vegana** Bent Martin Muus, Gasvaerksvej 10B, Stuen TV, 1656 Copenhaven V, Denmark **t** 0045 70 20 05 10 **e** info@vegana.dk **w** www.vegana.dk • **FRANCE Léa - Pour l'egalité animalé** 8 rue G. le Bigot, F-94800 Villejuif, France **w** www.ultimania.com/antispe • **Susan Morris/Trevor Warman** Le Guerrat, 09420 Rimont, France **t** 0033 5 61 96 37 03 • **GERMANY MUT Menschenrecht und Tierrecht e.v.** Gruneburgweg 154, D-60323 Frankfurt am Main, Germany **t** 0049 69 559589 • **GREECE Vegans in Greece Contact Group** Aris Skliros, Patission 341, 11144 Athens, Greece **t** 0030 1 22

81 964 • **ITALY Progetto Vivere Vegan** Merry Orling, Piazza Mentana 4, 50122 Firenze, Italy **t** 0039 55 214534 **e** megia@fi.flashnet.it **w** www.veganoutreach.org/ • **NETHERLANDS Dutch Vegan Society** Harm Breunis, Postbox 1087, 6801 BB Arnhem, Netherlands **t** 0031 70 350 3974 **e** schoen@xs4all.nl **w** www.veganisme.non-profit.nl • **NEW ZEALAND The Vegan Society NZ** Bruce Grenville (Secretary), PO Box 876, Auckland, New Zealand **t** 0064 25 7777 23 • **NORWAY Anita Saito** Soberveien 24, 1719 Greaker, Norway • **SWEDEN Swedish Vegan Society** Ulla Troeng, Kloverv 6, 64730 Mariefred, Sweden **t** 0046 159 34404 • **USA American Vegan Society** 56 Dinshah Lane, PO Box H, Malaga, NJ 08328, USA **t** 001 856 694 2887 • **ZIMBABWE** Edna Elliot-McColl, PO Box 824, Mutare, Zimbabwe **t** 00263 11 608 821 **e** eem@pci.co.zw

SOCIAL

Gay Veggies & Vegans Sun/Elsa, GV, BM Box 5700, London WC1N 3XX **t** 020 8690 4792. *Organise London socials and produce Green Queen magazine* • **Vegetarian & Vegan Gay Group** c/o 50 St Paul's Crescent, London NW1 9TN **t** 020 8690 5397 **e** vvgg@freeuk.com *Aimed at gay & bisexual men & women to socialise, organise events and provide advice & information on being gay and vegetarian/vegan* • **Vegetarian Friends** The Old Vicarage, Llangynog, Carmarthen SA33 5BS **t** 01267 241547 • **Vegetarian MatchMakers** Concord House, 7 Waterbridge Crt, Appleton, Cheshire WA4 3BJ **t** 01925 601609 **f** 01925 860442 **e** vmm@cybervillage.co.uk **w** www.cybervillage.co.uk/vmm/ • **Vegan Camp** John Strettle (Organiser), 30 Dinsdale Ave, Wallsend NE28 9JD **t** 0191 262 8844 (before 9pm). For info about each year's camp send 60p in stamps & SAE to Vegan Camp Enquiries, Rainbow Ctre, Nottingham NG21 3HW

SPORT

Vegetarian & Vegan Bodybuilding David & Gillian Fairclough, 17 Inglewood Rd, Rainford, St Helens, Lancs WA11 7QL. *Postal contact help group* • **Vegetarian Cycling & Athletic Club** Peter Simpson, 13 Peers La, Shenley Church End, Milton Keynes MK5 6BG **t** 01908 503919 **w** www.members.xoom.com/vegetarianac/vcachome.html

VEGAN SOCIETY LOCAL CONTACTS

Vegan Society Local Contacts are Vegan Society members who have offered to act, on a voluntary basis, as a point of contact for those interested in the Society's work. For a list, please see *The Vegan* magazine, published by the Vegan Society, or send a SAE marked 'Local Contacts' to: Vegan Society, Donald Watson Hse, 7 Battle Rd, St Leonard's-on-Sea, E Sussex TN37 7AA.

USEFUL ADDRESSES

Many of the groups listed below have limited funds and therefore would probably appreciate receiving an SAE with your enquiry.

ANIMAL EXPERIMENTS & ALTERNATIVES

• **British Anti-Vivisection Association** PO Box 82, Kingswood, Bristol BS15 1YF **t** 01246 230474 **e** bava@esmail.net **w** www.eurosolve.com/charity/bava • **British Union for the Abolition of Vivisection** 16a Crane Grove, London N7 8LB **t** 020 700 4888 • **Doctors & Lawyers for Responsible Medicine** 104b Weston Pk, London N8 9PP **t** 020 8340 9813 **e** DLRM@gn.apc.org **w** www.dlrmfreeserve.co.uk • **Dr Hadwen Trust for Humane Research** Dr Hadwen Hse, 84a Tilehouse St, Hitchin, Herts SG5 2DY **t** 01462 436819 **w** www.arrs.envirolink.org/drht/ • **FRAME** 96-98 North Sherwood St, Nottingham NG1 4EE **t** 0115 958 4740 **e** frame@frame-uk.demon.co.uk **w** www.frame-uk.demon.co.uk • **Humane Research Trust** Brook Hse, 29 Bramhall Lane South, Bramhall, Stockport, Cheshire SK7 2DN **t** 0161 439 8041 **e** members@humane.freeserve.co.uk **w** www.btinternet.com/~shawweb/hrt • **Lord Dowding Fund for Humane Research** see National Anti-Vivisection Society • **National Anti-Vivisection Society** 261 Goldhawk Rd, London W12 9PE **t** 020 8846 9777 **e** navs@cygnet.co.uk **w** www.cygnet.co.uk/navs • **Nurses' Anti-Vivisection Movement** PO Box 32, Matlock, Derbys DE4 3YJ **t** 01624 824718 • **People Against Vivisection** PO Box 70, N Shields, Tyne & Wear NE29 0YP **t** 0191 280 1771 **e** djurs@cableinet.co.uk • **Plan 2000** 234 Summergangs Rd, Hull HU8 8LL **t** 01482 786855 **w** www.eurosolve.com/charity/Plan2000 • **Quest Cancer Research** Woodbury, Harlow Rd, Roydon, Harlow, Essex CM19 5HF **t** 01279 792233 **e** questioncancer@btinternet.com **w** www.questcancer.org • **Uncaged Campaigns** 14 Ridgeway Rd, Sheffield S12 2SS **t** 0114 253 0020 **e** uncaged.anti-viv@dial.pipex.com **w** www.uncaged.co.uk

BLOODSPORTS

• **Campaign for the Abolition of Angling** BM Fish, London WC1N 3XX **t** 0870 458 4176 **e** caa@pisces.demon.co.uk **w** www.anti-angling.com • **Conservative Anti-Hunt Council** PO Box 193, Welwyn, Herts AL6 9HG **t** 01823 286398 • **Hunt Saboteurs Association** PO Box 2786, Brighton, E Sussex BN2 2AX **t** 01273 622827 • **League Against Cruel Sports** 83-87 Union St, London SE1 1SG **t** 020 7739 1000 • **National**

Anti-Hunt Campaign PO Box 66, Stevenage, Herts SG1 2TR **t** 01442 240246 **e** nahc@nahc.freeserve.co.uk

CIRCUSES & ZOOS

• **Captive Animals Protection Society** PO Box 43, Dudley DY3 2YP **t** 01384 456682 **e** caps-uk@dircon.co.uk **w** www.caps-uk.dircon.co.uk

DIET/LIFESTYLE

• **Bristol Cancer Help Ctre** Grove Hse, Cornwallis Gr, Clifton, Bristol BS8 4PG **t** 0117 980 9500 **e** jsen@bristolcancerhelp.org • **FRESH (Fruitarian & Raw Energy Support & Help) Network** PO Box 71, Ely, Cambs CB7 4GU **t** 0870 800 7070 **e** fresh@karenk.easynet.co.uk **w** www.easyweb.easynet.co.uk/karenk • **Friends Vegetarian Society** 9 Astons Cl, Woods La, Amblecote, Stourbridge DY5 2QT **t** 01384 423899 • **Institute for Plant Based Nutrition** 333 Bryn Mawr Ave, Bala Cynwyd, Pennsylvania 19004-2606, USA **t** 610 667 6876 **f** 610 667 1501 **w** plantbased.org • **International Vegetarian Union w** www.ivu.org • **London Vegetarian Info Centre** 2 Melcombe Gdns, Kenton, Middx HA3 9RH **t** 020 8204 1231 • **Movement for Compassionate Living** 47 Highlands Rd, Leatherhead, Surrey KT22 8NQ **t** 01372 372389 • **Physician's Committee for Responsible Medicine** 5100 Wisconsin Ave, NW, Suite 404, Washington, DC 20016, USA **w** www.pcrm.org • **Raw Times w** www.rawtimes.com • **Vegan Information Network & ESCAPE** Jasmine, PO Box 2801, Brighton, E Sussex BN1 3NH • **Vegan Response w** www.vegan-response.org.uk • **Vegan Views** Harry Mather, Flat A15, 20 Dean Pk Rd, Bournemouth BH1 1DB • **Vegetarian Society** Parkdale, Dunham Rd, Altrincham, Cheshire WA14 4QG **t** 0161 925 2000 **e** info@vegsoc.org **w** www.vegsoc.org • **Viva!** 12 Queen Sq, Brighton, E Sussex BN1 3FD **t** 01273 777688 **e** info@viva.org.uk **w** www.viva.org.uk • **Young Indian Vegetarians** 226 London Rd, W Croydon CR0 2TF **t** 020 8686 6931 **e** ahimsa@ahimsa.demon.uk **w** www.ahimsa.demon.co.uk

DIRECT ACTION

• **Animal Liberation Front Press Office** BM 4400, London WC1N 3XX **t** 01954 230542 • **Animal Liberation Front Supporters Group** BCM 1160, London WC1N 3XX **e** 100302.1616@compuserve.com

FARMING & GROWING

• **Compassion in World Farming** Charles Hse, 5a Charles St, Petersfield, Hants GU32 3EH **t** 01730 264708 **e** compassion@ciwf.co.uk **w** www.ciwf.co.uk • **Compassion in World Farming Trust** Charles Hse, 5a Charles St, Petersfield, Hants GU32 3EH **t** 01730 268070 **e** ciwftrust@ciwf.co.uk **w** www.ciwf.co.uk • **Farm & Food Society** 4 Willifield Way, London NW11 7XT **t** 020 8455 0634 • **Farm Animal Welfare Network** PO Box 40, Holmfirth, Huddersfield, W Yorks HD7 1QY **t** 01484 688650 • **Henry Doubleday Research Association** Centre for Organic Gardening, Ryton-on-Dunsmore, Coventry, W Midlands CV8 3LG **t** 020 7630 3517 • **National Organisation Working Against Live Exports** St Josephs, Souldern, Bicester, Oxon OX6 9LR **t** 01869 345243 • **Plants for a Future** The Field, Penpol, Lostwithiel, Cornwall PL22 0NG **t** 01208 872963 • **Soil Association** Bristol Hse, 40-56 Victoria St, Bristol BS1 6BY **t** 0117 929 0661 **e** info@soilassociation.org **w** www.soilassociation.org • **Vegan Organic Network** Anandavan, 58 High La, Chorlton, Manchester M21 9DZ **t** 0161 860 4869 **e** veganorganic@supanet.com **w** www.veganvillage.co.uk • **Veganic Garden Supplies/Information** c/o Weavers Way, Heath Farm Rd, Worstead, N Walsham, Norfolk NR28 9AH **t** 01692 404570

FUR & LEATHER

• **Campaign Against Leather & Fur** BM 8889, London WC1N 3XX **e** CALF@alrob.freeserve.co.uk • **Coalition to Abolish the Fur Trade** PO Box 38, Manchester M60 1NX **t** 020 7278 3068 **e** caft@caft.demon.co.uk

GENERAL

• **Advocates for Animals** 10 Queensferry St, Edinburgh EH2 4PG **t** 0131 225 6039 **f** 0131 220 6377 **e** advocates.animals@virgin.net • **Animal Aid** The Old Chapel, Bradford St, Tonbridge, Kent TN9 1AW **t** 01732 364546 **e** info@animalaid.org.uk **w** www.animalaid.org.uk • **Animal Concern Scotland** PO Box 3982, Glasgow G51 4WD **t** 0141 445 3570 • **Animal Defenders** see National Anti-Vivisection Society • **Animal Welfare Information Group** PO Box 8, Halesworth, Suffolk IP19 0JL **t** 01986 782280 • **Chickens' Lib** see Animal Aid • **Earthkind** Town Quay, Poole, Dorset BH15 1HJ **t** 01202 682344 **e** info@earthkind.org.uk **w** www.earthkind.org.uk • **IFAW** Warren Crt, Park Rd, Crowborough, E Sussex TN6 2GA **t** 01892 601900 **e** info@ifaw.org **w** www.ifaw.org • **London Greenpeace** 5 Caledonian Rd, London N1 9DX **t** 020 7713 1269 • **National Petwatch** PO Box 38, Blackpool FY2 2TQ **t** 01253 355856 • **People for the Ethical Treatment of Animals (Europe)** PO Box 3169, London SW18 4WJ **t** 020 8870 3966 **e** info@peta.demon.co.uk **w** www.peta/online.org • **Petsearch Register of Animals Lost & Found** 851 Old Lode La, Solihull B92 3JE **t** 0121 743 4133 • **Respect for Animals** PO Box 6500, Nottingham NG4 3GB **t** 0115 952 5440 **e** respect.for.animals@dial.pipex.com **w** www.respectforanimals.org • **RSPCA** Causeway, Horsham, W Sussex RH12 1HG **t** 01403 264181 **w** www.rspca.org.uk • **VIEW (Vegan Information concerning the Environment and 3rd World)** c/o 10 Duffryn Terrace, Wattsville, Gwent NP1 7QN • **World Society for the Protection of Animals** 2 Langley La, London SW8 1TJ **t** 020 7793 0540 • **World Wide Fund for Nature** Panda Hse, Weyside Pk, Godalming, Surrey GU7 1XR **t** 01483 426444

MARINE ANIMALS

• **Breach Marine Protection** 3 St John's St, Goole, E Yorks **t** 01405 769375 **e** breachenv@aol.com **w** www.members.aol.com/breachenv/home.htm • **British Divers Marine Life Rescue** 39 Ingram Rd, Gillingham, Kent ME7 1SB **t** 01634 281681 • **Cetacea Defence** PO Box 78, Shaftesbury, Dorset SP7 8BQ **e** cetaceadefence@hotmil.com **w** http://ds.dial.pipex.com/town/terrace/gdn22/NNP/Groups/CetDef • **Marine Conservation Society** 9 Gloucester Rd, Ross-on-Wye, Herefords HR9 5BU **t** 01989 566017 **e** mcsuk@mcmail.com **w** www.mcsuk.mcmail.com • **Shellfish Network** Springside, Forest Rd, E Horsley, Surrey KT24 5AZ **t** 01483 282995 **w** www.envirolink.ort/arrs/arc/shellfish • **Whale & Dolphin Conservation Society** Alexander Hse, James St West, Bath BA1 2BT **t** 01225 334511 **e** info@wdcs.org **w** www.wdcs.org

MISCELLANEOUS

• **Animal Cruelty Investigation Group** PO Box 8, Halesworth, Suffolk IP19 0JL **t** 01986 782280 • **McLibel Support Campaign** c/o 5 Caledonian Rd, London N1 9DX **t** 020 7713 1269 **e** mclibel@globalnet.co.uk **w** www.mcspotlight.org • **Vegan Bikers e** vb@eloi.nildram.co.uk **w** www.nildram.co.uk/veganmc • **Vegan/Vegetarian Esperanto Group** Brian Burnett, Nant Yr Hafod Cottage, Llandegla, Wrexham, Denbighshire LL11 3BG **t** 01978 790442 **e** brianthesquirrel@compuserve.com

PRISONERS' SUPPORT (ANIMAL RIGHTS/VEGAN)

• **Vegan Prisoners Support Group** POB 194, Enfield EN1 3HD
t 020 8292 8325 **e** hvpc@vpsg.freeserve.co.uk

RELIGIOUS

• **Anglican Society for the Welfare of Animals** Old Toll Gate, Hound
Green, Hook, Hants RG27 8LQ **t** 0118 932 6586 • **Animal Christian
Concern** PO Box 70, Horsforth, Leeds LS18 5BG • **Catholic Study
Circle for Animal Welfare** 39 Onslow Gdns, S Woodford, London E18
1ND **t** 020 8989 0478 • **Christian Ecology Link** 20 Carlton Rd,
Harrogate HG2 8DD **t** 01423 871616 **e** info@christian-ecology.org.uk
w www.christian-ecology.org.uk • **Christian Prayer Fellowship for
the Protection of Animals** 5 Wemyss Pl, Peebles EH45 8JT **t** 01721
722687 • **Eden Fellowship** c/o 59 Chapel Rd, Ramsgate, Kent CT11
0BS **t** 01843 589010 • **Jewish Vegetarian Society** 855 Finchley Rd,
London NW11 8LX **t** 020 8455 0692 **e** jvs@ivu.org
w www.ivu.org/jus/ • **Kindness Unlimited** The Old Vicarage, Llangynog, Carmarthen SA33 5BS **t** 01267 241547 • **Pagan Animal Rights**
110 Geoffrey Rd, Brockley, London SE4 1NU

SOYA MILK

• **Soya Source** 47a March Mont St, Bloomsbury, London WC1N 1AP
t 020 7833 3759 **e** bcl@dircon.co.uk

'THIRD WORLD'

• **Help International Plant Protein Organisation** The Old Vicarage,
Llangynog, Carmarthen SA33 5BS **t** 01267 241547
e hippo@gofornet.co.uk • **Vegfam** The Sanctuary, nr Lydford,
Okehampton, Devon EX20 4AL **t** 01822 820203
e vegfam@veganvillage.co.uk **w** www.veganvillage.co.uk/vegfam

WILD ANIMALS

• **Born Free Foundation** 3 Grove Hse, Foundry La, Horsham, W Sussex
RH13 5PL **t** 01403 240170 **e** wildlife@bornfree.org.uk
w www.bornfree.org.uk • **British Hedgehog Preservation Society**
Knowbury Hse, Knowbury, Ludlow, Shropshire SY8 3LQ **t** 01584
890801 • **Care for the Wild International** 1 Ashfolds, Horsham Rd,
Rusper, W Sussex RH12 4QX **t** 01293 871596
e info@careforthewild.org.uk **w** www.careforthewild.org.uk • **Fox**

Project The Old Chapel, Bradford St, Tonbridge, Kent TN9 1AW
t 01732 367397 **e** ap.wilson@btinternet.com
w www.innotts.co.uk/~robmel/foxproject.html • **International Primate Protection League** 116 Judd St, London WC1H 9NS **t** 020 7837 7227 • **Jenita Fox Rescue** Oak Tree, Main Rd, Colden Common, Winchester, Hants SO21 1TL **t** 023 8069 2309 • **London Wildlife Trust** Harling Hse, 47-51 Gt Suffolk St, London SE1 0BS **t** 020 7278 6612 **e** londonwt@cix.co.uk **w** www.wildlifetrust.org.uk/london/ • **National Federation of Badger Groups** Cloisters Hse, 8 Battersea Pk Rd, London SW8 4BG **t** 020 7498 3220 **e** elaine.king@ndirect.co.uk **w** www.geocities.com/rainforest/canopy/2626/ • **St Tiggywinkle's** Church Farm, Aston Rd, Haddenham, Aylesbury HP17 8AF **t** 01844 292292 • **Seal Sanctuary** Gweek, Cornwall **t** 01326 22361 • **Urban Wildlife Group** Unit 310, Jubilee Trade Ctre, 130 Pershore St, Birmingham B5 6ND **t** 0121 666 7474 • **Wildlife Hospital Trust** Aston Rd, Haddenham, Aylesbury, Bucks HP17 8AF **t** 01844 292292

YOUTH GROUPS

• **Animal Aid Youth Group** see Animal Aid (General) • **Earthlings** see Earthkind (General) • **Farm Animal Rangers** see Compassion in World Farming (Farming) • **Fox Cubs** PO Box 2786, Brighton, E Sussex BN2 2AX **t** 01273 622827 • **Go Wild Club** see World Wide Fund for Nature (General) • **Junior Elefriends** see Born Free Foundation (Wild Animals) • **Junior RSPCA** see RSPCA (General) • **SCREAM** see Vegetarian Society (Diet/Lifestyle) • **Viva! Activists** see Viva! (Diet/Lifestyle)

MULTIPLE OUTLET CONTACTS

Some companies listed below may not have product entries in the book.

• **Aldi** Holly La, Atherstone, Warks CV9 2SQ **t** 01827 711800 • **ASDA** ASDA Hse, Great Wilson St, Leeds LS11 5AD **t** 0113 243 5435 **w** www.asda.co.uk • **Body Shop** Hawthorne Rd, Wick, Littlehampton, W Sussex **t** 01903 731 500 **e** info@bodyshop.co.uk **w** www.bodyshop.co.uk • **Boots** Customer Services, PO Box 5300, 1 Thaine Rd West, Nottingham NG90 1AA **t** 0115 950 6111 • **Budgens** Stonefield Way, S Ruislip, Middx HA4 0JR **t** 020 8422 9511 • **Coop** PO Box 53, New Century Hse, Manchester M60 4ES **t** 0161 834 1212 **e** customer.relations@co-op.co.uk **w** www.co-op.co.uk • **Culpeper** Hadstock Rd, Linton, Cambridge CB1 6NJ **t** 01223 891196 **e** info@culpeper.co.uk **w** www.culpeper.co.uk • **Holland & Barrett** Samuel Ryder Hse, Townsend Dr, Attleborough Fields, Nuneaton CV11 6XW **t** 01455 251900 • **Iceland** Second Ave, Deeside Ind Pk, Deeside, Flintshire CH5 2NW **t** 01244 830100 • **Kwik Save** see Somerfield **w** www.kwiksave.co.uk • **Marks & Spencers** Michael Hse, Baker St, London W1A 1DN **t** 020 7935 4422 **w** www.marks-and-spencers.co.uk • **Netto** Elmsall Way, S Elmsall, nr Pontefract WF9 2XX **t** 01977 641212 • **Nisa Today** Pk Farm Rd, Foxhills Ind Est, Scunthorpe, N Lincs DN15 8QQ **t** 01724 282028 • **Safeway** 6 Millington Rd, Hayes, Middx UB3 4AY **t** 020 8848 8744 **w** www.safeway.co.uk • **Sainsbury's** Stamford Hse, Stamford St, London SE1 9LL **t** 0800 636262 **w** www.sainsburys.co.uk • **Somerfield** Somerfield Hse, Whitchurch La, Bristol BS14 0TJ **t** 0117 935 9359 • **Spar** 32 Headstone Dr, Harrow, Middx HA3 5QT **t** 0181 863 5511 • **Superdrug** 118 Beddington La, Croydon, Surrey CR0 4TB **t** 020 8684 7000 • **Tesco** Freepost SCO 2298, Dundee DD1 1YP **t** 0800 505555 **e** customer.services@tesco.co.uk **w** www.tesco.co.uk • **Thorntons** Thornton Pk, Somercotes, Derbys DE55 4JX **t** 01773 540550 **e** customer.services@thorntons.co.uk **w** www.thorntons.co.uk • **Waitrose** Southern Ind Est, Doncaster Rd, Bracknell, Berks RG12 8YA **t** 0800 188 884 **e** customer_service@waitrose.co.uk **w** www.waitrose.com • **Wine Rack** (also Thresher, Victoria Wine & Bottoms Up), First Quench, Sefton Hse, 42 Church Rd, Welwyn Garden City, Herts AL8 6PJ **t** 01717 385000

MAIL ORDER ADDRESSES

21st Century Health Freepost SCE9479, 3 Water Gdns, Stanmore, Middx HA7 3BR **t** 0800 026 0220 **e** 21st.century@easynet.co.uk **w** www.21stcenturyhealth.co.uk • **Absolute Aromas** 2 Grove Pk, Mill La, Alton, Hants GU34 2QG **t** 01420 549991 **e** oils@absolute-aromas.com • **Ainsworth's** 38 New Cavendish St, London W1M 7LH **t** 020 7935 5330 • **Aladdin Aromas** The Overwater Factory, Nenthead, Alston, Cumbria CA9 3NP **t** 01434 382820 **e** alaromas@aol.com • **Allergycare** 1 Church Sq, Taunton, Somerset TA1 1SA **t** 01823 325023 **e** info@allergyfreedirect.co.uk **w** www.allergyfreedirect.co.uk • **Allinson** see Ryvita • **Amber Essence** 9 Shorton Valley Rd, Paignton, Devon TQ3 1QY **t** 01803 529073 • **Ambrosian Vegetarian Foods** Highfield Lodge, 69 Occupation Rd, Albert Village, Swadlincote DE11 8HA **t** 01283 225055 **e** amb@ambrosian.screaming.net • **Animal Aid** The Old Chapel, Bradford St, Tonbridge, Kent TN9 1AW **t** 01732 364546 **e** info@animalaid.org.uk **w** www.animalaid.org.uk • **Aqua Natural** Unit 50, Leyland Trading Est, Wellingborough NN8 1RT **t** 01933 441818 **e** aqua.natural@virgin.net • **Aqua Source** 12 Oakfree Pl, Exeter, Devon EX2 8WA **t** 0800 454 715 **e** algae@aquasourceuk.demon.co.uk • **Aquarius Healthcare** see Natural Woman • **Arbonne** PO Box 5068, Milton Keynes MK4 3ZW **t** 01908 521200 **e** arbonneuk@aol.com • **Arovite** Freepost CV2390, PO Box 151, Warwick CV35 9BR **t** 0800 731 0732 • **Astonish** Valley Mills, Meanwood Rd, Leeds LS7 2JL **t** 0113 262 5206 **e** astonishproducts@clara.net **w** www.astonish.co.uk • **Australian Nougat Co** MS1537 Davis Rd, Tewantin, Queensland 4565, Australia **t** 0061 7 5485 3132 **e** ausnougat@email.tc **w** ausnougat.com.au • **Austrian Moor** Whiteladies, Maresfield, E Sussex TN22 2HH **t** 01825 762658 • **Avalon Vineyard** E Pennard, Shepton Mallet, Somerset BA4 6UA **t** 01749 860393 • **Baby Organix** Organix Hse, 4 Fairfield Cl, Christchurch BH23 1QZ **t** 01202 479701 (mail order dried products only) • **Beauty Through Herbs** 1 Sir John's Sq, Thurso, Caithness KW14 7AN **t** 01847 895558 **w** www.bth.co.uk • **Beauty Without Cruelty** Devonshire Rd Ind Est, Millom, Cumbria **t** 01229 775185 • **Beer Shop** 14 Pitfield St, London N1 6EY **t** 020 7739 3701 • **Bickiepegs** 5 Blackburn Ind Est, Kinellar, Aberdeen AB21 ORX **t** 01224 790626 • **Biddenden Vineyards** Little Whatmans, Biddenden, Kent TN27 8DH **t** 01580 291726 • **Bio-D** 64 St Nicholas Gate, Hedon, Kingston-Upon-Hull HU12 8HS **t** 01482 229950 **e** tribe@ecodet.karoo.co.uk **w** www.naked-earth.homepage.com • **Biocare** see Natural Woman • **Biorganic** 17 Tedworth Green, Leices-

ter LE4 2NG **t** 0116 236 2958 • **Birkenstock** The Boot Tree, 1 Addison Bridge Pl, London W14 8XP **t** 020 7602 2866
e birkenstock@boottree.demon.co.uk • **Biz Niz** see Natural Woman
• **Blue Green Planet** PO Box 1454, Slough, Berks SL3 9YS
t 01753 544002 **e** helpdesk@blue-green-planet.com
w www.blue-green-planet.com • **Body Reform** Vale Business Pk, Cowbridge, Vale of Glamorgan CF71 7PF **t** 01446 771483
e sales@body-reform.co.uk • **Bodyline** Oaktree Hse, Aspen Way, Yalberton Ind Est, Paignton, Devon TQ4 7QZ **t** 01803 555582
f 01803 528012 **e** info@bodyline.co.uk • **Borve Brew House** Ruthven, Huntly, Aberdeenshire AB54 4SG **t** 01466 760343 •
Bramble Foods Ltd 5 Crowe St, Stowmarket, Suffolk IP14 1DL
t 020 8450 9419 **f** 020 8208 1551 • **Butterfly Effect, The** PO Box 2365, Hove BN3 3FY **t** 01273 722343
e thebutterflyeffect@hotmail.com
w www.thebutterflyeffect.freeserve.co.uk • **Buxton Foods**
12 Harley St, London W1N 1AA **t** 020 7637 5505
e buxton@stamp-collection.co.uk **w** www.stamp-collection.co.uk •
Cachet see Network Health & Beauty • **Calder Valley** Unit 10, Hanson La Enterprise Ctr, Hanson La, Halifax HX1 5PG **t** 01422 362202 • **Caledonian Brewing Co** see Vinceremos • **Caledonian Curry Co** Unit 2, South Bonar Est, Bonar Bridge, Sutherland IV24 3AP **t** 01863 766025 **w** info@caledoniancurry.co.uk
w www.caledoniancurry.co.uk • **Camilla Hepper** 51 St Marys St, Wallingford, Oxon OX10 0EY **t** 01491 826196 • **Carabay** Moycullen, Co Galway, Ireland **t** 00 353 91 555112 **e** carabay@esatclear.ie •
Care for Life Websters Hse, Bow St, Langport, Somerset TA10 9PS
t 01458 251559 **e** suecfl@aol.com **w** www.careforlife.co.uk • **Cariad** Rivernook Farm, Sunnyside, Walton-on-Thames, Surrey KT12 2ET
t 01932 269962 **e** cariad@compuserve.com • **Carole Monteith** 4 Stanford Cl, Hampton TW12 3XZ **t** 020 879 7473
e monteith@btinternet.com • **Chapel Chocolates** The Pebbles, St Davids, Pembrokeshire SA62 6RD **t** 01437 720023
e chocolates@chapchoc.demon.co.uk • **Charles Wells** Eagle Brewery, Havelock St, Bedford MK40 4LU **t** 01234 272766
w www.charleswells.co.uk • **Chimans** 73 Windsor Rd, Barnstaple, Devon EX31 4AG **t** 01271 374416 **e** chimans@sosi.net • **Chirali Old Remedies** 210 High St, Eltham, London SE9 1BG **t** 020 8859 5818
e ilkay@ilkaychirali.co.uk **w** www.ilkaychirali.co.uk • **Christy** see Network Health & Beauty • **Clearspring** 19a Acton Pk Est, London W3 7QE **t** 020 8749 1781 **e** mailorder@clearspring.co.uk
w www.clearspring.co.uk • **Clive Lowe** 111 Oaklands Pk, Buckfastleigh, Devon TQ11 0NR **t** 01364 642279 • **Coles Traditional Foods** Station Approach, London Rd, Gt Chesterford, Saffron

Walden, Essex CB10 1PG **t** 01799 531053 • **Condomi** Studio 13, Brockley Cross Bus Ctre, Endwell Rd, London SE4 2PD **t** 020 7277 6630• **Conscience Cosmetics** PO Box 5180, Matlock, Derbys DE4 4ZW **t** 01629 822972 **e** conscience@bodycarezi.freeserve.co.uk • **Courtneys** see Clearspring • **Cotswold Health Products** 5/8 Tabernacle Rd, Wotton-under-Edge, Glos GL12 7EF **t** 01453 843694 **e** sales@cotsherb.demon.co.uk • **Culpeper Ltd** Hadstock Rd, Linton, Cambridge CB1 6NJ **t** 01223 894054 **f** 01223 893104 **e** info@culpeper.co.uk **w** www.culpeper.co.uk • **D&D Chocolates** 261 Forest Rd, Loughborough LE11 3HT **t** 01509 216400 • **Daler Rowney** 12 Percy St, Tottenham Ct Rd, London W1A 2BP **t** 020 7636 8241 **w** www.daler-rowney.com • **Daniel Field Direct** PO Box 105, Thame DO, Oxon OX9 2YR **t** 020 7437 1490 **w** www.daniel-field.com • **Danival** see Clearspring • **De Vere** see Natural Woman • **Desert Essence** Revital Mail Order, 35 High Rd, Willesden, London NW10 2TE **t** 020 8459 3382 **e** consac@clara.net • **Disos** Disos Bus Ctr, 50 Springfield Rd, Gatley, Cheadle, Cheshire SK8 4PF **t** 0161 428 7666 • **Dolma** 19 Royce Ave, Hucknall, Nottingham NG15 6FU **t** 0115 963 4237 **e** dolma@veganvillage.co.uk **w** www.veganvillage.co.uk/dolma • **Doves Farm** Salisbury Rd, Hungerford, Berks RG17 0RT **t** 01488 684880 (mail order bulk only) • **Dr Hadwen Trust** Dr Hadwen Hse, 84a Tilehouse St, Hitchin, Herts SG5 2DY **t** 01462 436819 • **Dragonfly** 2a Mardle Way, Buckfastleigh, Devon TQ11 0NR **t** 01364 642700 **e** boreham@beany.co.uk **w** www.beany.co.uk **&** www.tofu.co.uk • **Droyt Products** Progress Mill, Progress St, Chorley, Lancs PR6 0RZ **t** 01257 417251 **e** sales@droyts.com • **Dunkerton's** Pembridge, Leominster, Herefords HR6 9ED **t** 01544 388653 • **Earth Force** see Desert Essence • **Ella Drinks** Alloa Bus Ctr, Alloa FK10 3SA **t** 01259 721905 **e** anne.thomson@sol.co.uk • **Erewhon** see Clearspring • **Escential Botanicals** Unit 25, Mountbatten Rd, Kennedy Way, Tiverton, Devon EX16 6SW **t** 01884 257612 **e** mayfield.labs@btinternet.com • **Essential Oil Co** Dept Freepost BZ704, Basingstoke, Hants RG21 3LH **t** 01256 332737 **e** essoil@aol.com • **Essentially Oils** 8-10 Mount Farm, Churchill, Chipping Norton, Oxon OX7 6NP **t** 01608 659544 **e** sales@essentiallyoils.com **w** www.essentiallyoils.com • **Ethical Wares** Caegwyn, Temple Bar, Felinfach, Lampeter, Ceredigion SA48 7SA **t** 01570 471155 **f** 01570 471166 **e** ethicalwares@veganvillage.co.uk **w** www.veganvillage.co.uk/ethicalwares• **Everfresh Natural Foods** Gatehouse Cl, Aylesbury, Bucks HP19 3DE **t** 01296 425333 **e** sunnyvaleo@aol.com • **Everett Healthcare** Poundshill Clinic, Poundshill, Crediton, Devon EX17 1AA **t** 01363 772029

e everetthe@btinternet.com **w** www.everetthe.oaktree.co.uk •
Faith In Nature see Natural Woman • **Faith Products** 5 Kay St, Bury
BL9 6BU **t** 0161 764 2555 **e** sales@faithproducts.com • **Farrow &
Humphries** Wellow Hurst, Wellow, Bath BA2 8PU **t** 01225 840880
e sales@farrowhumphreys.co.uk **w** www.farrowhumphreys.co.uk •
Felici see Natural Woman • **First Quality Foods** Unit 4, The Alpha
Ctr, Armstrong Way, Yate, Bristol BS37 5NG **t** 01454 880044
e mailorder@quality-foods.freeserve.co.uk • **Fleur Aromatherapy**
Health Pack, Langston Factory Mews, Kingham, Oxon OX7 6UP
t 01608 658816 • **Food Safe** Winwick Hall, Winwick,
Northampton NN6 7PD **t** 01788 510415
e bruce.green@pipemedia.co.uk • **Four Seasons** PO Box 436, Norwich NR3 1LL **t** 0800 783 1262 **e** sales@4-seasons.net • **Freerangers**
9b Marquis Ct, Low Prudhoe, Northumberland NE42 6PJ **t** 01661
831781 **e** sales@freerangers.co.uk • **Good Food Distributors** Unit
35, Ddole Rd Ind Est, Llandrindod Wells, Powys LD1 6DF **t** 01597
824720 **e** gfd.wholesale@btinternet.com
w www.goodfooddistributors.co.uk • **Goodness Foods** South
March, Daventry, Northants NN11 4PH **t** 01327 706611 **f** 01327
300436 **e** info@goodness.co.uk **w** www.goodness.co.uk/goodness/
• **GR Lane** Sisson Rd, Gloucester GL1 3QB **t** 01452 524012
e jlane@laneshealth.com • **Grandma Vine's** see Natural Woman •
Green & Blacks see Whole Earth • **Green Ark** Unit 7b, Lineholme
Mill, Burnley Rd, Todmorden, W Yorks OL14 7DH **t** 01282 606810
e greenark@cwcom.net **w** www.greenark.mcmail.com • **Green City
Wholefoods** 23 Fleming St, Dennistoun, Glasgow G31 1PQ **t** 0141
554 7633 **e** greencity@net.ntl.com • **Green Gourmet** PO Box 25,
Congleton, Cheshire CW12 4FG **t** 01477 500703 **e** ggfood1@aol.com
w www.greengourmet.com • **Green People** Brighton Rd, Hand-
cross, Haywards Heath, W Sussex RH17 6BZ **t** 01444 401444 • **Green
Shoes** 69 High St, Totnes, Devon TQ9 5PB **t** 01803 864997
e greenshoes@shines.swis.net **w** www.greenshoes.co.uk •
Growganic Littleton Mill, Semington, Trowbridge, Wilts BH4 6LQ
t 01380 871050 **e** growganic@aol.com • **Gusto** see Whole Earth •
Hambleden Herbs Court Farm, Milverton, Somerset TA4 1NF
t 01823 401104 **e** info@hambledenherbs.co.uk
w www.hambledenherbs.co.uk • **Harbingers of a New Age** 717 E
Missoula Ave, Troy, MT 59935, USA **t** 001 406 295 4944 • **Har-
bourne Vineyard** Wittersham, Tenterden, Kent TN30 7NP **t** 01797
270420 **e** sales@harvin.globalnet.co.uk
w www.users.globalnet.co.uk/~harvin • **Harlow Lubricants**
Freepost, Stanmore, Middx HA7 3BR **t** 01992 460525
e sales@harlube.co.uk **w** www.harlube.co.uk • **Health Imports**
Nutripost, Freepost BD2932, Bradford, W Yorks BD8 7BR

t 01274 484212 **e** health-imports.co.uk • **Healthy Hampers** PO Box 1001, Sandhurst, Berks GU46 7YY **t** 01252 878698 • **Healthy Herbs** PO Box 22, Warrington WA3 6GE **t** 01925 822502 **e** p.2364850@aol.com • **Heartland Products** Box 250, Dakota City, Iowa 50529, USA **t** 001 515 332 3087 • **Hemp Food Industries Association** PO Box 204, Barnet, Herts EN5 1EP **t** 07000 436748 • **Hemp Union** 24 Anlaby Rd, Hull HU1 2PA **t** 01482 225328 **e** sales@hemp-union.karoo.co.uk **w** www.karoo.co.uk/hemp-union • **Hendersons (Sheffield)** 41 Leavygreave Rd, Sheffield S3 7RA **t** 0114 272 5909 • **Hermitage Oils** East Morton, Keighley BD20 5UQ **t** 01274 565957 **w** www.hermitt.com • **Hollytrees** see Humane Research Trust or J&D Black • **Homecare Products** Broomhill Rd, London SW18 4JQ **t** 020 8871 5027 **e** sales@homecareproducts.co.uk • **Honesty** Lumford Mill, Bakewell, Derbys DE45 1GS **t** 01629 814888 **e** honesty.cosmetics@virgin.net • **House of Dorchester** Victor Jackson Ave, Poundbury, Dorchester, Dorset DT1 3GY **t** 01305 264257 • **Humane Research Trust** Brook Hse, 29 Bramhall La South, Bramhall, Stockport, Cheshire SK7 2DN **t** 0161 439 8041 **e** members@humane.freeserve.co.uk **w** www.btinternet.com/~shawweb/hrt • **ID Aromatics** 12 New Station St, Leeds LS1 5DZ **t** 0113 2424 983 • **Imagine** see Clearspring • **Indra** see Natural Woman • **Innoxa** see Network Health & Beauty • **J&D Black** 3 Kennet Cl, Ash, nr Aldershot, Hants GU12 6NN **t** 01252 344010 • **J&E Imports** 171 Chester Rd, Hazel Grove, Stockport, Cheshire SK7 6EN **t** 01625 876406 • **James White** Whites Fruit Farm, Ashbocking, Ipswich IP6 9JS **t** 01473 890111 **e** info@jameswhite.co.uk • **Janus** Mounts Farm, Shalford Rd, Rayne, Braintree, Essex CM7 5XA **t** 01376 342111 • **Jethros** Unit 1, Sheddingdean Bus Ctr, Burgess Hill, W Sussex RH15 8QY **t** 01444 244311 **e** marinade@easynet.co.uk **w** www.jethros.co.uk • **JP Textiles** 13 Maltkiln Row, Cawthrone, Barnsley, S Yorks S75 4HH **t** 01226 791358 **e** john.parkinson@virgin.net • **Kent Cosmetics** Kent Hse, Ashford Rd, Harrietsham, Kent ME17 1BW **t** 01622 859898 **e** kent-cosmetics.freeserve.co.uk • **Kettle Valley** Cornwallis Hse, Howard Chase, Basildon, Essex SS14 3BB **t** 01268 282341 • **Kobashi** 2 Fore St, Ide, nr Exeter, Devon EX2 9RQ **t** 01392 217628 **e** sales@kobashi.com **w** www.kobashi.com • **Le Myosotis** see Clearspring • **LG Harris** Stoke Prior, Bromsgrove, Worcs B60 4AE **t** 01527 575441 **e** lgharris@compuserve.com • **LifeSPRING** see Natural Woman • **Lima** see Clearspring • **Linpharma** see Natural Woman • **Lothian Herbs** see Shirley Price Aromatherapy • **Lunn-Links** Greenbrier, Victoria Rd, Brixham, S Devon TQ5 9AR **t** 01803 853579 **e** llorganic@aol.com • **Lush** 29 High St, Poole, Dorset BH15 1AB **t** 01202 668545 **w** www.lush.co.uk • **Lyme Regis Fine Foods**

Unit D, Station Ind Est, Liphook, Hants GU30 7DR **t** 01428 722900
e info@lyme-regis-foods.co.uk **w** www.lyme-regis-foods.co.uk/lrf •
M&M see Vinceremos • **MacSween** Dryden Rd, Bilston Glen, Loan-
head, Edinburgh EH20 9LZ **t** 0131 440 2555
e haggis@macsween.co.uk **w** www.macsween.co.uk • **Made to Last**
8 The Crescent, Hyde Pk, Leeds LS6 2NW **t** 0113 230 4983 • **Markal**
see Clearspring • **Martha Hill** Old Vicarage, Laxton, nr Corby,
Northants NN17 3AT **t** 0800 980 6662 **e** order@marthahill.com
• **Mason's** 2 Schofield St, Durn, Littleborough, Lancs OL15 OJS
t 01706 379817 **e** dogoil@zen.co.uk
w www.zen.co.uk/home/page/dogoil • **Maxicrop** Weldon Rd, Corby, Northants NN17 5US **t** 01536 402182 **e** info@maxicrop.co.uk •
Maxim Fragrance Unit Ten, Nasmyth Row, Elsecar Heritage Ctr, Elsecar, S Yorks S73 8HJ **t** 01226 749073 • **Maxim Marketing** 4 Allison
Rd, London W3 6JE **t** 020 8993 2528 • **Meadow Sweet Oils** 18 Dal-
ston Gdns, Stanmore, Middx HA7 1BU **t** 020 8204 4441 **f** 020 8204
4440 • **Meadowsweet** Unit 1, Uplands Courtyard, Stowupland Rd,
Stowmarket, Suffolk IP14 5AN **t** 01449 676940
e sales@meadowsweet **w** www.meadowsweet.co.uk • **Meridian**
see Clearspring • **Micheline Arcier** 7 William St, Knightsbridge, London SW1X 9HL **t** 020 7235 3545 • **Mitoku** see Clearspring • **Mole-
naartje** see Clearspring • **Montagne Jeunesse** Eco-Factory, Clos Llyn
Cwm, Valley Way, Swansea Enterprise Pk, Swansea SA6 8QP **t** 01792
310306 **e** katen@montagnejeunesse.co.uk • **Mrs Moon's** Willow
Food Traders, Walton Farm, Kilmersdon, Bath BA3 5SY **t** 01761
432383 **e** sales@mrsmoons.com • **Murphy & Son** Alpine St, Old
Basford, Nottingham NG6 OHQ **t** 0115 978 5494
e info@murphy&son.co.uk **w** www.murphy&son.co.uk • **Natrababy**
see Natural Woman • **Natracare** see Natural Woman • **Natural
American Spirit** Marble Head Brand Development, PO Box 16785,
London W11 OZJ **t** 0800 731 1500 **e** mbdltd@compuserve.com •
Natural Collection see XV • **Natural Flow** see Clearspring • **Natural
Woman** 21 Wellington Pk, Clifton, Bristol BS8 2UW **t** 0117 946 6649
f 0117 970 6988 **e** sales@natural-woman.com • **Nature's Gold** 783a
Fulham Rd, Fulham, London SW6 5HD **t** 020 7736 1600 • **Nature's
Own** Unit 8, Hanley Workshops, Hanley Rd, Hanley Swan, Worcs
WR8 ODX **t** 01684 310022 • **Nature's Source** see Natural Woman •
Neal's Yard Remedies 29 John Dalton St, Manchester M2 6DS
t 0161 831 7875 **f** 0161 835 9322 • **Nelson** 73 Duke St, Grosvenor
Sq, London W1M 6BY **t** 020 7495 2404 **e** alanc@nelsons-co.uk • **Net-
work Health & Beauty** Fenwicks, 39 Northumberland St, Newcastle,
Tyne & Wear NE99 1AR **t** 0191 232 5100 x 2343
e networkm@globalnet.com • **New Seasons** The Old Post Office,
Lockinge, Wantage, Oxon OX12 8QD **t** 01235 821110

e abreaks376@aol.com • **Nirvana Natural** Monks Pond Cottage, Monks Alley, Binfield, Berks RG42 5PA t 01344 360931 • **Noir** see Network Health & Beauty • **Norfolk Truffle Co** Hall Farm, Bungay Rd, Hempnall, Norfolk NR15 2LJ t 01508 471003

e colin@giver.freeserve.co.uk • **Norwood House Chocolate** The Chocolate Society, Clay Pit La, Roecliffe, Boroughbridge, N Yorks YO51 9LS t 01423 322230 e info@chocolate.co.uk • **Organic Gardening Catalogue** Riverdene Bus Pk, Molesey Rd, Hersham, Surrey KT12 4RG t 01932 253666 e chaseorg@aol.com • **Organic Valley** Blackhorse Rd, Letchworth, Herts SG6 1HL t 01462 643333

e info@organicvalley.co.uk w www.organicvalley.co.uk • **Organic Wine Company** PO Box 81, High Wycombe, Bucks HP13 5QN t 01494 446557 e afm@lineone.net

w www.organicwinecompany.com • **Orgran** see Bramble Foods • **Perfumers Guild** 61 Abbots Rd, Abbots Langley, Herts WD5 0BJ t 01923 260502 e parfumalex@aol.com • **Phillips Nutritionals** see Natural Woman • **Phyto Products** Park Works, Park Rd, Mansfield Woodhouse, Notts NG19 8EF t 01623 644334 e info@phyto.co.uk • **Pinetum Products** Pinetum Lodge, Churcham, Glos GL2 8AD t 0452 750 554 • **Pitfield Brewery** see Beer Shop • **Planet V** 43 Zoar St, Lower Gornal, Dudley, W Midlands DY3 2PA t 0800 783 9378 e sales@planetv.co.uk • **Power Health Products Ltd** 10 Central Ave, Airfield Est, Pocklington, York YO42 1NR t 01759 302595 f 01759 304286 • **Probiotics International** Matts La, Stoke-sub-Hamdon, Somerset TA14 6QE t 01935 822921

e enquiries@probiotics-international.ltd.uk

w www.probiotics-international.ltd.uk • **Purple Flame Aromatherapy** Clinton La, Kenilworth CV8 1VE t 01926 855908

e purple.flame@zetnet.co.uk w www.purpleflame.co.uk • **Quinessence Aromatherapy** Unit 2, Forest Ct, Lindon Way, Coalville, Leicester LE67 3JY t 01530 838358 f 01530 814171

e enquiries@quinessence.com w www.quinessence.com • **Radfords** Devon Fudge Direct, 2a Barton Hill Rd, Torquay, Devon TQ2 8JH t 01803 316020 • **Redwood** Unit 6, Alexander Ct, Fleming Rd, Earlstrees Est, Corby, Northants NN8 3TF t 01536 400557 • **Renahall** 61 Lime Tree Ave, Rugby CV22 7QT t 01788 811454 • **Rococo Chocolates** 321 Kings Rd, London SW3 5EP t 020 7352 5857

e venus@rococochocolates.demon.co.uk

w www.rococochocolates.com • **Romanda Healthcare** Romanda Hse, Ashley Wk, London NW7 1DU t 020 8346 0784 • **RTR Safety** Claydon Industrial Pk, Gipping Rd, Great Blakenham, Ipswich IP6 0NL t 01473 833770 e sales@rtrsafety.co.uk • **Ryvita** Old Wareham Rd, Poole, Dorset BH12 4QW t 01202 743090 • **St Peter's Brewery** see Vinceremos • **Salus** 17 Grosvenor Grange, Woolston, Warring-

ton, Cheshire WA1 4SF **t** 01925 825679 **e** salusuk@aol.com.uk •
Sanchi see Bramble Foods • **Scottish Herbal Supplies** 108 Kinnell
Ave, Glasgow G52 3RZ **t** 0141 882 7001 **e** sshm@cqm.co.uk •
Seabrook Seabrook Hse, Allerton Rd, Bradford, W Yorks BD15 7QU
t 01274 546405 • **Seagreens** see Clearspring • **Sedlescombe Vine-
yard** Cripp's Corner, Sedlescombe, nr Robertsbridge, E Sussex TN32
5SA **t** 01580 830715
e rcook91137@aol.com **w** www.tor.com.uk/sedlescombe/ • **Septico**
184 Henwood Rd, Tettenhall, Wolverhampton, W Midlands WV6
8NZ **t** 01902 752242 • **Shanti** 5 Templar Rd, Temple Ewell, nr Dover,
Kent CT16 3DL **t** 01304 820129 • **Shepherd Neame** 17 Court St,
Faversham, Kent ME13 7AX **t** 01795 542222 • **Shepherdboy**
Healthcross Hse, Syston, Leics LE7 2JG **t** 01162 602992 • **Shirley
Price Aromatherapy** Essentia Hse, Upper Bond St, Hinckley, Leics
LE10 1RS **t** 01455 615466 **e** shirleypricearoma@compuserve.com
w www.shirleypricearoma.co.uk • **Soap Tub, The** 20 The Grove,
Fartown, Huddersfield HD2 1BL **t** 01484 323606
e service@thesoaptub.co.uk **w** www.thesoaptub.co.uk • **Source
Foods** see Clearspring • **Soyfoods** 66-68 Snow Hill, Melton Mow-
bray, Leics LE13 1PD **t** 01664 560572 • **SPR** Greenfields Farm,
Fontwell Ave, Eastergate, Chichester, Sussex PO20 6RU
e d.bland@zetnet.co.uk **w** www.users.zetnet.co.uk/spr/ •
Speakeasy see Bramble Foods • **Sunblest** see Ryvita • **Tamar
Organics** 5a Westbridge Est, Tavistock, Devon PL19 8DE **t** 01822
618765 **e** tamarorganics@compuserve.com • **Tasunami Wave** see
Natural Woman • **The Spice Village Ltd** Gallamore La Ind Est, Market Rasen, Lincs LN8 3HZ **t** 08001951956 **f** 0800 195 5611
e info@spice-trail.com **w** www.spice-trail.co.uk • **TIGI** TIGI Hse,
Bentinck Rd, West Drayton, Middx UB7 7RQ **t** 020 8338 1300 **f** 020
8338 1302 • **Terrasana** see Clearspring • **Trefriw Wells Spa** Freepost Spatone, Trefriw Wells Spa, Trefriw, N Wales LL27 0BR **t** 01492
640057 **e** spatone.iron@virgin.net •
Tropical Source see Bramble Foods • **Vegan Society** Donald Watson
Hse, 7 Battle Rd, St Leonard's-on-Sea, E Sussex TN37 7AA **t** 01424
427393 **e** info@vegansociety.com **w** www.vegansociety.com • **Veganline** Freepost LON10506, London SW14 1YY **t** 0800 458 4442
e animal@animal.nu • **Vegetarian Shoes** 12 Gardner St, Brighton, E
Sussex BN1 1UP **t** 01273 691913
e information@vegetarian-shoes.co.uk
w www.vegetarian-shoes.co.uk • **Veggies** 180 Mansfield Rd, Nottingham NG1 3HW **t** 0115 958 5666 **e** info@veggies.org.uk • **Village
Bakery** Melmerby, Penrith, Cumbria CA10 1HE **t** 01768 898437
f 01768 897700 **e** andrew@village-bakery.com
w www.village-bakery.com • **Vinceremos** 261 Upper Town St, Leeds

LS13 3JT **t** 0113 257 7545 **f** 0113 257 6906 **e** info@vinceremos.co.uk **w** www.vinceremos.co.uk • **Vindotco** 11a Elwes St, Brigg, N Lincs DN20 8LB **t** 01652 652444 **e** vindotco@compuserve.com • **Vink Sales BV** PO Box 448, 3840 AK Harderwijk, Holland **t** 0031 341 432623 **f** 0031 341 432724 **e** info@yarrah.com **w** www.yarrah.com • **Vintage Roots** Farley Farms, Bridge Farm, Reading Rd, Arborfield, Berks RG2 9HT **t** 0118 976 1999 • **Viva!** 12 Queen Sq, Brighton, E Sussex BN1 3FD **t** 01273 777688 **e** info@viva.org.uk **w** www.viva.org.uk • **Wassen** 14 The Mole Business Pk, Leatherhead, Surrey KT22 7BA **t** 01372 379828 **e** wassen@globalnet.co.uk • **Waterfront** Clark Foods Ltd, Unit B, Manor Ind Est, Flint, CH6 5UY **t** 01352 735522 **f** 01352 733828 **e** jclark@clarkfood.u-net.com • **Weleda** Heanor Rd, Ilkeston, Derby DE7 8DR **t** 0115 944 8200 **e** weledauk@compuserve.com **w** www.weleda.co.uk • **Weston & Sons, H** The Bounds, Much Marcle, Herefords HR8 2NQ **t** 01531 660233 **e** tradition@westons-cider.co.uk • **What on Earth** 6 Sleaford St, Chelsea Bridge, London SW8 5AB **t** 020 7720 4410 • **Whole Earth** Fresh Food Co, 326 Portobello Rd, London W10 5RU **t** 020 8969 0351 **e** organic@freshfood.co.uk **w** www.freshfood.co.uk • **Wholistic Research Co** Brighton Haven, Robin's La, Lolworth, Cambridge CB3 8HH **t** 01954 781074 • **Wicken Fen** Duns, Berkwicks TD11 3HS **t** 01361 883150 **e** wickenfoods@freeserve.co.uk • **William Santus** The Toffee Works, Dorning St, Wigan WN1 1HE **t** 01942 243464 **e** unclejoe@uncle-joes.com • **Worlds End Trading** 4 Florence Terrace, Falmouth TR11 3RR **t** 01326 316528 **e** sales@worldsend.co.uk **w** www.worldsend.co.uk • **XV** Ecohouse, Monmouth Pl, Bath BA1 2DQ **t** 01225 442288 **f** 01225 469673 **e** natcoll@ecotrade.co.uk **w** www.greenstore.co.uk • **Xynergy** Elsted, Midhurst, W Sussex GU29 OJT **t** 01730 813642 **e** orders@xynergy.co.uk **w** www.xynergy.co.uk • **Yin Yang** New Yatt Bus Ctr, Witney, Oxon OX8 6TJ **t** 01993 868912 **e** health@yinyang.co.uk **w** www.yinyang.co.uk • **Your Body** Unit 52-54, Millmead Ind Ctr, Mill Mead Rd, London N17 9QU **t** 020 8808 2662 **e** sales@yourbody.co.uk

INDEX

acknowledgements	6
additives	228
additives, animal-derived	228
additives, possibly animal-derived	228
addresses, mail order	255
addresses, useful	248
adhesives, note	211
aftershave	146
air freshener	204
alcopops	92
Aldi, note	ii
Alldays, note	ii
alternative healthcare, note	181
animal care	215
animal deterrents	217
animal experiments	13, 248
animal food	216
animal-free criteria	226
animal-free shops	235
animal health	216
animal rights/welfare	8
animal substances, glossary	231
animal testing criteria	3, 227
animal tests, statistics	13
animal welfare groups	250
antibiotics	16
antiperspirants	127
apéritifs	102
aromatherapy oil	122
Artex, note	211
artists' materials	222
ASDA, note	ii
baby care	185
baby food	186
bagels	26
bags	192
baked beans	64
banana chips, note	85
bak notes, note	211
baps	26
base oils	128
bath products	120
beds, note	211
beer	92
beers, note	116
bees	10
belts	192
beta-carotene, note	85
beverages	91
biscuits	24
bleach	206
bloodsports	248
blusher	157
Body Shop, note	ii
Body Shop, toiletries/cosmetics, note	166
books	236
boots	193, 197
Boots, note	ii
bovine spongiform encephalopathy (BSE)	9
bread	26
bread mix	26
bread, note	85
breakfast foods	34
brushes, artists'	222
brushes, general	206
brushes, DIY paint	209
brushes, personal use	124
BSE	9
Budgens, note	ii
'burgers'	37
Cadbury's, note	85
cake decorations	47
cakes	39
cake mixes	39
calves	9
cancer, prevention of	15
candles	206

capsules, note	181	contacts, business	242
Care for Life, note	166	contacts, communities	242
carpet products	207	contacts, families	243
cat food	216	contacts, local	243, 247
ceramics, note	211	contacts, international	245
cereals	34	contacts, projects	242
cereals, note	85	contacts, social	246
champagne	94	contacts, sport	246
Charles Wells Ltd, note	116	contents	i
'cheese'	40	contraceptives	169
'cheese' spreads	40	contraceptives, note	181
child care	185	compost	222
children's clothing	187	cooking aids, savoury	46
chocolate	41	cooking aids, sweet	47
chocolate, cooking	41	cook-in sauce	57
chocolate, note	85	Co-op, note	ii
Christmas pudding	72	cordial	97
chutney	57	cosmetics	119
cider	95	Cosmetics Industry Coalition	
cigarette papers	223	for Animal Welfare (CICAW)	4
circuses	249	Courts, note	212
CJD	16	crackers	48
cleaners, all purpose	207	crafts materials	222
cleaners, floor	209	cranberry sauce	57
cleaners, footwear	197	cream replacer	50
cleaners, general	207	Creutzfeldt Jakob Disease	
cleaners, industrial	208	(CJD)	16
cleaners, outdoor	222	crispbreads	48
cleaners, toilet	209	crisps	74
cleansers, skin	147	crisps, note	85
clothing	192	crumpets	26
clothing, children's	187	Culpeper, note	ii
cochineal	13	custard powder	47
coffee whitener	50		
cologne	141	D_2, note	181
composts	222	dairy	9
conditioner, hair	125	dairy allergy/ intolerance	15
condoms	169	Daler Rowney, note	212
condoms, note	181	dental products, note	166
confectionery	43	denture cleaner	164
conserves, note	85	deodorant	127
contact lenses, note	166	desserts	50
contact lens solution	132	desserts, frozen	50
contact networks	242	di-calcium phosphate, note	85

diet/lifestyle	249
dips	51
direct action	249
dishwasher products	208
disinfectant	209
dog food	216
dressings	51
drink	91
drink, children's	186
drinking chocolate	96
drinks, carbonated	97
drinks, hot	96
drinks, low/non-alcoholic	96
drinks, soft	97
drugs, note	181
E coli	15
ecology	17
Ecover, note	166
egg replacer	53
eggs	10
envelopes, note	211
Environment Emergency Hotline	18
essential oil	128
ethical considerations, other	4
eye liner	132
eye pencils	132
eye products	132
fabric conditioner	209
fabric dyes, note	211
Falmer, note	198
farming, animal	8
faming/growing	250
fats	56
Femidom, note	181
feminine hygiene	133
fertiliser	222
film, note	224
fire-lighters	209
fish	9
fixed cut-off date	
(animal testing)	4
flapjacks	24
floor covering, note	211
floor products	209
food	23
food poisoning	15
foot care	170
footwear, children's	134
footwear, general	187
footwear, sports	193
footwear, note	197
fruit, gift box	198
fruit, note	85
fur	11, 250
furniture, note	211
furniture polish	209
gardening products	222
gelatine	12
gelatine carrier, note	85
genetically-modified organisms (GMOs)	16
gift boxes/packs	135
glass, note	211
global warming	17
glossary of animal substances	231
gravy	53
groups, animal welfare	250
groups, international	245
groups, local	243
groups, national	248
groups, youth	253
guidelines	iv
hair care	125
hair dye	136
hair gel	137
hair removal	137
hairspray	137
hampers	54
hand care	138
hand cream	138
Happidog, note	218
health	14

health care 169
health care, children's 187
Holland & Barrett, note ii
home furnishings 209
home products 203
homoeopathy, note 181
honey 10
hot cross buns 72
Humane Cosmetics Standard 3
Humane Research Trust, note 218
humane traps/deterrents 217
Humbrol adhesives/thinners, note 211
Humbrol Airfix, note 224
hummus 80

'ice cream' 55
ice cream cones 55
Iceland, note ii
incense 204
incense sticks, note 212
infant care 185
infant formula 186
infant formula, note 189
insect repellent, body 172
insect repellent, room 217
introduction 1
Inveresk Plc, note 212

jackets 192
jam 82
jam, note 85
Janus, note 218
jeans, note 198
jellies, note 85
jellies, ready to eat 50
jelly crystals 50
John Dickenson, note 212

key iii
Kwik Save, note ii

lager 92
land use 17

lanolin 11
Larkhall Green Farm, note 218
Leaf, note 85
leather 11, 250
leg care 134
leisure products 221
Levi, note 198
lifestyle/diet 249
Lindt & Sprungli, note 85
lip products 140
lip salve 140
lipstick 140
Lo Cost Stores, note ii
Londis Holdings, note ii
lollies 55
lubricants, personal 170

magazines 241
magazines, 'talking' 241
mail order addresses 255
margarine 56
marine animals/sealife 9, 251
Marks & Spencer, note ii
Marks & Spencer chocolate, note 85
marmalade, note 85
mascara 132
massage oil 128
matches, note 212
mattresses, note 211
mayonnaise 51
meal replacements 170
meat 8
'meat' slices 37
microbiological testing 5
milk, soya 77, 252
milk, other non-dairy 77
mincemeat 72
mince pies 72
minerals 177
miso 83
moisturiser 147
motorcyclist clothing, note 198

mouse traps	217
mouthwash	164
muesli	34
multiple outlet contacts	254
multiple outlet quick reference guide	ii
musical instruments, note	224
mustard	57
nail polish	140
nail products	140
nappies	187
nappies, note	189
Netto Foodstores Ltd, note	ii
night lights	206
Nike, note	198
Nisa Today, note	ii
Not Tested on Animals Cosmetics Standard	3
nut cutlets	37
office products	203
olives	57
oral contraceptives, note	181
oral hygiene	164
paint, note	212
paints, artists'	222
panty liners	133
paper, note	212
Parmesan seasoning	40
pasta sauce	57
pasties	64
pastry	57
Patak's, note	86
pâté	80
peanut butter	80
peanuts	74
perfume	141
perry	95
PERSONA, note	181
pet food	216
pets, note	218
photographic film, note	224
pickle	57
pies	64
pillows, note	211
pizza bases	26
Plasticine, note	224
plum pudding	72
polish, furniture	209
polish, general purpose	209
polish, nail	140
polish, shoe	197
popcorn	43
poppadums, note	86
postage stamps, note	212
pottery, note	211
poultry	8
prescriptions, note	182
preserves, note	85
prevention (illness), note	182
prisoners support group	252
processing aids, note	86
purses	192
quiche base	57
reading, suggested	236
religious/spiritual	19, 252
relish	57
remedies	172
remedies, children's	187
resource use	18
rice cakes	48
rolls	26
rubber gloves, note	212
rubber, note	212
running shoes, note	198
Safeway, note	ii
Safeway, toileteries /cosmetics, note	166
Sainsbury's note	ii
salads, chilled	66
salt, note	86
sandals	193

'sausages'	37
sauce, savoury	57
sauce, sweet	47
savouries, canned/bottled	64
savouries, chilled/fresh	66
savouries, dried	69
savouries, frozen	70
sea life/marine animals	9, 251
seasonal food	72
seitan	83
Sellotape, note	211
shampoo	142
shaving cream	146
shaving products	146
shellac	13
shoe polish	197
shoes	193
shower gel	120
silk	12
skin care	147
skin make up	157
slaughter statistics	8
smoking products	223
snack pots	69
snacks, savoury	74
snacks, sweet	43
soap	158
soft drinks, note	116
Somerfield, note	ii
sorbet	55
soup	76
soya milk	77, 252
spaghetti, tinned	64
Spar, note	ii
spices	78
spirits	102
spirits, note	116
spiritual/religious	19, 252
spreads, savoury	80
spreads, sweet	82
stain remover	207
starch (washing)	210
stock	53
stout	92

stuffing	46
suet, vegetable	56
sugar, note	86
suggested reading	236
sun care	162
sun-tan lotion	162
Superdrug, note	ii
supplements	170, 177
supplements, animals'	216
supplements, children's	177, 187
sweets	43
talcum powder	163
'talking magazines'	241
tanneries	18
tempeh	83
tennis balls, note	224
Tesco, note	ii
textiles, note	198
'third world'	252
Thorntons, note	ii
Thornton's chocolate, note	85
tofu	83
toilet cleaner	209
toilet products	209
toiletries	119
toiletries, children's	187
toothpaste	164
training shoes, note	198
useful addresses	248
Vegan Society Trade Mark	230
video cassette tapes, note	212
vinegar, note	86
vinegars	57
vitamins	177
vivisection	13
Waitrose, note	ii
wallets	192
washing powder	210
washing up liquid	210
washing up products	210

water filters, note	212
water, note	116
water pollution	18
water use	18
waterproofers, footwear	197
WH Smith, note	212
whiteners, note	86
wild animals	252
wine	104
Wine Rack, note	ii
wines, note	116
wipes	207, 208
wool	11
World Cancer Research Fund (WCRF)	15
yeast extract	80
'yoghurts'	84
youth groups	253
zoos	249

NOTES

NOTES

NOTES

NOTES

NOTES

NOTES

NOTES

MEMBERSHIP APPLICATION

Promoting ways of living which avoid the use of animal products – for the benefit of people, animals and the environment

□ Individual £17
□ Unwaged Individual £11

□ Family/Joint★ £23
□ Unwaged Family/Joint★ £15
□ Life £275

Eire & overseas: all applicants must add £5

Please tick as appropriate:

□ I adhere to a vegan diet and wish to become a Vegan Society member. I undertake to abide by the Society's *Memorandum amd Articles of Association*★★

□ Although not a vegan I support the Society's work and wish to become a supporter member

Membership subscription	£	
Memo & Arts (£2)	£	
Donation	£	
TOTAL	£	

□ I enclose a cheque/PO payable to 'The Vegan Society' *(Eire & overseas: payment must be made by sterling International Money Order or sterling cheque drawn on a British bank)*

□ I would like to pay by standing order. Please send me a form

☐ I am a UK taxpayer and would like to help the Society claim the income tax I have paid. Please send me gift aid details.

☐ Please debit my *(delete not applicable)* Visa/Mastercard/Access/Eurocard/Switch/Visa Delta/Connect card number

☐☐☐☐☐☐☐☐☐☐☐☐☐☐☐☐☐☐☐☐

Name on card _____

Signature _____

Start date ☐☐☐☐   Expiry date ☐☐☐☐

Today's date ☐☐☐☐   Switch issue no. ☐☐

Name _____
Address _____
_____
_____

Post code _____ Tel _____
Skills/Profession _____
_____

Return to: Membership Assistant,
The Vegan Society, Donald Watson House,
7 Battle Road, St Leonards-on-Sea, East Sussex
TN37 7AA, UK

t 01424 427393   f 01424 717064
e memb@vegansociety.com
w www.vegansociety.com

★   All applicants must reside at the same address – please supply names on separate sheet

★★   £2 – or may be viewed at the Society's office

Membership includes The Vegan *magazine. This form may be photocopied. Please send both parts.*